PACEMAKER®

Algebra 1

TEACHER'S ANSWER EDITION

GLOBE FEARON

Pearson Learning Group

Contents

Pacemaker® Algebra 1, Second Edition

We thank the following educators, who provided valuable comments
and suggestions during the development of the first edition of this book:

REVIEWERS

Ann Dixon, Teacher, Allegheny Intermediate Unit, South Park High School,
Library, PA 15129
Ravi Kamat, Math Teacher, Dallas, TX 75203
Janet Thompson, Teacher, St. Louis, MO 63107
Linda White, Teacher, Riverview Learning Center, Daytona Beach, FL 32118

PROJECT STAFF
Exect…ive Editor: Eleanor Ripp; *Supervising Editor*: Stephanie Cahill; *Senior Editor*: Phyllis Dunsay;
Editor: Theresa McCarthy; *Production Editor*: Travis Bailey; *Designers*: Susan Brorein, Jennifer Visco;
Market Manager: Katie Kehoe-Erezuma; *Research Director*: Angela Darchi; *Cover Design*: Susan Brorein,
Jennifer Visco; *Editorial Development*: GTS; *Electronic Composition*: GTS, Phyllis Rosinsky;
Manufacturing Supervisor: Mark Cirillo

About the Cover: Algebra 1 is important in mathematics and in everyday life. The images on the
cover represent some of the things you will be learning about in this book. The pattern in the
nautilus shell is an example of a number pattern called the Fibonacci numbers. The graph of the
equation $x = y$ shows how you can connect Algebra and Geometry. The running cheetah is an
example of the familiar relationship between distance, rate, and time. The coins represent problems
about discount, sale price, and the cost of items. The ruler is one of the tools you will use to
measure the world around you. What other images can you think of to represent Algebra 1?

ISBN: 0-130-23630-6

Printed in the United States of America

7 8 9 10   07 06 05

1-800-321-3106
www.pearsonlearning.com

Proven Solution for Today's Classrooms from Globe Fearon

Students and educators alike face increased challenges in the twenty-first century. Students need preparation for the rigors of more difficult standards and proficiency tests, as well as the ability to successfully apply learning to daily challenges—including the challenges of the workplace. Educators must meet the needs of diverse classrooms, keep learning up-to-date and relevant, and create supportive learning environments for a range of learning styles. Both students and educators will need teaching and learning tools to meet the challenges of the twenty-first century classroom.

Globe Fearon's *Pacemaker® Algebra 1* has always supplied educators and students with materials and techniques that are accessible, predictable, age-appropriate, and relevant. This new edition continues to provide a solid, well-balanced approach to teaching Algebra 1.

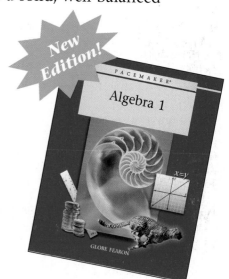

The Second Edition of *Algebra 1* retains these successful features:

- concise, manageable lessons
- concepts presented in a predictable format
- frequent opportunities for review
- pre-taught vocabulary and controlled reading level
- high-interest, age-appropriate design
- solid teacher support

The Second Edition of *Algebra 1* is enhanced with features teachers asked for:

- a full-color Student Edition that engages students
- margin notes that provide support
- features that provide relevance for student learning
- visuals that address a variety of learning styles
- a Workbook that parallels each chapter in the Student Edition
- more teacher support—The new Teacher's Answer Edition provides answers on the student pages.
- an improved Classroom Resource Binder with an abundant variety of teacher support

A Complete Program!

STUDENT EDITION includes:
- unit openers that list chapters for planning.
- chapter openers that introduce vocabulary, state chapter objectives, and a chapter project.
- content divided into manageable lessons.
- stepped out examples.
- ample review for reinforcement.
- features such as *People in Math, Math Connection, On-the-Job Math,* and *Math in Your Life* make content relevant.
- chapter reviews that assess vocabulary and content retention.
- unit reviews for standardized test practice.

TEACHER'S ANSWER EDITION includes:
- answers at point-of-use.
- instruction on how to use programs in the classroom.

WORKBOOK includes:
- complete practice for every chapter.
- skill practice worksheets that provide essential practice and encourage student mastery of content.
- critical thinking questions that provide opportunities to extend content.

CLASSROOM RESOURCE BINDER includes:
- a variety of reproducibles that review, reinforce, and enrich key skills and concepts.
- a variety of assessment opportunities.
- organizational and planning charts for classroom management.

SEPARATE ANSWER KEY includes:
- answers for Student Edition, Workbook, and Classroom Resource Binder.

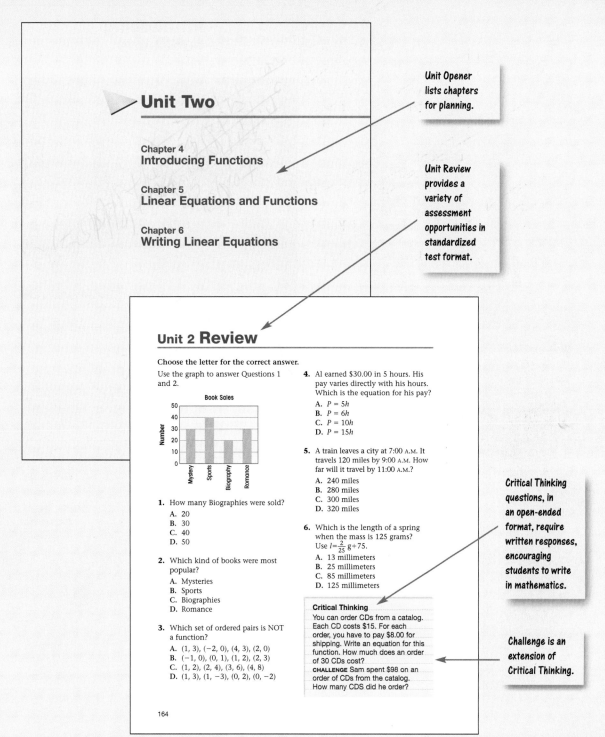

▷ **Unit Two**

Chapter 4
Introducing Functions

Chapter 5
Linear Equations and Functions

Chapter 6
Writing Linear Equations

Unit Opener
lists chapters
for planning.

Unit Review
provides a
variety of
assessment
opportunities in
standardized
test format.

Unit 2 Review

Choose the letter for the correct answer.

Use the graph to answer Questions 1 and 2.

Book Sales

Number

50
40
30
20
10
0

Mystery   Sports   Biography   Romance

1. How many Biographies were sold?
A. 20
B. 30
C. 40
D. 50

2. Which kind of books were most popular?
A. Mysteries
B. Sports
C. Biographies
D. Romance

3. Which set of ordered pairs is NOT a function?
A. (1, 3), (−2, 0), (4, 3), (2, 0)
B. (−1, 0), (0, 1), (1, 2), (2, 3)
C. (1, 2), (2, 4), (3, 6), (4, 8)
D. (1, 3), (1, −3), (0, 2), (0, −2)

4. Al earned $30.00 in 5 hours. His pay varies directly with his hours. Which is the equation for his pay?
A. $P = 5h$
B. $P = 6h$
C. $P = 10h$
D. $P = 15h$

5. A train leaves a city at 7:00 A.M. It travels 120 miles by 9:00 A.M. How far will it travel by 11:00 A.M.?
A. 240 miles
B. 280 miles
C. 300 miles
D. 320 miles

6. Which is the length of a spring when the mass is 125 grams? Use $l = \frac{2}{25}g + 75$.
A. 13 millimeters
B. 25 millimeters
C. 85 millimeters
D. 125 millimeters

Critical Thinking
You can order CDs from a catalog. Each CD costs $15. For each order, you have to pay $8.00 for shipping. Write an equation for this function. How much does an order of 30 CDs cost?
CHALLENGE Sam spent $98 on an order of CDs from the catalog. How many CDS did he order?

Critical Thinking
questions, in
an open-ended
format, require
written responses,
encouraging
students to write
in mathematics.

Challenge is an
extension of
Critical Thinking.

164

Sample pages from Unit 2 of the Student Edition.

High interest photo connects algebra to the real world.

Detailed caption supports understanding and provides a springboard for discussion of algebra in real life.

Words to Know introduces students to key algebraic vocabulary in the chapter.

High-interest project engages students and gears them up for the algebra ahead.

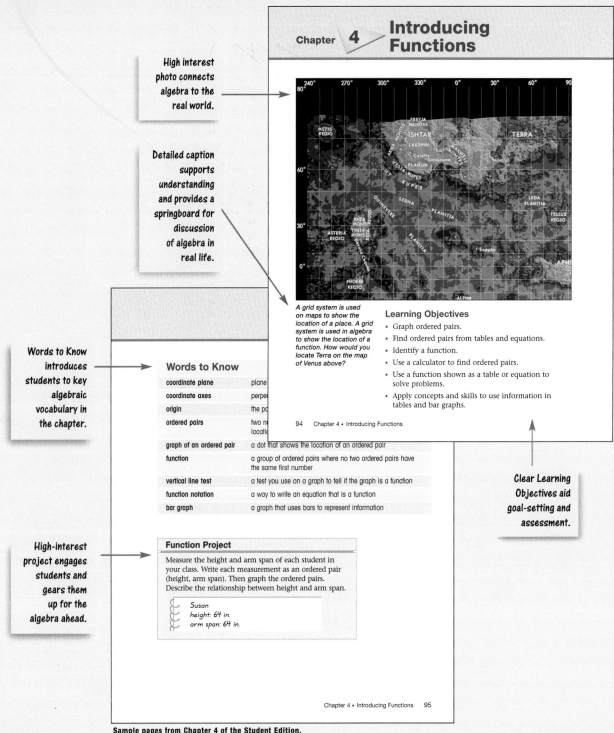

Chapter **4** | Introducing Functions

A grid system is used on maps to show the location of a place. A grid system is used in algebra to show the location of a function. How would you locate Terra on the map of Venus above?

94   Chapter 4 • Introducing Functions

Learning Objectives
- Graph ordered pairs.
- Find ordered pairs from tables and equations.
- Identify a function.
- Use a calculator to find ordered pairs.
- Use a function shown as a table or equation to solve problems.
- Apply concepts and skills to use information in tables and bar graphs.

Clear Learning Objectives aid goal-setting and assessment.

Words to Know

coordinate plane	plane
coordinate axes	perpe
origin	the p
ordered pairs	two n
	locati
graph of an ordered pair	a dot that shows the location of an ordered pair
function	a group of ordered pairs where no two ordered pairs have the same first number
vertical line test	a test you use on a graph to tell if the graph is a function
function notation	a way to write an equation that is a function
bar graph	a graph that uses bars to represent information

Function Project

Measure the height and arm span of each student in your class. Write each measurement as an ordered pair (height, arm span). Then graph the ordered pairs. Describe the relationship between height and arm span.

> Susan
> height: 64 in.
> arm span: 64 in.

Chapter 4 • Introducing Functions   95

Sample pages from Chapter 4 of the Student Edition.

Step-by-Step lessons make content accessible.

Stepped-out examples build algebra skills.

Clear, visual presentation of algebra concepts help students.

Cooperative Learning provides an opportunity for students to work together and write about algebra.

4-3 Tables and Ordered Pairs

You can show ordered pairs in tables. The first column of the table contains the first number of an ordered pair. The second column of the table contains the second number.

▶ **EXAMPLE 1**

Write the ordered pairs from the table.

Time	Distance
1 second	2 feet
2 seconds	4 feet
3 seconds	6 feet

Write each row as an ordered pair.
(1, 2), (2, 4), (3, 6)

The ordered pairs are (1, 2), (2, 4), and (3, 6).

You can graph the ordered pairs. Use the heading of the first column for the horizontal axis. Use the heading of the second column for the vertical axis.

▶ **EXAMPLE 2**

Write the ordered pairs from the table. Label the coordinate axes. Then, graph the ordered pairs.

Minutes	°Celsius
4	−4
5	−2
6	0

Write each row as an ordered pair.
(4, −4), (5, −2), (6, 0)

Label the horizontal axis with the heading from the first column.

Label the vertical axis with the heading from the second column.

Graph the ordered pairs.

100   Chapter 4 • Introducing Functions

Try These

1. Write the ordered pairs
   Write the rows as ordered p

   The ordered pairs are (1
   and ▦, ▦).

2. Label the axes. Graph t
   Label the horizontal axis wi
   from the first column.
   Label horizontal axis: Hours.
   Label the vertical axis with the heading from the second column.
   Label vertical axis: ▦.
   Graph the ordered pairs.

Practice

Write the ordered pairs from each table. Use graph paper. Label the axes. Then, graph the ordered pairs.

1.
Day	Temperature
1	−5
2	0
3	5

2.
Quarts	Pints
2	4
4	8
6	12

Cooperative Learning

3. Explain to a partner how to write the ordered pairs in number 2 in **Practice**.

4. Make a table containing three pairs of numbers. Ask a partner to write the ordered pairs. Be sure to put labels in the table.

Chapter 4 • Introducing Functions   101

4-7 Calculator: Finding Ordered Pairs

Some equations have large numbers. You can use a calculator to find ordered pairs for these equations.

▶ **EXAMPLE 1**

Complete this table of ordered pairs for the equation $y = 25(x + 3)$.

x	$25(x + 3)$	y
.2	$25(.2 + 3)$	?
1.4	$25(1.4 + 3)$	?
.06	$25(.06 + 3)$	?

Remember
Do the work in the parentheses first.

Use .2 for x.   Display
PRESS: . 2 + 3 =   3.2

Then multiply.
PRESS: × 2 5 =   80
The first ordered pair is (.2, 80).

Use 1.4 for x.
PRESS: 1 . 4 + 3 =

Then multiply.
PRESS: × 2 5 =
The second ordered pair is (1.4, 110).

Use .06 for x.
PRESS: . 0 6 + 3 =

Then multiply.
PRESS: × 2 5 =
The third ordered pair is (.06, 76.5).

108   Chapter 4 • Introducing Functions

→ Feature Lessons, such as Calculator lessons, encourage students to grasp algebraic principles.

Practice
Complete each table of ordered pairs.

1. $y = 0.5x + 18$

x	$0.5x + 18$	y
2	$0.5(2) + 18$	?
4	?	?
6	?	?
8	?	?

2. $y = 10(x + 6)$

x	$10(x + 6)$	y
2	$10(2 + 6)$	?
4	?	?
6	?	?
8	?	?

On-the-Job Math

MAKING MAPS

There are many kinds of maps. Some maps show natural places, like rivers and deserts. Others show things like streets and cities. Maps can show large areas, such as continents. They can also show small places, like a town or even your school.

One thing maps have in common is how they are made. Mapmakers, also called *cartographers*, start with a photograph of the place they are mapping. The photograph may be taken from an airplane or even a satellite. They study the photograph carefully so they don't make mistakes. From the air, many things can look alike. A park and a forest need to be labeled correctly.

Labels make reading a map easier. Some maps are labeled with a special coordinate plane. One axis is numbered, and the other axis is lettered. A grid divides the map into squares. Each square on the map is located by its number and letter. This is like finding a point on a graph by its ordered pair.

Chapter 4 • Introducing Functions   109

Every chapter has a boxed feature, such as On-the-Job Math, People in Math, Math Connection, or Math in Your Life. →

Sample pages from Chapter 4 of the Student Edition.

T8

Problem-solving strategy builds students' proficiency in solving word problems.

Examples with models build problem-solving skills.

Consistent problem-solving method is given from chapter to chapter.

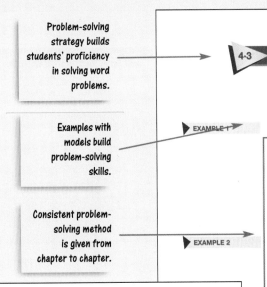

4·3 ▶ **Tables and Ordered Pairs**

You can show ordered pairs in tables. The first column of the table contains the first number of an ordered pair. The second column of the table contains the second number.

▶ EXAMPLE 1 ▶

Write the ordered pairs from the table.

Write each row as an ordered pair.
(1, 2), (2, 4), (3, 6)

Time	Distance
1 second	2 feet
2 seconds	4 feet
3 seconds	6 feet

The ordered pairs are (1, 2), (2, 4), and (3, 6)

You can graph the ordered pairs. Use the heading of the first column for the horizontal axis. Use the heading of the second column for the vertical axis.

▶ EXAMPLE 2

Write the ordered pairs from the table. Label the coordinate axes. Then, graph the ordered pairs.

Minutes	°Celsius
4	−4
5	−2
6	0

Write each row as an ordered pair.
(4, −4), (5, −2), (6, 0)

Label the horizontal axis with the heading from the first column.

Label the vertical axis with the heading from the second column.

Graph the ordered pairs.

ntroducing Functions

Try These

Answer each question using the table or equation.

1. How much do 100 CDs cost?

Use the ▦.

Substitute 100 for c.

Simplify.

$t = 12c + 4$

$t = 12\,(▦) + 4$

$t = ▦ + 4$

$t = ▦$

100 CDs cost ▦.

2. How much do 2 CDs cost?

Use the ▦.

c	$12c + 4$	t
1	$12(1) + 4$	16
2	$12(2) + 4$	28
3	$12(3) + 4$	40

2 CDs cost ▦.

Guided problem-solving practice promotes skill building.

Practice

Tell whether you would use the table or equation. Then, answer the question.

1. How much does 1 CD cost?

2. How much do 8 CDs cost?

3. How much do 5 CDs cost?

4. How much do 50 CDs cost?

5. As the number of CDs you buy increases, what happens to the cost?

Cooperative Learning

6. Explain to a partner how to decide which method to use in number **3** in **Practice**.

7. Choose a number between 6 and 20. Ask a partner to find the cost to order that many CDs.

Chapter 4 • Introducing Functions   111

T9

▶ Applications connect math to the real world.

Application Lesson applies algebra skills to what students learned in the chapter.

Examples relate and apply skills to real-life problems.

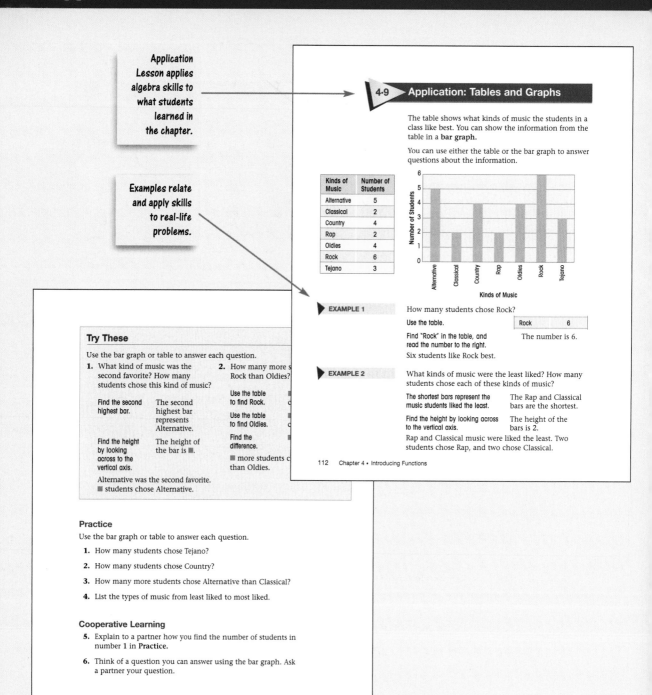

4-9 **Application: Tables and Graphs**

The table shows what kinds of music the students in a class like best. You can show the information from the table in a **bar graph.**

You can use either the table or the bar graph to answer questions about the information.

Kinds of Music	Number of Students
Alternative	5
Classical	2
Country	4
Rap	2
Oldies	4
Rock	6
Tejano	3

EXAMPLE 1

How many students chose Rock?

Use the table.

Rock	6

Find "Rock" in the table, and read the number to the right.   The number is 6.

Six students like Rock best.

EXAMPLE 2

What kinds of music were the least liked? How many students chose each of these kinds of music?

The shortest bars represent the music students liked the least.   The Rap and Classical bars are the shortest.

Find the height by looking across to the vertical axis.   The height of the bars is 2.

Rap and Classical music were liked the least. Two students chose Rap, and two chose Classical.

112   Chapter 4 • Introducing Functions

Try These

Use the bar graph or table to answer each question.

1. What kind of music was the second favorite? How many students chose this kind of music?

Find the second highest bar.   The second highest bar represents Alternative.

Find the height by looking across to the vertical axis.   The height of the bar is ■.

Alternative was the second favorite. ■ students chose Alternative.

2. How many more s Rock than Oldies?

Use the table to find Rock.

Use the table to find Oldies.

Find the difference.

■ more students c than Oldies.

Practice

Use the bar graph or table to answer each question.

1. How many students chose Tejano?

2. How many students chose Country?

3. How many more students chose Alternative than Classical?

4. List the types of music from least liked to most liked.

Cooperative Learning

5. Explain to a partner how you find the number of students in number **1** in **Practice.**

6. Think of a question you can answer using the bar graph. Ask a partner your question.

Chapter 4 • Introducing Functions   113

Sample pages from Chapter 4 of the Student Edition.

Chapter Review assesses concept retention, builds study skills, and prepares students for tests.

Chapter Quiz questions assess chapter objectives.

Chapter Summary provides a graphic presentation of main chapter ideas to use as a study aid.

Essential Vocabulary Review reinforces word retention.

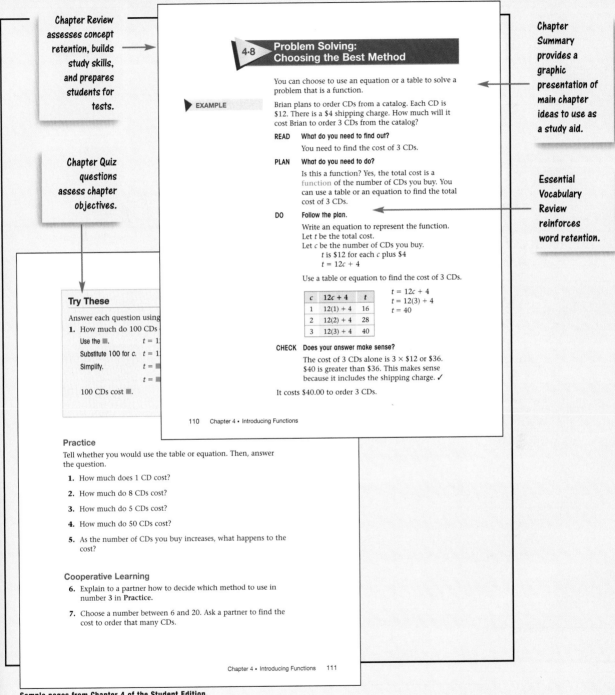

4·8 Problem Solving: Choosing the Best Method

You can choose to use an equation or a table to solve a problem that is a function.

▶ EXAMPLE

Brian plans to order CDs from a catalog. Each CD is $12. There is a $4 shipping charge. How much will it cost Brian to order 3 CDs from the catalog?

READ What do you need to find out?

You need to find the cost of 3 CDs.

PLAN What do you need to do?

Is this a function? Yes, the total cost is a function of the number of CDs you buy. You can use a table or an equation to find the total cost of 3 CDs.

DO Follow the plan.

Write an equation to represent the function.
Let t be the total cost.
Let c be the number of CDs you buy.
t is $12 for each c plus $4
$t = 12c + 4$

Use a table or equation to find the cost of 3 CDs.

c	$12c + 4$	t
1	12(1) + 4	16
2	12(2) + 4	28
3	12(3) + 4	40

$t = 12c + 4$
$t = 12(3) + 4$
$t = 40$

CHECK Does your answer make sense?

The cost of 3 CDs alone is $3 \times \$12$ or $36. $40 is greater than $36. This makes sense because it includes the shipping charge. ✓

It costs $40.00 to order 3 CDs.

110   Chapter 4 • Introducing Functions

Try These

Answer each question using

1. How much do 100 CDs

Use the ■. $t = 1$

Substitute 100 for c. $t = 1$

Simplify. $t = $ ■

                  $t = $ ■

100 CDs cost ■.

Practice

Tell whether you would use the table or equation. Then, answer the question.

1. How much does 1 CD cost?

2. How much do 8 CDs cost?

3. How much do 5 CDs cost?

4. How much do 50 CDs cost?

5. As the number of CDs you buy increases, what happens to the cost?

Cooperative Learning

6. Explain to a partner how to decide which method to use in number 3 in **Practice**.

7. Choose a number between 6 and 20. Ask a partner to find the cost to order that many CDs.

Chapter 4 • Introducing Functions   111

Sample pages from Chapter 4 of the Student Edition.

A component reference annotation corresponds to Workbook page.

Introductory activity begins every lesson.

More practice is provided in Exercise 20 of the Workbook.

4·3 Tables and Ordered Pairs

Getting Started
Have students read tables from newspapers in order to help them interpret information in tables.

You can show ordered pairs in tables. The first column of the table contains the first number of an ordered pair. The second column of the table contains the second number.

▶ **EXAMPLE 1**

Write the ordered pairs from the table.

Write each row as an ordered pair.
(1, 2), (2, 4), (3, 6)

Time	Distance
1 second	2 feet
2 seconds	4 feet
3 seconds	6 feet

The ordered pairs are (1, 2), (2, 4), and (3, 6)

You can graph the ordered pairs. Use the heading of the first column for the horizontal axis. Use the heading of the second column for the vertical axis.

▶ **EXAMPLE 2**

Write the ordered pairs from the table. Label the coordinate axes. Then, graph the ordered pairs.

Minutes	°Celsius
4	−4
5	−2
6	0

Write each row as an ordered pair.
(4, −4), (5, −2), (6, 0)

Label the horizontal axis with the heading from the first column.

Label the vertical axis with the heading from the second column.

Graph the ordered pairs.

troducing Functions

Try These

1. Write the ordered pairs from the table.
   Write the rows as ordered pairs.   (1, ■)
                                      (2, ■)
                                      (■, ■)

Hours	Feet
1	2
2	−2
3	−6

   The ordered pairs are (1, ■), (2, ■), and ■, ■).

2. Label the axes. Graph the ordered pairs.

   Label the horizontal axis with the heading from the first column.

   Label horizontal axis: Hours.

   Label the vertical axis with the heading from the second column.

   Label vertical axis: ■. Feet

   Graph the ordered pairs.

Practice

Write the ordered pairs from each table. Use graph paper.
Label the axes. Then, graph the ordered pairs.

1.
Day	Temperature
1	−5
2	0
3	5

(1, −5)
(2, 0)
(3, 5)

See Additional Answers, p. 471.

2.
Quarts	Pints
2	4
4	8
6	12

(2, 4)
(4, 8)
(6, 12)

See Additional Answers, p. 471.

Cooperative Learning

3. Explain to a partner how to write the ordered pairs in number 2 in **Practice.** Possible answer: Use the first column to write the first number in the ordered pair. The second column is for the second number in the ordered pair.
4. Make a table containing three pairs of numbers. Ask a partner to write the ordered pairs. Be sure to put labels in the table. Answers will vary.

Chapter 4 • Introducing Functions   101

This hardcover teacher tool provides answers right on student pages.

Annotations offer support for ease of classroom management.

Workbook provides practice for every chapter.

Name_____ Date_____

4 ▷ **Tables, Equations, and Ordered Pairs**   **Exercise 20**

Lessons 4.3 and 4.4

A. Graph and label the ordered pairs.

1.

Point	Time	Temperature
A	0	−1
B	1	−3
C	2	−5
D	3	−4
E	4	0

B. Complete each table.

2. $y = x + 1$

x	x + 1	y
−2		
−1		
0		
1		
2		

3. $y = -2x$

x	−2x	y
−2		
−1		
0		
1		
2		

4. $y = 3x + 2$

x	3x + 2	y
−2		
−1		
0		
1		
2		

5. $y = 2(x - 3)$

x	2(x − 3)	y
−2		
−1		
0		
1		
2		

Sample page from Chapter 4 of the Workbook.

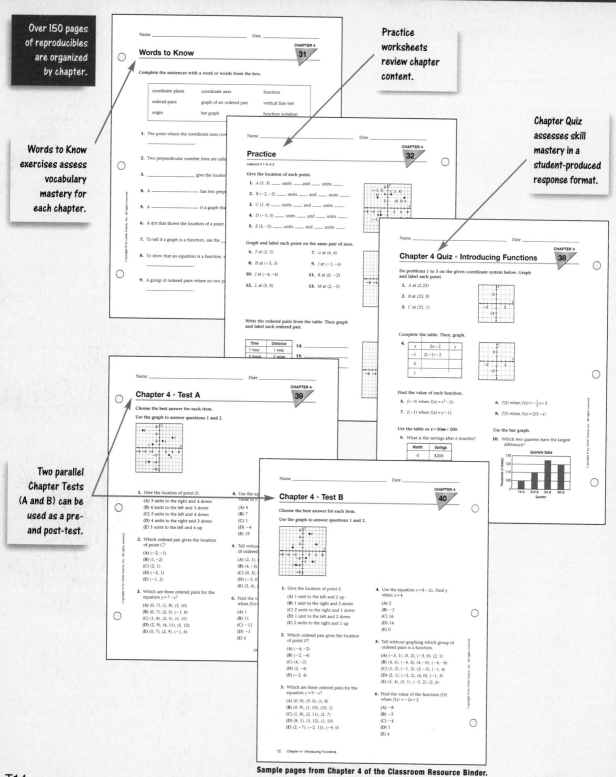

Over 150 pages of reproducibles are organized by chapter.

Words to Know exercises assess vocabulary mastery for each chapter.

Practice worksheets review chapter content.

Chapter Quiz assesses skill mastery in a student-produced response format.

Two parallel Chapter Tests (A and B) can be used as a pre- and post-test.

Sample pages from Chapter 4 of the Classroom Resource Binder.

T14

Visuals provide both study aids and tools for hands-on activities.

Name _____ Date _____

VISUAL
C

The Coordinate Plane

Three-column tables allow students to create their own functions.

Name _____ Date _____

VISUAL
F

Three-Column Table

x	x²−1	y
-1	(-1)²	0

Name _____ Date _____

Diagnostic Test • Chapters 1–15

Simplify.

1. ⁻2 + ⁻8   2. ⁻5 − ⁻15   3. ⁻7 • ⁻6

4. 9 ÷ ⁻3   5. ⁻6 + 9 + ⁻15   6. (⁻5)³

7. Evaluate the variable expression 15x + 5 when x is 3.

Simplify.

8. 30 − 3 × 2³   9. ⁻5(w − 2)   10. 6x² − 3y + 3x² − 7y

11. Use the formula V = lwh to find the volume of the box. l is 12 in., w is 6 in., h is 7 in.

12. Tell whether the number is a solution of the equation. 45; b ÷ 3 = 3

Solve each equation.

13. d + 5 = 3   14. a − 12 = ⁻5   15. ⁻9 = c/2

16. ⁻3b = 15   17. 2m − 3 = 7   18. ⁻2(n − 1) = 10

19. 300 students at a high school study a language. 85% of those students study Spanish. How many students study Spanish?

20. What is the sale price of a $26 pair of sunglasses on sale for 20% off?

Write the ordered pairs from the table. Then graph the ordered pairs.

Day	Temperature
1	⁻2
2	0
3	3

21. (,)
22. (,)
23. (,)

(Go on to next page)
Test Preparation • T3

Diagnostic test aids student placement and success within the program.

Name _____ Date _____

Final • Chapters 1–15

Simplify.

1. ⁻9 ÷ 2   2. ⁻7 − 8   3. 9 • ⁻6

4. ⁻28 + ⁻7   5. ⁻12 + 4 + ⁻6   6. ⁻2⁴

7. Evaluate the variable expression 3x² + 5x when x is 2.

Simplify.

8. 10 + 54 ÷ 3²   9. ⁻6(2w + 3)   10. 8p² + 2p − 3p² + 5p

11. Use the formula V = lwh to find the volume of the box. l is 8 cm, w is 5 cm, h is 6 cm

12. Tell whether the number is a solution of the equation. ⁻4; 20 − 3y = 32

Solve each equation.

13. 8 + x = ⁻2   14. ⁻3 = k − 5   15. 12 = y/⁻3

16. 7d = ⁻42   17. 6b + 3 = 15   18. 4(z + 5) = 32

19. 520 students at a high school study a language. 65% of those students study French. How many students study French?

20. What is the sale price of a $38 pair of pants on sale for 15% off?

Write the ordered pairs from the table. Then graph the ordered pairs.

Hours	Feet
1	3
2	0
3	⁻3

21. (,)
22. (,)
23. (,)

(Go on to next page)

T14 • Test Preparation

Final Exam parallels the Diagnostic Test to ensure student mastery.

Use these Globe Fearon programs and worktexts for extra practice, reteaching, reinforcement, enrichment, and test preparation.

Math for Proficiency

helps students develop
the mastery and
confidence they need
to succeed on tests.

Writing in Mathematics

shows your entire class
how to communicate
clearly in mathematics.

Pacemaker® Pre-Algebra

takes arithmetic, geometry,
statistics, and other topics of
basic math and relates them to
such algebra fundamentals as
evaluating expressions, solving
equations, writing equations,
and graphing.

Success in Math

is a five-book series that takes
core math concepts and breaks
them into short, manageable
lessons that assume little
background knowledge.

*Globe Fearon offers additional materials to help tailor instruction
to meet the diverse needs of your students.*

*For more information on Globe Fearon worktexts,
call 1-800-848-9500.*

PACEMAKER®

Algebra 1

GLOBE FEARON

Pearson Learning Group

Pacemaker® Algebra 1, Second Edition

We thank the following educators, who provided valuable comments and suggestions during the development of the first edition of this book:

REVIEWERS

Ann Dixon, Teacher, Allegheny Intermediate Unit, South Park High School, Library, PA 15129

Ravi Kamat, Math Teacher, Dallas, TX 75203

Janet Thompson, Teacher, St. Louis, MO 63107

Linda White, Teacher, Riverview Learning Center, Daytona Beach, FL 32118

PROJECT STAFF

Executive Editor: Eleanor Ripp; *Supervising Editor*: Stephanie Petron Cahill; *Senior Editor*: Phyllis Dunsay
Editor: Theresa McCarthy; *Production Editor*: Travis Bailey; *Lead Designer*: Susan Brorein
Market Manager: Douglas Falk; *Cover Design*: Susan Brorein, Jennifer Visco
Editorial, Design, and Production Services: GTS Graphics; *Electronic Composition*: Phyllis Rosinsky

Photo Credits appear on page 470.

About the Cover: Algebra 1 is important in mathematics and in everyday life. The images on the cover represent some of the things you will be learning about in this book. The pattern in the nautilus shell is an example of a number pattern called the Fibonacci numbers. The graph of the equation $x = y$ shows how you can connect Algebra and Geometry. The running cheetah is an example of the familiar relationship between distance, rate, and time. The coins represent problems about discount, sale price, and the cost of items. The ruler is one of the tools you will use to measure the world around you. What other images can you think of to represent Algebra 1?

ISBN: 0-130-23638-1
Printed in the United States of America
9 10   06 05

Globe Fearon
Pearson Learning Group

1-800-321-3106
www.pearsonlearning.com

Contents

UNIT FIVE — 327

Chapter 13 — Radicals and Geometry — 328

Chapter 14 Rational Expressions and Equations — 356

A Note to the Student

Welcome to algebra! The purpose of this book is to make your journey through algebra a success. Your journey will be comfortable and interesting. You will build new skills based on what you already know. As you work through and review each topic, your algebra skills will grow.

Each lesson presents clear models and examples. The lessons give you a chance to try out your skills in **Try These**. Then, you go on and use the skills in **Practice**. From lesson to lesson, you share what you have learned with a partner in **Cooperative Learning**. Margin notes are there to give you helpful hints.

Application lessons show you how you can apply what you know to science, geometry, statistics, and business. **Problem Solving** lessons show different ways to solve problems using what you have learned. **Calculator** lessons show you another tool you can use with your algebra skills.

Math Connections, People in Math, On-the-Job Math, and **Math in Your Life** are features that contain interesting information about people and careers in math. They also give interesting facts about math in other subjects that you might study.

There are many other study aids in the book. At the beginning of every chapter, you will find **Learning Objectives**. They will help you focus on the important points covered in the chapter. You will also find **Words to Know**. This is a look ahead at new vocabulary you may find difficult. At the end of each chapter, you will find a **Chapter Review**. This will give you a review of what you have just learned. A **Unit Review** comes after each unit.

Everyone who put this book together worked hard to make it useful, interesting, and enjoyable. The rest is up to you.

We wish you well on your journey through algebra. Our success comes from your success.

Unit One

Balloon pilots use numbers to keep track of air temperature, wind speed, and altitude. As a balloon rises, the air temperature gets colder. What numbers could you use for this air temperature?

Learning Objectives

- Graph integers on a number line.
- Find the absolute value of integers.
- Add, subtract, multiply, and divide with positive and negative numbers.
- Use a calculator to add, subtract, multiply, and divide positive and negative numbers.
- Guess, check, and revise to solve problems.
- Apply concepts and skills to find information from broken-line graphs.

Words to Know

positive numbers	the numbers to the right of zero on the number line
negative numbers	the numbers to the left of zero on the number line
integers	the numbers ... $^-3$, $^-2$, $^-1$, 0, 1, 2, 3,...
absolute value	the distance between 0 and a number on the number line
opposites	numbers with the same absolute value on opposite sides of zero on the number line; $^-3$ and 3 are opposites
expression	a number, or a group of numbers written with operation signs
simplify	perform the operations; find the value
base	a factor; In 3^2, 3 is the base used as a factor 2 times
exponent	the number that tells how many times the base is used as a factor
power	the product when factors are the same; in $3^2 = 9$, 9 is the power
revise	change; to change a guess when you have more information
broken-line graph	a graph made up of pieces of straight lines; used to display information

Line Graph Project

Measure the outdoor temperature each hour, starting at 9:00 A.M. and ending at noon. Record each temperature reading in your notebook. After you have completed Lesson 1.11, draw a broken-line graph to show your data. At what time was the temperature the highest? When was it the lowest?

Time	Temperature
9:00	48°
10:00	51°

Project See the Classroom Resource Binder for a scoring rubric to assess this project.

More practice is provided in Exercises 1 and 2 of the Workbook.

1·1 ▸ The Number Line

Getting Started
Using an outdoor thermometer, discuss temperatures above and below zero. Decide how such temperatures might be written.

Look at the number line below. **Positive numbers** are to the right of 0. **Negative numbers** are to the left of 0. Zero is not positive or negative.

Math Fact
+ is a positive sign.
− is a negative sign.

Read $^+4$ as "positive four" or "four." 4 is the same as $^+4$. Read $^-5$ as "negative five."

The **integers** are the numbers...$^-2$, $^-1$, 0, 1, 2...You can graph integers on a number line.

▸ **EXAMPLE 1**

Graph $^-5$ on a number line.

Count 5 places to the left of zero.
Draw a dot.

You can also use a number line to compare integers. On the number line, the integer to the left of another integer is less than that integer. The integer to the right of another integer is greater than that integer.

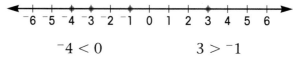

Math Fact
> means *is greater than.*
< means *is less than.*

$$^-4 < 0 \qquad\qquad 3 > {}^-1$$

$^-4$ is less than 0   3 is greater than $^-1$

▸ **EXAMPLE 2**

Compare $^-4$ and 3. Use > or <.
$^-4$ is to the left of 3 on the number line. $^-4 < 3$
$^-4$ is less than 3.

▸ **EXAMPLE 3**

Compare $^-1$ and $^-3$. Use > or <.
$^-1$ is to the right of $^-3$ on the number line. $^-1 > {}^-3$
$^-1$ is greater than $^-3$.

Try These

Graph on a number line.

1. ⁻6

Count 6 places to the ■ of 0. left

2. 5

Count 5 places to the ■ of 0. right

Compare. Use > or <.

3. ⁻7 and ⁻2

⁻7 is to the ■ of ⁻2 on the number line. left

⁻7 is ■ than ⁻2. less

⁻7 ■ ⁻2
  <

4. 3 and ⁻5 right

3 is to the ■ of ⁻5 on the number line.

3 is ■ than ⁻5. greater

3 ■ ⁻5
  >

Practice

Graph on a number line.

1. 2

⁻3 ⁻2 ⁻1 0 1 2 3

2. ⁺5

⁻1 0 1 2 3 4 5

3. ⁻7

⁻10 ⁻9 ⁻8 ⁻7 ⁻6 ⁻5 ⁻4

4. ⁻1

⁻4 ⁻3 ⁻2 ⁻1 0 1 2

5. 4

⁻1 0 1 2 3 4 5

6. ⁻8

⁻10 ⁻9 ⁻8 ⁻7 ⁻6 ⁻5 ⁻4

7. ⁻4

⁻7 ⁻6 ⁻5 ⁻4 ⁻3 ⁻2 ⁻1

8. ⁻3

⁻4 ⁻3 ⁻2 ⁻1 0 1 2

Compare. Use > or <.

9. 2 and ⁻1 >   **10.** ⁻4 and 0 <   **11.** ⁺3 and 4 <   **12.** ⁻8 and ⁻9 >

13. 1 and ⁻3 >   **14.** ⁻2 and 8 <   **15.** ⁻12 and 4 <   **16.** ⁻11 and 10 <

Cooperative Learning

17. Explain to a partner how to use a number line to compare the integers in number **9** in **Practice.** Draw a number line. Draw a dot at 2 and at ⁻1. Show that 2 is farther right than ⁻1. Therefore, 2 > ⁻1.

18. Pick an integer between ⁻10 and 10. Have a partner graph the integer on a number line. Check the work. Answers will vary.

1·2 ▶ Absolute Value

Getting Started
Discuss integers on the number line. The sign tells if the point is to the right or to the left of zero. The number gives the distance from zero. Have students give examples.

The **absolute value** of a number is its distance from 0. Distance is never negative. It is zero or positive.

The absolute value of ⁻4 is 4. It is 4 units from 0. The absolute value of ⁻4 is written as |⁻4|.

The absolute value of 4 is 4. It is 4 places from 0. The absolute value of 4 is written as |4|.

EXAMPLE 1

Find |⁻6|.

⁻6 is 6 units from 0.

The absolute value of ⁻6 is 6.

EXAMPLE 2

Find |0|.

0 is 0 units from 0.

The absolute value of 0 is 0.

Opposites have the same absolute value. One is positive and one is negative. ⁻2 and 2 are opposites.

EXAMPLE 3

Find the opposite of ⁻3.

⁻3 is negative. The opposite is positive.

The opposite of ⁻3 is 3.

EXAMPLE 4

Find the opposite of 5.

5 is positive. The opposite is negative.

The opposite of 5 is ⁻5.

Try These

Find each absolute value.

1. $|8|$
8 is ■ 8 places from 0.
$|8|$ = ■ 8

2. $|^-12|$
$^-12$ is ■ 12 places from 0.
$|^-12|$ = ■ 12

Find the opposite of each integer.

3. $^-15$
$^-15$ is ■. negative
The opposite is ■. positive
The opposite of $^-15$ is ■. 15

4. 20
20 is ■. positive
The opposite is ■. negative
The opposite of 20 is ■. $^-20$

Practice

Find the absolute value of each integer.

1. $|^-2|$ 2
2. $|1|$ 1
3. $|^-3|$ 3
4. $|^-7|$ 7

5. $|5|$ 5
6. $|10|$ 10
7. $|^-1|$ 1
8. $|^-9|$ 9

9. $|^-8|$ 8
10. $|^+6|$ 6
11. $|9|$ 9
12. $|^-15|$ 15

Find the opposite of each integer.

13. $^-5$ 5
14. 10 $^-10$
15. 7 $^-7$
16. 4 $^-4$

17. $^-22$ 22
18. 15 $^-15$
19. 0 0
20. $^-2$ 2

Cooperative Learning

21. Explain to a partner how to use a number line to find the absolute value in number **4** in **Practice**. Draw a number line. Draw a dot at $^-7$. Count the spaces between $^-7$ and 0. The distance between $^-7$ and 0 is 7. Therefore, 7 is the absolute value.

22. Write a positive integer and a negative integer. Ask a partner to find the opposite of each. Check the work. Answers will vary. Possible answer: Write 6 and $^-8$. The opposite of 6 is $^-6$. The opposite of $^-8$ is 8.

More practice is provided in Exercise 2 of the Workbook.

1·3 Addition

Getting Started
Help students show consecutive moves on the number line. Have them begin at 0 and name the points on which they land. For example, 4 then 2 (6); ⁻4 then ⁻2 (⁻6).

You can use a number line to add integers.

Move to the right to add positive numbers.

$$2 + 3 = 5$$

Move to the left to add negative numbers.

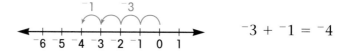

$$^-3 + {}^-1 = {}^-4$$

You can also add integers using absolute values. When the signs of the integers are the same, add the absolute values. The sign of the sum is the same as the sign of the integers.

▶ **EXAMPLE 1**

Add.   ⁻4 + ⁻2

Find the absolute values. $|^-4| = 4$ $|^-2| = 2$
Add the absolute values. $4 + 2 = 6$
The sum is negative.   ⁻6

$$^-4 + {}^-2 = {}^-6$$

When the signs of the integers are different, subtract the smaller absolute value from the larger. Use the sign of the integer with the larger absolute value.

▶ **EXAMPLE 2**

Add.   5 + ⁻7

Math Fact
⁻7 has the larger absolute value.

Find the absolute values. $|^-5| = 5$ $|^-7| = 7$
Subtract the smaller from the larger. $7 - 5 = 2$
The sum is negative.   ⁻2

$$5 + {}^-7 = {}^-2$$

Try These

Add.

1. $5 + {}^-5$

The signs are different.	$5 + {}^-5$
Find the <u>absolute value</u> ▨.	$|5| = $ ▨ 5 $|{}^-5| = $ ▨ 5
<u>subtract</u> ▨ the absolute values.	$5 - 5 = $ ▨ 0
Zero does not have a sign.	▨ 0

$5 + {}^-5 = $ ▨ 0

2. $^-3 + 4$

The signs are different.	$^-3 + 4$
Find the <u>absolute value</u> ▨.	$|{}^-3| = $ ▨ 3 $|4| = $ ▨ 4
<u>subtract</u> ▨ the smaller from the larger.	$4 - 3 = $ ▨ 1
4 ▨ has the larger absolute value.	

$^-3 + 4 = $ ▨ 1

Practice

Add.

1. $6 + {}^-3$ 3

2. $4 + {}^-2$ 2

3. $^-4 + {}^-5$ $^-9$

4. $8 + {}^-5$ 3

5. $3 + {}^-9$ $^-6$

6. $^-5 + 7$ 2

7. $^-1 + {}^-5$ $^-6$

8. $^-4 + 0$ $^-4$

9. $3 + 3$ 6

10. $8 + {}^-8$ 0

11. $0 + {}^-9$ $^-9$

12. $^-3 + {}^-2$ $^-5$

13. $^-4 + {}^-3$ $^-7$

14. $^-10 + 10$ 0

15. $^-1 + 7$ 6

Cooperative Learning

16. Explain to a partner how to add the integers in number 6 in **Practice.** Possible answer: Find the absolute values of $^-5$ and 7. Subtract the smaller from the larger. 7 has a larger absolute value. So, the answer is positive 2.

17. Write an addition problem with integers. Ask a partner to add the integers. Check the work with a number line. Possible answer: $4 + {}^-6$; $\|4\| = 4$, $\|{}^-6\| = 6$; $6 - 4 = 2$; $\|{}^-6\|$ is larger than $\|4\|$, so the sign on 2 is negative; $4 + {}^-6 = {}^-2$.

Check:

1·4 ▶ Subtraction

Getting Started
Draw a number line on the chalkboard. Have students use the number line to subtract whole numbers. Point out that subtraction is a move to the left.

You can use a number line to see how subtracting integers is like adding integers.

This shows the subtraction: $5 - 3 = 2$

This shows the addition: $5 + {}^-3 = 2$

Subtracting 3 is the same as adding $^-3$.

Remember
3 is the opposite of $^-3$.

Subtracting an integer is the same as adding its opposite. You can write subtraction as addition.

▶ **EXAMPLE 1**

Subtract. $^-2 - {}^-4$

Change to adding the opposite of $^-4$. $^-2 + {}^+4$

Find the absolute values. $|{}^-2| = 2$ $|{}^+4| = 4$

Subtract the smaller from the larger. $4 - 2 = 2$

$^+4$ has a larger absolute value. $^+2$

$^-2 - {}^-4 = 2$

▶ **EXAMPLE 2**

Subtract. $^-3 - 6$

Change to adding the opposite of 6. $^-3 + {}^-6$

Find the absolute values. $|{}^-3| = 3$ $|{}^-6| = 6$

Add the absolute values. $3 + 6 = 9$

$^-3$ and $^-6$ are both negative. $^-9$

$^-3 - 6 = {}^-9$

▶ **EXAMPLE 3**

Subtract. $5 - {}^-2$

Remember
$^+2$ is the same as 2.

Change to adding the opposite of $^-2$. $5 + {}^+2$

Add the integers. $5 + 2 = 7$

$5 - {}^-2 = 7$

Try These

Subtract.

1. $^-1 - 4$

Change to adding the opposite of 4. $^-1 + \blacksquare$ $^-4$

Find the absolute values. $|^-1| = 1$
$|^-4| = 4$

Add the absolute values. $4 \blacksquare 1 = \blacksquare$ $^+$ 5

$^-1$ and $^-4$ are negative. $\blacksquare$ $^-5$

$^-1 - 4 = \blacksquare$ $^-5$

2. $^-7 - ^-3$

Change to adding the opposite of $\blacksquare$. $^-3$ $^-7 + \blacksquare$ $^+3$

Find the absolute values. $|^-7| = 7$
$^+3 |\blacksquare| = 3$

Subtract the larger from the smaller. $7 \blacksquare 3 = \blacksquare$ $^-$ 4

$^-7$ has the larger absolute value.

$^-7 - ^-3 = \blacksquare$ $^-4$

Practice

Subtract.

1. $^-1 - ^-3$ 2

2. $6 - ^-3$ 9

3. $5 - 6$ $^-1$

4. $^-4 - ^-5$ 1

5. $8 - ^-5$ 13

6. $0 - 8$ $^-8$

7. $2 - ^-4$ 6

8. $^-3 - 1$ $^-4$

9. $4 - 6$ $^-2$

10. $7 - 7$ 0

11. $0 - ^-9$ 9

12. $^-3 - ^-11$ 8

13. $^-10 - 13$ $^-23$

14. $^-20 - ^-30$ 10

15. $25 - ^-25$ 50

16. Write the problem: $^-4 - ^-5$. Change to adding the opposite of $^-5$: $^-4 + 5$. Find the absolute values: $|^-4| = 4, |5| = 5$. Subtract 4 from 5. 5 has the larger absolute value, so the answer is positive. $^-4 - ^-5$ is 1.

Cooperative Learning

16. Explain to a partner how to change the subtraction to addition in number **4** in **Practice**. See above.

17. Write a negative and a positive number. Ask a partner to subtract the negative number from the positive number. Check your partner's work. Answers will vary. Possible answer: Write $^-5$ and 4. Subtract $4 - ^-5$. $4 - ^-5$ is 9.

1·5 ▶ **Multiplication**

Getting Started
Discuss the many ways to indicate multiplication. 2×7, 2(7), (2)(7) and $2 \cdot 7$ all mean *two times seven*.

You can use repeated addition to multiply an integer by a whole number.

Math Fact
$2(^-3)$ means
2 times $^-3$.

Addition: $^-3 + ^-3 = ^-6$

Multiplication: $2(^-3) = ^-6$

The product of a positive and a negative integer is negative.

▶ **EXAMPLE 1**

Multiply. $^-2 \cdot 4$

Find the absolute values.

Multiply the absolute values.

The product of a negative and a positive integer is negative.

$^-2 \cdot 4$

$|^-2| = 2$ $|4| = 4$

$2 \cdot 4 = 8$

$^-2 \cdot 4 = ^-8$

The product of two positive integers is positive.
$(2)(3) = 6$

Look at the pattern in these products to find the sign of the product of two negative integers.

$$2 \cdot ^-3 = ^-6$$
$$1 \cdot ^-3 = ^-3$$
$$0 \cdot ^-3 = 0$$
$$^-1 \cdot ^-3 = ?$$
$$^-1 \cdot ^-3 \text{ is } 3.$$

The product of two negative integers is positive.

▶ **EXAMPLE 2**

Math Fact
$(^-4)(^-5)$ means
$^-4$ times $^-5$.

Multiply. $(^-4)(^-5)$

Find the absolute values.

Multiply the absolute values.

The product of two negative integers is positive.

$(^-4)(^-5)$

$|^-4| = 4$ $|^-5| = 5$

$4 \cdot 5 = 20$

$(^-4)(^-5) = ^+20$

Try These

Multiply.

1. $(^-7)(^-3)$

Multiply the
absolute values.

The product of two
negative integers is ■.
positive

$(^-7)(^-3) = $ ■
21

$7 \cdot 3 = $ ■ 21

$(^-7)(^-3) = $ ■ 21

2. $^-4 \cdot 8$

Multiply the ■. absolute values

The product of a negative
integer and a ■ is ■. negative
positive integer

$^-4 \cdot 8 = $ ■
$^-32$

$4 \cdot 8 = $ ■ 32

$^-4 \cdot 8 = $ ■
$^-32$

$^-4 \cdot 8 = $ ■
$^-32$

3. $(5)(^-6)$

Multiply the ■. absolute values
positive

The product of a ■ and
a negative integer is ■.
negative

$(5)(^-6) = $ ■
$^-30$

$5 \cdot $ ■ $ = $ ■ 6 30

$(5)(^-6) = $ ■
$^-30$

4. $(^-3)(0)$

Multiply the ■. absolute values

zero ■ does not have a sign.

$(^-3)(0) = $ ■ 0

3 ■ $\cdot 0 = $ ■ 0

$(^-3)(0) = $ ■
0

Practice

Multiply.

1. $3 \cdot 5$ 15

2. $(2)(^-5)$ $^-10$

3. $^-1 \cdot {}^-7$ 7

4. $(^-4)(^-3)$ 12

5. $6 \cdot 3$ 18

6. $^-6 \cdot 4$ $^-24$

7. $(9)(^-5)$ $^-45$

8. $^-2 \cdot 10$ $^-20$

9. $1 \cdot 6$ 6

10. $2 \cdot {}^-8$ $^-16$

11. $(^-9)(^-2)$ 18

12. $^-11 \cdot 3$ $^-33$

13. $4 \cdot {}^-7$ $^-28$

14. $9 \cdot 3$ 27

15. $(^-10)(^-20)$ 200

Cooperative Learning

16. Explain to a partner how to find the product in number **11**
in **Practice.** Find the absolute values: $|^-9| = 9, |^-2| = 2$. Multiply the absolute values:
$9 \cdot 2 = 18$. Both integers are negative, so the answer is positive: $(^-9)(^-2) = 18$.

17. Write a positive integer and a negative integer. Have a partner
find the product of the numbers. Check the work.
Answers will vary. Possible answer: Write 5 and $^-2$. $5 \cdot {}^-2 = {}^-10$.

More practice is provided in Exercise 3 of the Workbook.

1·6 ▸ Division

Getting Started
Discuss the different ways to indicate division: $9 \div 3$ and $\frac{9}{3}$ both mean *9 divided by 3*. Then have students show the different ways to write 12 divided by 4.

You can use what you know about multiplying integers to divide integers.

$$(^+2)(^+3) = {}^+6 \qquad \longrightarrow \qquad (^+6) \div (^+3) = {}^+2$$
$$(^+2)(^-3) = {}^-6 \qquad \longrightarrow \qquad (^-6) \div (^-3) = {}^+2$$

The quotient of two negative integers is positive.

▸ **EXAMPLE 1**

Divide. $\qquad ^-12 \div {}^-4$

Find the absolute values. $\qquad |^-12| = 12 \qquad |^-4| = 4$

Divide the absolute values. $\qquad 12 \div 4 = 3$

The quotient of two negative integers is positive. $\qquad ^-12 \div {}^-4 = 3$

Look at these products and quotients to find the sign of the quotient of a positive and a negative integer.

$$(^-2)(^-3) = {}^+6 \qquad \longrightarrow \qquad (^+6) \div (^-3) = {}^-2$$
$$(^-2)(^+3) = {}^-6 \qquad \longrightarrow \qquad (^-6) \div (^+3) = {}^-2$$

The quotient of a positive and a negative integer is negative.

▸ **EXAMPLE 2**

Math Fact
$\frac{^-49}{7}$ means $^-49 \div 7$.

Divide. $\qquad \dfrac{^-49}{7}$

Find the absolute values. $\qquad |^-49| = 49 \qquad |7| = 7$

Divide the absolute values. $\qquad 49 \div 7 = 7$

The quotient of a positive integer and a negative integer is negative. $\qquad \dfrac{^-49}{7} = {}^-7$

There are important and helpful facts to know when using division.

Math Fact
$\frac{0}{2}$ means $0 \div 2$.

Zero divided by any number is 0. $\qquad \dfrac{0}{2} = 0$

You cannot divide by 0. $\qquad \dfrac{3}{0}$ is undefined.

Any number divided by itself is 1. $\qquad \dfrac{5}{5} = 1$

Try These

Divide.

1. $^-27 \div ^-9$

Divide the absolute values.

$27 \div \blacksquare = \blacksquare$ 9   3

The quotient of two negative integers is ■. positive

$^-27 \div ^-9 = \blacksquare$ 3   3

$^-27 \div ^-9 = \blacksquare$ 3

2. $\dfrac{0}{23}$

Zero divided by an integer is ■.0

$\dfrac{0}{23} = \blacksquare$ 0

$\dfrac{0}{23} = \dfrac{\blacksquare}{\blacksquare}$ 0

3. $24 \div ^-6$

Divide the ■.   absolute values   24   6   4

The quotient of a ■ integer and a negative integer is negative.   positive

$\blacksquare \div \blacksquare = \blacksquare$ $24 \div ^-6 = \blacksquare$ $^-4$

$24 \div ^-6 = \blacksquare$ $^-4$

4. $\dfrac{^-30}{5}$

Divide the ■.   absolute values   30   5   6

The quotient of a negative integer and a positive integer is ■. negative

$\blacksquare \div \blacksquare = \blacksquare$ $\dfrac{^-30}{5} = \blacksquare$ $^-6$

$\dfrac{^-30}{5} = \blacksquare$ $^-6$

Practice

Divide.

1. $\dfrac{25}{5}$ 5   **2.** $24 \div ^-3$ $^-8$ **3.** $^-10 \div 10$ $^-1$ **4.** $^-9 \div 3$ $^-3$

5. $0 \div ^-11$ 0   **6.** $\dfrac{28}{^-7}$ $^-4$ **7.** $\dfrac{32}{8}$ 4   **8.** $\dfrac{^-18}{0}$ undefined

9. $\dfrac{^-8}{^-4}$ 2   **10.** $^-9 \div ^-9$ 1   **11.** $^-12 \div 4$ $^-3$ **12.** $72 \div 9$ 8

13. $42 \div 0$ undefined   **14.** $\dfrac{^-56}{8}$ $^-7$ **15.** $\dfrac{^-24}{4}$ $^-6$ **16.** $\dfrac{^-30}{^-2}$ 15

Cooperative Learning

17. Explain to a partner how to find the quotient in number **14** in **Practice.** Find the absolute values: $|^-56| = 56$, $|8| = 8$. Divide the absolute values: $56 \div 8 = 7$. The signs are different, so the answer is negative: $^-56 \div 8 = ^-7$.

18. Pick an even number. Ask a partner to find the quotient of the even number divided by $^-2$. Answers will vary. Check the signs of students' work.

1·7 Simplifying Number Expressions

Getting Started
Using a number line, show how to start with $20, spend $5, receive $10 as a present, and end up with $25.

A group of numbers written with operation signs is called an **expression.** You **simplify** an expression when you do the addition, subtraction, multiplication, or division.

You can use the rules that you know about adding and subtracting to add and subtract more than two integers.

▶ **EXAMPLE 1**

Simplify.　　$^-28 + {}^-2 + 15$

Add $^-28$ and $^-2$.　　　　　　$^-28 + {}^-2 + 15$

Add $^-30$ and 15.　　　　　　　$^-30 + 15$

　　　　　　　　　　　　　　　　$^-15$

$^-28 + {}^-2 + 15 = {}^-15$

▶ **EXAMPLE 2**

Simplify.　　$^-3 - 7 + 8$

Rewrite subtraction as addition.

Add $^-3$ and $^-7$.　　　　　　$^-3 + {}^-7 + 8$

Add $^-10$ and 8.　　　　　　　$^-10 + 8$

　　　　　　　　　　　　　　　　$^-2$

$^-3 - 7 + 8 = {}^-2$

Sometimes a minus sign is used in place of a plus sign and negative sign that are next to each other.

　　　$^-5 + {}^-8 = {}^-13$
　　　　　　　　　　　Both mean $^-5$ plus $^-8$ equals $^-13$.
　　　$^-5 - 8 = {}^-13$

▶ **EXAMPLE 3**

Remember
$2 - 12$ means $2 + (^-12)$.

Simplify.　　$^-8 + 10 - 12$

Add $^-8$ and 10.　　　　　　$^-8 + 10 - 12$

Add 2 and $^-12$.　　　　　　　$2 - 12$

　　　　　　　　　　　　　　　　$^-10$

$^-8 + 10 - 12 = {}^-10$

Try These

Simplify each expression.

1. ⁻6 − ⁻2 + 10
      addition
Rewrite as ▪.
Add.

                +
                ⁻6 ▪ 2 + 10
                ⁻4 ▪ + 10
                      ▪
                      6

⁻6 − ⁻2 + 10 = ▪ 6

2. ⁻11 − 15 + 6
Add. ⁻11 and ⁻15.
Add ⁻26 and 6.

                        ⁻15
              ⁻11 + ▪ + 6
              ⁻26 ▪ + 6
                    ▪
                    ⁻20

⁻11 − 15 + 6 = ▪ ⁻20

3. ⁻5 − 15
Add ⁻5 and ⁻15.

                  ⁻15
          ⁻5 + ▪
               ▪
            ⁻20

⁻5 − 15 = ▪ ⁻20

4. ⁻12 − 8 + 14
Add ⁻12 and ▪. ⁻8
Add ▪ and 14.

          ⁻12 + ⁻8 + 14
          ⁻20 ▪ + 14
        ⁻20
                    ▪
                    ⁻6

⁻12 − 8 + 14 = ▪ ⁻6

Practice

Simplify.

1. 2 − ⁻3 + 10   15

2. ⁻5 − 1 + 6   0

3. 6 − ⁻10 + ⁻4   12

4. 8 − 17 − 8   ⁻17

5. ⁻4 − ⁻3 + ⁻1   ⁻2

6. ⁻3 + 9 − 12   ⁻6

7. ⁻8 + ⁻8 − 16   ⁻32

8. 0 + ⁻5 − 3   ⁻8

9. ⁻5 − ⁻12 − 16   ⁻9

10. ⁻3 + 10 − 9   ⁻2

11. ⁻7 − 4 + 11   0

12. ⁻8 − 4 + ⁻10   ⁻22

13. ⁻8 + 14   6

14. ⁻5 + 5   0

15. ⁻3 − 3   ⁻6

16. 4 − 10 − 26   ⁻32

17. ⁻16 + 9 − 5   ⁻12

18. 25 − 12 − 13   0

Cooperative Learning

19. Explain to a partner how to simplify the expression in number 5 in **Practice.** Rewrite the expression as an addition problem: ⁻4 + 3 + ⁻1. Add ⁻4 and 3: ⁻4 + 3 = ⁻1. Add ⁻1 and ⁻1: ⁻1 + ⁻1 = ⁻2.

20. Write an expression in which you add two negative numbers. Have a partner simplify the expression. Check the work. Answers will vary. Possible answer: Write ⁻8 + ⁻3; −8 + ⁻3 = −11.

More practice is provided in Exercise 3 of the Workbook.

1·8 ▶ Exponents

Getting Started
Show students that a number can be multiplied by itself several times. For example, $3 \times 3 \times 3$ or $2 \times 2 \times 2 \times 2$. Have students find the product of each repeated multiplication.

There is a shorter way to show multiplication when the factors are the same.

exponent
↓

$$4 \cdot 4 \cdot 4 = 4^3 \qquad 4^3 = 64 \leftarrow \text{power}$$

base 4 is a factor ↑
3 times   base

In 4^3, 4 is the **base**, and 3 is the **exponent**. The exponent tells how many times the base is used as a factor. The exponent also tells the **power** of the base. 64 is the third power of 4. You can use other numbers as exponents. Read these examples.

$$4^1 = 4 \qquad\qquad \text{4 is a factor 1 time.}$$
$$4^2 = 4 \cdot 4 = 16 \qquad \text{4 is a factor 2 times.}$$

▶ **EXAMPLE 1**

Find the power. 6^2 $\qquad$ 6^2

Use 6 as a factor 2 times. $\qquad$ $6 \cdot 6 = 36$

$6^2 = 36$

Watch for the sign of the base. Parentheses can be used to show the base.

$$^-2^3 \qquad\qquad (^-12)^2$$
2 is the base. $\qquad$ $^-12$ is the base.

▶ **EXAMPLE 2**

Find the power. $^-2^3$ $\qquad$ $^-(2)^3$

Use 2 as a factor 3 times. $\qquad$ $^-(2 \cdot 2 \cdot 2) = {}^-8$

$^-2^3 = {}^-8$

▶ **EXAMPLE 3**

Remember
The product of two negative numbers is positive.

Find the power. $(^-12)^2$ $\qquad$ $(^-12)^2$

Use $^-12$ as a factor 2 times. $\qquad$ $(^-12)(^-12) = 144$

$(^-12)^2 = 144$

Try These

Find the power.

1. $(^-5)^3$

    Use $^-5$ as a factor $(^-5)^3$
    3 ■ times.

    Multiply. $(^-5) \cdot (\overset{^-5}{■}) \cdot (\overset{^-5}{■})$
                        $\underset{^-125}{■}$

    $(^-5)^3 = $ ■ $^-125$

2. 3^4

    Use $\overset{3}{■}$ as a factor 3^4
    4 times.

    Multiply. $\overset{3}{■} \cdot \overset{3}{■} \cdot \overset{3}{■} \cdot \overset{3}{■}$
                        $\underset{81}{■}$

    $3^4 = $ ■ 81

Practice

Find the power.

1. 6^2 36

2. 8^2 64

3. 2^3 8

4. 5^3 125

5. $^-13^2$ $^-169$

6. 50^2 2,500

7. $(^-30)^3$ $^-27,000$

8. 5^4 625

9. 9^4 6,561

10. $^-10^4$ $^-10,000$

11. $(^-4)^2$ 16

12. $(^-11)^2$ 121

13. $^-(3)^3$ $^-27$

14. $(^-7)^2$ 49

15. $(^-4)^3$ $^-64$

16. $(^-10)^4$ 10,000

17. 4^3 64

18. $^-(5)^2$ $^-25$

19. $(^-1)^4$ 1

20. $(^-1)^3$ $^-1$

Cooperative Learning

21. Explain to a partner how to find the power in number **10**
in **Practice.** The base is 10 and the exponent is 4. So, use 10 as a factor 4 times. The negative
sign stays on the outside. $^-(10)(10)(10)(10) = {}^-10,000.$

22. Write a power with a negative number as the base and a positive
number as the exponent. Make sure you use parentheses to show
the base. Have a partner find the power. Check the work.
Possible answer: Write $(^-6)^3.$ $(^-6)(^-6)(^-6) = {}^-216.$

Getting Started
Be sure that
students can
enter a negative
number on their calculators.
On some calculators the
number is entered first and
then made negative.

1·9

Calculator: Performing Operations

You can use a calculator to perform operations with positive and negative numbers. Follow the same rules you learned for adding, subtracting, multiplying, and dividing with integers.

▶ **EXAMPLE 1**

Add. $^-53.62 + 180.8$

Find the absolute values.

$$|^-53.62| = 53.62$$
$$|180.8| = 180.8$$

Subtract the smaller absolute value from the larger. $180.8 - 53.62$ **Display**

Enter 180.8
by pressing:

| 1 | 8 | 0 | . | 8 |

180.8

Remember
The number with the larger absolute value is positive.

Subtract 53.62
by pressing:

| − | 5 | 3 | . | 6 | 2 | = |

127.18

$^-53.62 + 180.8 = 127.18$

▶ **EXAMPLE 2**

Divide. $\dfrac{546}{^-13}$

Find the absolute values.

$$|546| = 546$$
$$|^-13| = 13$$

Divide the absolute values. $546 \div 13$ **Display**

Enter 546
by pressing:

| 5 | 4 | 6 |

546

Remember
The quotient of a positive number and a negative number is negative.

Divide by 13
by pressing:

| ÷ | 1 | 3 | = |

42

$\dfrac{546}{^-13} = {^-42}$

▶ **EXAMPLE 3**

Subtract. $30 - 45$ **Display**

Enter 30
by pressing:

| 3 | 0 |

30

Subtract 45
by pressing:

| − | 4 | 5 | = |

-15

$30 - 45 = {^-15}$

Practice

Use your calculator. Find the sum, difference, product, or quotient.

1. $^-125 - 159$ $^-284$
2. $99 + (^-54)$ 45
3. $^-100 + 76$ $^-24$
4. $^-231 + 149$ $^-82$
5. $\frac{^-598}{^-23}$ 26
6. $(^-29)(^-57)$ $1,653$
7. $^-23(71)$ $^-1,633$
8. $\frac{^-247}{13}$ $^-19$

Math Connection

ELEVATION

One way to describe a place is by its elevation. Elevation tells how high a place is above *sea level*. Sea level is where the land meets the sea. Elevation can also tell you how far a place is below sea level.

Elevation can be shown on a map. At sea level, a place is at zero elevation. Like the points on a number line, elevation tells the distance from zero. Heights above sea level are like the positive numbers. Distances below sea level are like the negative numbers. Both tell the distance from zero, but in different directions.

The tallest mountain in the world is Mount Everest. It is 29,028 feet above sea level at the top. The floors of the oceans have deep trenches. Some trenches are more than 35,000 feet below sea level.

Elevation can affect how you live. In higher places, the air is thinner. If you go from a lower to a higher place, you might feel some changes. Your ears might "pop." You might find it hard to breathe at first. You could even have trouble baking a cake. Knowing about elevation helps people adjust to these changes no matter where they live.

Getting Started
Give examples
of everyday
situations in
which guesses are made
and then revised, such as
how much time they need for
homework. Ask students to
provide more examples.

1·10 | # Problem Solving: Guess, Check, Revise

You can guess an answer to a problem and check to see if the guess is the correct answer. If the guess is not correct, **revise** or change your guess until you get the right answer.

▶ **EXAMPLE**

José drove a total of 80 miles in two days. He drove 20 miles less on the first day than on the second day. How many miles did José drive on each day?

READ **What do you need to find out?**
You need to find how many miles José drove on each day.

PLAN **What do you need to do?**
You can guess how many miles José drove on the second day. Use the guess to find how many miles he drove on the first day. Then see if the two numbers add up to 80 miles.

DO **Follow the plan.**
Guess for second day: 60 miles
Subtract 20 to find miles
driven first day: $60 - 20 = 40$ miles
Add: $60 + 40 = 100$; too big

Revise guess for second day: 40 miles
Subtract 20 to find miles
driven first day: $40 - 20 = 20$ miles
Add: $40 + 20 = 60$; too small

Revise guess for second day: 50 miles
Subtract 20 to find miles
driven first day: $50 - 20 = 30$ miles
Add: $50 + 30 = 80$; correct

CHECK **Does your answer make sense?**
Total miles driven are $30 + 50 = 80$. ✓

José drove 30 miles the first day and 50 miles the second.

Try These

1. Sue buys a shirt and jeans for $42.00. The jeans cost $14.00 more than the shirt. How much does each cost?

   Guess for shirt: $15
   Jeans cost $14 more: ■. $29
   Check: $15 + $29 = $44   Too big, but close.
   Revise guess for shirt: $14
   Jeans cost $14 more: ■. $28
   Check: $14 + ■ = $42   Correct.
   $28
   So, the jeans cost ■ and the shirt costs ■. $14 $28

2. The product of two integers is 32. One integer is twice the other. What are the integers?

   Guess for first integer: 3   6
   Second integer is twice the first: ■.
   Check: 3 • ■ = 18   Too small. 6
   Revise guess for integer: 4
   Second integer: ■. 8
   Check: 4 • ■ = 32   Correct.
   8
   So, the integers are ■ and ■.
   8   4

Practice

Guess, check, and revise to solve each problem.

1. Alexandra put some money in her savings account in July. She put three times that amount into her savings account in August. She saved a total of $140.00 in July and August. How much did she save each month? $35.00 in July, $105.00 in August

2. The sum of two integers is 9. The product of the integers is 14. What are the integers? 7, 2

3. The drama club sold 240 tickets to the play. They sold 20 more student tickets than adult tickets. How many of each type of ticket did they sell? 110 adult tickets, 130 student tickets

Cooperative Learning

4. Explain to a partner how to find the integers in number 2 in **Practice**. Answers will vary. Guess: 3 and 6. Test: 3 + 6 = 9, but (3)(6) = 18. Too high. Revise: 7 and 2. Test: 7 +2 = 9, and (7)(2) = 14. Correct.

5. Write a problem about the product of two integers. Make one integer three times the other. Find the product of the two integers. Ask a partner to find the two integers by looking only at the product. Answers will vary. Possible answer: The product of two integers is 27. One integer is three times the other. What are the two integers? 3 and 9: 3(3) = 9, 3 • 9 = 27.

1·11 ▶ # Application: Information from Broken-Line Graphs

Information from graphs can be used to solve problems. The graph below is a **broken-line graph**. It shows a company's earnings over 6 months.

Months	Earnings
January	5
February	6
March	−8
April	−6
May	−2
June	4

Earnings Over Six Months
in Thousands of Dollars

▶ **EXAMPLE 1**

What were the company's earnings in May?

Find the point above May.
Read across to the number to the left.   ⁻2

The company's earnings were ⁻$2,000 in May.
The company lost money in May.

▶ **EXAMPLE 2**

Which month had the highest earnings?
What were the company's earnings for that month?

Find the highest point.   The highest point is
Read the month for this point.   above February.

Find the earnings for February.
Read across to the number to the left.   6

The highest earnings were in February.
The company earned $6,000.

Try These

Use the graph about earnings to answer the questions.

1. Which month had the lowest earnings? What were the company's earnings that month?

The lowest point is above ■. March

Read across to the number to the left.
$\overline{}8$ ■

March ■ has the lowest earnings. Earnings were $\overline{}$\$■,000.
$\quad\quad\quad\quad 8$

2. What is the difference between the highest earnings and lowest earnings?

Find the highest point.
$\begin{array}{c}6\\■\end{array}$

Find the lowest point. $\overline{}8$ ■

Subtract. $6\,■ - ■\,\overline{}8$

The difference between the highest and lowest earnings is \$■,000.
$\quad 14$

Practice

Use this graph to answer the questions.

1. Which month had the highest temperature? December

2. Which had the lowest? February

3. How much higher is the temperature in December than in February? 7°

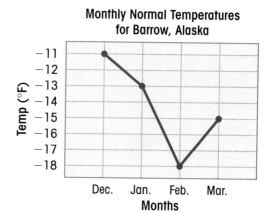

Monthly Normal Temperatures for Barrow, Alaska

Cooperative Learning

4. Explain to a partner how to use the graph to answer number 3 in **Practice.** Find the highest point: ⁻11. Find the lowest point: ⁻18. Subtract ⁻18 from ⁻11: ⁻11 − ⁻18 = 7.

5. Ask a partner to find the total of the normal temperatures. Check the work. Add the absolute values of each month's normal temperature. The sign is negative. Answer: ⁻57.

Summary

The absolute value of a number is its distance from zero. Opposites have the same absolute value.
To add two integers with the same sign, add their absolute values. Use the sign of the integers as the sign of the sum.
To add integers with different signs, subtract the absolute values. Use the sign of the integer with the larger absolute value as the sign of the sum.
To subtract an integer, add its opposite.
The product or quotient of a positive integer and a negative integer is negative. The product or quotient of two negative integers is positive.
Guess, check, and revise is a way to solve problems.
You can use a broken-line graph to find information.

More vocabulary review is provided in Exercise 1 of the Classroom Resource Binder.

positive numbers
negative numbers
integers
absolute value
opposites
expression
exponent
base
power
revise
broken-line graph

Vocabulary Review

Complete the sentences with words from the box.

1. In 3^2, 3 is called the ____. base

2. The ____ are the numbers to the right of zero. positive numbers

3. When you change a guess, you ____. revise

4. Numbers that are the same distance from zero but on opposite sides are ____. opposites

5. The ____ are the numbers to the left of zero. negative numbers

6. The distance of a number from 0 is called the absolute value

7. The exponent tells how many times the base is a factor.

8. A ____ is a graph that is made up of pieces of straight lines. broken-line graph

9. The numbers . . . $^-3, ^-2, ^-1, 0, 1, 2, 3, . . .$ are ____. integers

10. Numbers with operation signs make an ____. expression

11. A ____ is the result of multiplying when factors are the same. power

Chapter Quiz   More assessment is provided in the Classroom Resource Binder.

Graph on a number line.

1. ⁻5

-6 -5 -4 -3 -2 -1 0

2. 3

-2 -1 0 1 2 3 4

3. ⁻1

-3 -2 -1 0 1 2 3

Compare. Use > or <.

4. ⁻10 and ⁻8 <

5. 4 and ⁻5 >

6. 2 and 9 <

Find the absolute value of each integer.

7. |7| 7

8. |⁻10| 10

9. |0| 0

Find the opposite of each integer.

10. ⁺6 ⁻6

11. ⁻12 12

12. 8 ⁻8

Simplify.

13. ⁻5 + ⁻7 ⁻12

14. 8 + ⁻10 ⁻2

15. ⁻2 − ⁻5 3

16. ⁻5 − 9 ⁻14

17. (⁻2)(⁻6) 12

18. (3)(⁻9) ⁻27

19. ⁻27 ÷ 3 ⁻9

20. ⁻6 ÷ ⁻6 1

21. (⁻4)² 16

22. ⁻5 + 9 − 14 ⁻10

23. ⁻2 − 2 − 4 ⁻8

24. 9 − 15 + 6 0

Guess, check, and revise to solve this problem.

25. The sum of two integers is 9 and their product is 18. What are the integers? 6, 3

Use the graph of Alex's savings to answer the question.

26. How much more money did Alex save in August than in June? $40.00

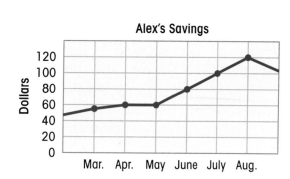

Additional Practice for this chapter is provided on p. 413 of this text.

To play an instrument, you need to know how to read notes and keep a beat. Algebra has its own symbols and rules. What are some rules about integers?

Learning Objectives

- Use order of operations.
- Simplify number and variable expressions.
- Evaluate variable expressions.
- Identify an equation as true or false.
- Use a calculator to evaluate variable expressions.
- Solve problems by writing equations for word statements.
- Apply concepts and skills to using geometry formulas.

Words to Know

Order of Operations	rules that tell you which operations to do first
variable	a letter that represents a number
terms	parts of an expression separated by a + or − sign
constants	numbers, or quantities, that do not change
coefficient	a number that multiplies a variable
like terms	terms that have the same variables with the same exponents
substitute	replace a variable with a number or expression
equation	a statement that two expressions are equal
Commutative Property	the order of two numbers does not matter when you add or multiply
Associative Property	the grouping of more than two numbers does not matter when you add or multiply
Identity Property	adding 0, or multiplying by 1, does not change a number
Addition Property of Opposites	the sum of a number and its opposite is 0
Zero Property of Multiplication	the product of any number and 0 is 0
Distributive Property	multiply a sum or difference by a number by multiplying each term of the sum or difference by the number

Recipe Project

Choose a simple recipe. Copy the ingredients and directions onto an index card. Trade recipes with a partner. Discuss any abbreviations, such as tsp. or °F, you find in each other's recipe. Then change the order of the directions in the recipe and describe what might happen.

Project See the Classroom Resource Binder for a scoring rubric to assess this project.

2-1 ▶ Order of Operations

Getting Started
Discuss the need for an Order of Operations in everyday life. Then apply the need to math. Show how $3 + 6 \times 2$ can be evaluated as 9×2 or $3 + 12$.

Numbers and operation signs are used to write expressions. You simplify an expression when you perform the operations. When there is more than one operation, you must follow the **Order of Operations**.

1. First, multiply and divide from left to right.
2. Then, add and subtract from left to right.

▶ **EXAMPLE 1**

Simplify.　　$16 - 6 \cdot 2$

Multiply first.　　　　　　　　　　　$16 - 6 \cdot 2$

Subtract next.　　　　　　　　　　　$16 - 12$
　　　　　　　　　　　　　　　　　　　4

The value of $16 - 6 \cdot 2$ is 4.

▶ **EXAMPLE 2**

Simplify.　　$2 + 12 \div 4 - 10$

Divide first.　　　　　　　　　$2 + 12 \div 4 - 10$

Add.　　　　　　　　　　　　　$2 + 3 - 10$

Subtract.　　　　　　　　　　　$5 - 10$
　　　　　　　　　　　　　　　　　-5

The value of $2 + 12 \div 4 - 10$ is -5.

Sometimes, an expression contains a power. Find the value of the power first.

▶ **EXAMPLE 3**

Remember
2^2 means $2 \cdot 2$.

Simplify.　　$3 + 8 \div 2^2$

Find the value of the power.　　$3 + 8 \div 2^2$

Divide.　　　　　　　　　　　$3 + 8 \div 4$

Add.　　　　　　　　　　　　$3 + 2$
　　　　　　　　　　　　　　　　5

The value of $3 + 8 \div 2^2$ is 5.

Practice

Simplify.

1. $3 \cdot 1 + 4$ 7

2. $8 \div 4 + 4 \cdot 2$ 10

3. $5 + 8 \cdot 3 + 2$ 31

4. $14 \div 7 + 3$ 5

5. $2 \cdot 4 - 9$ -1

6. $10 \cdot 3 + 1 - 16$ 15

7. $2 + 3^2$ 11

8. $32 - 30 \div 10$ 29

9. $-2 + 3 - 6 + 2$ -3

10. $28 \div 7 \cdot 2$ 8

11. $10 - 5 \cdot 3$ -5

12. $10 \div 2 + 8$ 13

13. $30 + 5 \div 5$ 31

14. $9 + 15 \div 15 - 10$ 0

15. $15 - 2 \cdot 2$ 11

16. $2 + 12 \cdot 2 \div 6$ 6

17. $5 \cdot 4 \div 2^2$ 5

18. $24 - 25 \div 5^2$ 23

19. $-9 \div 3 + 4 \cdot 7$ 25

20. $5 + 2 \cdot 4^2 - 25$ 12

21. $24 \div 4 - 6$ 0

Cooperative Learning

22. Explain to a partner how to simplify the expression in number **16** in **Practice.** Possible answer: Multiply 2 by 12; Divide 24 by 6; Add 2 and 4.
       $2 + [(12 \cdot 2) \div 6] = 6.$

23. Work with a partner to simplify $9 \cdot 5 \div 15 - 3$. Take turns doing the steps. Check each other's work. $9 \cdot 5 \div 15 - 3 = 45 \div 15 - 3 = 3 - 3 = 0$

2-2 ► Grouping Symbols

Getting Started
Review Order of Operations. Have a volunteer simplify
$4 \cdot 7 - 3$. (25)

Sometimes, expressions contain parentheses. Be sure to do the operations inside the parentheses first.

► **EXAMPLE 1**

Simplify. $4 \cdot (7 - 3)$

Do the subtraction in parentheses first. $4 \cdot (\underline{7 - 3})$

Multiply. $4 \cdot 4$

    $\underline{16}$

$4 \cdot (7 - 3)$ is 16.

► **EXAMPLE 2**

Simplify. $(4 + 5) \div 3^2$

Do the addition in parentheses first. $(\underline{4 + 5}) \div 3^2$

Remember
3^2 means $3 \cdot 3$.

Find the value of the power. $9 \div 3^2$

Divide. $9 \div 9$

    $\underline{1}$

$(4 + 5) \div 3^2$ is 1.

► **EXAMPLE 3**

Simplify. $-(3 - 8) - 9$

Do the subtraction in parentheses first. $-(\underline{3 - 8}) - 9$

    $-(-5) - 9$

Math Fact
$-(-5)$ means $-1(-5)$.

Multiply. $\underline{-1(-5)} - 9$

Subtract. $\underline{5 - 9}$

    $\underline{-4}$

$-(3 - 8) - 9$ is -4.

Try These

Simplify.

1. $20 - (8 - 4) \div 2$
subtraction
Do ▨ in parentheses.	$20 - (8 - 4) \div 2$
Divide.	$20 - 4 ▨ \div 2$
Subtract.	$20 - \quad 2 ▨$
	$18 ▨$

$20 - (8 - 4) \div 2$ is ▨. 18

2. $2^3 - (2 + 6)$
addition
Do ▨ in parentheses.	$2^3 - (2 + 6)$
Find the value of the ▨. power	$2^3 - \quad ▨ 8$
Subtract.	$▨ - \quad ▨ 8$
	8
	$▨$
	0

$2^3 - (2 + 6)$ is ▨. 0

Practice

Simplify.

1. $(5 + 3) \bullet 2$ 16

2. $6 \div (6 - 3)$ 2

3. $3(2 + 7) - 7$ 20

4. $10 \div (5 \bullet 2)$ 1

5. $12 + 2(9 - 5)$ 20

6. $-6(1 - 3)$ 12

7. $(9 - 5) \div 2$ 2

8. $3^2 \div (4 - 3)$ 9

9. $(5 - 6) \bullet 3$ -3

10. $2(7 - 3)$ 8

11. $-(4 - 6)$ 2

12. $2^3(3 - 2)$ 8

13. $3(4 + 6) \div 5$ 6

14. $(4 + 16) \div 5 \bullet 2$ 8

15. $14 - (8 - 4)$ 10

16. $3(2 - 6) \div 2$ -6

17. $9 - (4 - 2)$ 7

18. $-2(3 \bullet 3)$ -18

19. $4^2 - 3(2 + 1)$ 7

20. $(12 - 8) \div 2 \bullet 3$ 6

21. $4^3 \div 8(12 - 11)$ 8

Cooperative Learning

22. Possible answer: Add 4 and 6; Multiply 10 by 3; Divide 30 by 5. $[3(4 + 6)] \div 5 = 6$.

22. Listen while a partner explains how to simplify the expression in number **13** in **Practice**. Follow the steps as your partner explains. See above.

23. Simplify $6 - 4 \div 2$. Have a partner simplify $(6 - 4) \div 2$. Compare your answers. Why are they different? When the first problem is simplified, the answer is 4, because you must divide before you subtract. The second problem is 1, because the parentheses mean you now subtract before you divide.

2-3 ▶ Variable Expressions

A **variable** is a letter that stands for a number. Any letter can stand for any number. The letter t could be used to stand for a time like 4 hours.

You can write expressions with variables, operations, and numbers. The variable expressions below contain addition and subtraction.

$$4 + t \qquad t - 5 \qquad t + h$$

You can show multiplication in different ways.

$$3 \text{ times } a \rightarrow 3 \times a \quad \text{or} \quad 3 \cdot a \quad \text{or} \quad 3a \quad \text{or} \quad 3(a)$$
$$c \text{ times } d \rightarrow c \times d \quad \text{or} \quad c \cdot d \quad \text{or} \quad cd \quad \text{or} \quad c(d)$$

Show division with a fraction bar or a division sign.

$$4x \text{ divided by } 5 \rightarrow \frac{4x}{5} \quad \text{or} \quad 4x \div 5$$

▶ **EXAMPLE 1**

Complete. xy means x ? y

xy means x ? y

xy means x times y.

xy means $x \cdot y$

▶ **EXAMPLE 2**

Complete. $3s^2$ means 3 ? s ? s

$3s^2$ means 3 ? s^2

$3s^2$ means 3 times s^2.

$3s^2$ means $3 \cdot s^2$

s^2 means s times s.

$3s^2$ means $3 \cdot s \cdot s$

▶ **EXAMPLE 3**

Complete. $\frac{3x}{2}$ means 3 ? x ? 2

$\frac{3x}{2}$ means 3 ? x ? 2

$3x$ means 3 times x.

$\frac{3x}{2}$ means $3 \cdot x$? 2

$\frac{3x}{2}$ means $3x$ divided by 2.

$\frac{3x}{2}$ means $3 \cdot x \div 2$

Practice

Complete. Replace ? with +, −, •, or ÷.

1. $3y$ means 3 ? y. •

2. $\frac{k}{4}$ means k ? 4. ÷

3. $4b - 3$ means 4 ? b ? 3. •, −

4. $7a^2$ means 7 ? a ? a. •, •

5. $2d + 9$ means 2 ? d ? 9 •, +

6. $3a^2 + 1$ means 3 ? a ? a? 1. •, •, +

7. r^3 means r ? r ? r. •, •

8. $-8n + 3$ means -8 ? n ? 3. •, +

9. $\frac{2m}{4}$ means 2 ? m ? 4. •, ÷

10. $3x^2 - 1$ means 3 ? x ? x ? 1. •, •, −

11. $a + 4b$ means a ? 4 ? b. +, •

12. $pq - 3$ means p ? q ? 3. •, −

13. $\frac{6x}{y}$ means 6 ? x ? y. •, ÷

14. $-6 + 3w$ means -6 ? 3 ? w. +, •

15. $2x^2 + 3y$ means 2 ? x ? x ? 3 ? y.
          •, •, +, •

16. $-8a - 2b^2$ means -8 ? a ? 2 ? b? b.
          •, −, •, •

Cooperative Learning

17. Explain to a partner how to complete number **10** in **Practice**.
Possible answer: $3x^2 - 1$ means "3 times x times x minus 1."

18. Write a variable expression using addition and multiplication. Have a partner write the meaning. Check the work.
Possible answer: $3y + 4$; This means: $3 \cdot y + 4$.

More practice is provided in Exercises 7 and 11 of the Workbook.

2·4 ▶ Like Terms

The different parts of an expression are called the
terms of an expression. They are the parts separated
by addition or subtraction. Numbers alone are
called **constants**.

$-4xy$	$x^2 - 16$	$-4y + 6x - xy$
one term	two terms	three terms

▶ **EXAMPLE 1**

Remember
4 x − 2 x is the same as
4 x + (−2 x).

Name the terms and constant in $4x - 2x + 7$.

Look for the parts separated by + or −. $4x - 2x + 7$

There are three terms: $4x$, $-2x$, and 7.
7 is a constant.

A **coefficient** is a number that multiplies a variable.

$3x \rightarrow$	$3 \bullet x$	3 is the coefficient of x.
$a^2 \rightarrow$	$1 \bullet a^2$	1 is the coefficient of a^2.
$-y \rightarrow$	$-1 \bullet y$	-1 is the coefficient of y.

▶ **EXAMPLE 2**

Math Fact
− x means −1 • x.

Name the coefficients in $3x^2 - x + 4$.

Look for the numbers that multiply variables. $3x^2 - 1x + 4$

The coefficients are 3 and -1.

Like terms have the same variables with the same
exponents. All numbers are like terms.

Math Fact
yx is the same as xy.

Like terms	Unlike terms
$3xy$ and $-yx$	x and y
$4a$ and $3a$	a and ab
$-5x^2$ and $2x^2$	x and x^2

▶ **EXAMPLE 3**

Are $3x^2y$ and yx^2 like or unlike?

Same variables with same exponents $3x^2y$ and yx^2

$3x^2y$ and yx^2 are like terms.

Practice

Name the terms in each expression.

1. $3n + 4p + 2$ 3n, 4p, 2   **2.** $-g^2 + 8k + 9$ $-g^2; 8k, 9$ **3.** $7a^3b^2c$ $7a^3b^2c$

Name the coefficients in each expression.

4. $3a$ 3

5. $x - 7y + 8$ 1, −7

6. $-ab + 9a$ −1, 9

7. $-2a^2 + 3a$ −2, 3

8. $y^2 - 2y - 15$ 1, −2

9. $x^2 + 2xy + y^2$ 1, 2, 1

Are the terms like or unlike?

10. $3n$ and $3n^2$ unlike

11. $12wc$ and $12cw$ like

12. 10 and −2   like

Cooperative Learning

13. Explain to a partner how to decide if the terms are like or unlike in number **7** in **Practice.** Exponents are different, so they are unlike.

14. Write a variable expression with like terms. Have a partner name the terms, the coefficients, and the like terms. Check the work.
Possible answer: $2x + 4x - 5y^2 + y^2$; terms are 2x, 4x, $-5y^2$, and y^2; coefficients are 2, 4, −5, and 1; like terms are 2x, 4x and $-5y^2$, y^2.

More practice is provided in Exercise 8 of the Workbook.

Getting Started
Point out that when you combine quantities, the units need to be alike. Use objects to show that 3 pens $+4$ pens $= 7$ pens, but 3 books $+ 4$ pens $\neq 7$ pens. Apply this to math. $\$3 + \$4 = \$7$, but $3¢ + \$4 \neq \$7$.

2·5 Combining Like Terms

You can simplify variable expressions by combining terms. You can only combine like terms.

$$2a \quad + \quad 3a \quad = \quad 5a$$

$$\underbrace{a + a}_{} + \underbrace{a + a + a}_{} \qquad \underbrace{a + a + a + a + a}_{}$$

So, $\quad 2a + 3a = 5a$

You combine like terms by adding the coefficients. For number terms, just add or subtract the numbers.

▶ **EXAMPLE 1**

Simplify. $\quad 5n + n$

Look for like terms. $\qquad\qquad\qquad\qquad\qquad 5n + n$

Math Fact
n means $1 \cdot n$.

Add the coefficients. $\qquad\qquad\qquad\qquad\quad 5n + 1n$

$$\underbrace{\qquad}_{6n}$$

$5n + n$ is the same as $6n$.

Sometimes, you need to combine more than two terms. Combine them two at a time. Combine all like terms in an expression.

▶ **EXAMPLE 2**

Simplify. $\quad 6x^2 + x^2 - 9x^2$

Look for like terms. $\qquad\qquad\qquad 6x^2 + x^2 - 9x^2$

Add the coefficients. $\qquad\qquad\qquad 6x^2 + 1x^2 - 9x^2$

$$\underbrace{\qquad\qquad}_{7x^2 - 9x^2}$$

$$\underbrace{\qquad\qquad}_{-2x^2}$$

$6x^2 + x^2 - 9x^2$ is the same as $-2x^2$

Some expressions contain like terms and unlike terms. Be sure to combine only the like terms.

▶ **EXAMPLE 3**

Simplify. $\quad 3x - 6x - 2y + 8y$

Look for like terms. $\qquad\qquad\qquad 3x - 6x - 2y + 8y$

Remember
$3x - 6x$ means $3x + (-6x)$.

Add the coefficients. $\qquad\qquad\qquad 3x - 6x - 2y + 8y$

$$\underbrace{\qquad}_{-3x} \quad + \quad \underbrace{\qquad}_{6y}$$

$-3x$ and $6y$ are unlike terms.

$3x - 6x - 2y + 8y$ is the same as $-3x + 6y$.

Try These

Simplify by combining like terms.

1. $8x - 2x$

Look for ■. Like terms $\quad 8x - 2x$

Combine the coefficients. $\quad 8x - 2x$

$$■$$

$$6x$$

2. $5y - 10y + 3y$

Look for ■. Like terms $\quad 5y - 10y + 3y$

Combine the coefficients. $\quad ■ + 3y$

$$-5y \quad ■$$

$$-2y$$

3. $7a - a - 9 - 5$

Look for like terms. $\quad 7a - a - 9 - 5$

Combine the $\qquad 7a - 1a - 9 - 5$

coefficients. $\qquad 6a \quad 14$

$$■ - ■$$

4. $c^2 + c^2 + c$

Look for ■. Like terms $\quad c^2 + c^2 + c$

Combine the $\qquad 1c^2 + 1c^2 + c$

coefficients. $\qquad 2c^2$

$$■ + c$$

Practice

Simplify.

1. $3x^3 + 7x^3 \quad 10x^3$

2. $12n - 2n \quad 10n$

3. $-5b - 6b \quad -11b$

4. $a + a + 2a \quad 4a$

5. $-7a + 10a \quad 3a$

6. $6x^2 - 8x^2 \quad -2x^2$

7. $r + 2r + 3s \quad 3r + 3s$

8. $-4p^2 - 3p^2 + 5q + 2q \quad -7p^2 + 7q$

9. $-5x + x + 8y^2 - 6y^2 \quad -4x + 2y^2$

10. $4r - 3r \quad r$

11. $-6a + 2a + 5b - 2b \quad -4a + 3b$

12. $10n^2 + 4n^2 + 3n \quad 14n^2 + 3n$

13. $5t - t + 2 + 8 \quad 4t + 10$

14. $c + 9c + 2 \quad 10c + 2$

15. $2x + x + 7x^2 - 10x^2 \quad 3x - 3x^2$

16. $2y - 5y + 8 + 3 \quad -3y + 11$

Cooperative Learning

17. Explain to a partner how to simplify the expression in number **10** in **Practice**. Since $4r$ and $-3r$ are like terms, you can add the coefficients (4 and -3) to get $1r$ or r.

18. Write a variable expression with like terms. Have a partner simplify. Check the work. Possible answer: $3y + y + 2$; Simplified as $4y + 2$.

Getting Started
Review exponents. Have students find the value of each expression.
3^2 (9) 2^3 (8)
5^2 (25) 4^2 (16)

2-6 ► Evaluating Variable Expressions

You **evaluate** a variable expression when you **substitute** numbers for the variables. You will then have a number expression. Then, find the value of the number expression.

► **EXAMPLE 1**

Evaluate $a^2 + 3$ when a is 4.

Substitute 4 for a.	$a^2 + 3$

Remember
4^2 means $4 \cdot 4$.

Find the value of the power.	$4^2 + 3$
Add.	$16 + 3$
	19

The value of $a^2 + 3$ is 19 when a is 4.

► **EXAMPLE 2**

Find the value of $3x$ when x is -2.

Remember
$3x$ means 3 times x.

Substitute -2 for x. Use parentheses around the negative number.	$3x$
Multiply.	$3(-2)$
	-6

The value of $3x$ is -6 when x is -2.

You can evaluate variable expressions with more than one variable.

► **EXAMPLE 3**

Evaluate $2b - c$ when b is 3 and c is -4.

Substitute 3 for b and -4 for c.	$2b - c$

Remember
Follow the Order of Operations.

Multiply.	$2 \cdot 3 - (-4)$
	$6 - (-4)$
Add.	$6 + 4$
	10

The value of $2b - c$ is 10 when b is 3 and c is -4.

Try These

Evaluate each variable expression.

1. $\frac{6a}{4}$ when a is -2

Substitute ■ for a. $\frac{6a}{4}$
    -2

Multiply. $\frac{6(-2)}{4}$

Divide. $\frac{-12}{4}$

    ■ -3

The value of $\frac{6a}{4}$ is ■ when a is -2.
    -3

2. $3x^2 - y$ when x is 2 and y is -4
     x

Substitute 2 for ■ and $3x^2 - y$
-4 for ■. y

Find the value of the $3 \bullet$ ■$^2 -$ ■
power. 2 -4

Multiply. $3 \bullet$ ■ $-(-4)$
       4

Add. $12 +$ ■ 4

    16 ■

The value of $3x^2 - y$ is ■ when
x is 2 and y is -4. 16

Practice

Evaluate each variable expression.

1. $t + 5$ when t is 3   8

2. $9 + w$ when w is -7 2

3. $18 \div c$ when c is -2 -9

4. $8x$ when x is 0   0

5. $4 - s^2$ when s is 4 -12

6. $2r + r^2$ when r is 4   24

7. $\frac{5p}{-1} + q$ when p is 21 and q is 9 -96

8. $8(a + b)$ when a is 5 and b is 3   64

9. $3m + 9 \div n$ when m is 4 and n is -3 9

10. $\frac{3x}{12}$ when x is 8   2

Cooperative Learning

11. Explain to a partner how to find the value of the variable expression in number **8** in **Practice**. Possible answer: Substitute 5 for a and 3 for b. Simplify the parentheses by adding 5 and 3. Multiply 8 and 8.

12. Pick three numbers for x. Ask a partner to evaluate $3(x - 1)$ for each of the numbers. Check the work. Possible answer: $x = 2$, $x = 5$, and $x = -3$. $3(x - 1) = 3$ when $x = 2$; $3(x - 1) = 12$ when $x = 5$; $3(x - 1) = -12$ when $x = -3$.

2·7 Meaning of an Equation

Getting Started
Have students evaluate the expressions $3 - 9$ and $-12 \div 2$. (Both expressions are equal to -6.) Then, ask students for expressions that equal 5.

When expressions have the same value, they are **equivalent.** You can write a statement when two expressions are equal. This is called an **equation.**

$$9 = 9 \qquad 7 - 9 = 2 - 4 \qquad 12 \div 3 = 4$$
$$\text{true} \qquad\qquad \text{true} \qquad\qquad \text{true}$$

These equations are all true. Both sides of the equal sign have the same value. If the two expressions have different values, you do not have an equation.

 EXAMPLE 1

Tell whether $2 + 6 = 11 - 3$ is true or false.

Simplify each expression. $2 + 6 \; ? \; 11 - 3$

$$8 \;\; = \;\; 8 \quad \text{true}$$

$2 + 6 = 11 - 3$ is true.

When an equation contains variables, you can substitute a value for the variable. Then, tell whether the number equation is true or false.

 EXAMPLE 2

Tell whether $2a = a + a$ when a is 3.

Remember
$2a$ means 2 times a.

Substitute 3 for a. $2a = a + a$

Simplify each side. $2(3) \; ? \; 3 + 3$

$$6 = 6 \text{ true}$$

$2a = a + a$ when a is 3.

 EXAMPLE 3

Tell whether $3(x + 2) = 3x + 2$ when x is -1.

Remember
Follow the Order of Operations to simplify.

Substitute -1 for x. $3(x + 2) = 3x + 2$

Simplify each side. $3(-1 + 2) \; ? \; 3(-1) + 2$

$$3(1) \; ? \; -3 + 2$$

Math Fact
$\neq$ means *not equal to.*

$$3 \neq -1$$

$3(x + 2) \neq 3x + 2$ when $x = -1$.

1. Tell whether $\frac{4 + 6}{2} = 2 \cdot 5 - 5$ is true or false.

Simplify each side. $\frac{4 + 6}{2} = 2 \cdot 5 - 5$

$$\frac{10}{2} = 10 - 5$$

$$5 \blacksquare = \blacksquare 5$$

$\frac{4 + 6}{2} = 2 \cdot 5 - 5$ is $\blacksquare$.
true

2. Tell whether $3x + 4 = 4x$ when $x = 5$.

Substitute 5 for $\blacksquare$. x $\quad 3x + 4 = 4x$

Simplify each side. $3 \cdot \blacksquare + 4 \,?\, 4 \cdot \blacksquare$

$$15 \blacksquare + 4 \,?\, \blacksquare 20$$

$$19 \blacksquare \neq \blacksquare 20$$

$3x + 4 \,\blacksquare\, 4x$ when $x = 5$.
$\neq$

Practice

Tell whether the expressions form an equation. Write *yes* or *no*.

1. $24 \div 3$ and $16 - 8$ yes

2. $2 \cdot 4$ and $10 - 4$ no

3. $3z + 2 = 5$ when z is 1   yes

4. $x \cdot x = 2x$ when x is 3   no

5. $2k = 6$ when k is 3   yes

6. $10 \div b = 25$ when b is -2 no

7. $a \div 5 = 6$ when a is 35   no

8. $3(x + 2) = 3x + 6$ when x is 1   yes

9. $2(x - 5) = 3x - 5$ when x is 15   no

10. $5n + n = 30$ when n is 6   no

11. $\frac{b}{3} + 6 = 12$ when b is 12   no

12. $4a - 10 = -26$ when a is -4 yes

13. $7y + 3y = 20$ when y is 2   yes

14. $-16 = -4x - 8$ when x is 2   yes

Cooperative Learning

15. Explain to a partner how to decide if the equation in number **3** in **Practice** is true or false. Possible answer: 3(1) + 2 is 5, so 5 = 5 and the equation is true.

16. Pick two values for k. Have your partner decide if $2(k - 1) = 2k - 2$ for each value of k. Choices for k will vary, but equation must always be true. Possible answer: Choose $k = 0$ and $k = 1$; $-2 = -2$ true, 0 = 0 true.

More practice is provided in Exercises 7 and 10 of the Workbook.

2·8 ▶ Properties of Addition

Getting Started
Help students to recognize that the order of the addends can be different but the sum will be the same. Have students evaluate $-10 + 3$ and $3 + -10$. (-7)

There are addition properties that are always true.

Commutative Property of Addition
The order of two numbers in addition does not matter.
$3 + 2 = 2 + 3$

Associative Property of Addition
The grouping of numbers in addition does not matter.
$(1 + 7) + 4 = 1 + (7 + 4)$

Identity Property of Addition
Adding 0 to any number does not change the number.
$0 + (-5) = -5$

Math Fact
The opposite of a positive integer is negative.

Addition Property of Opposites
The sum of a number and its opposite is 0.
$8 + (-8) = 0$

▶ **EXAMPLE 1**

Name the property shown. $(2x + 3) + 5 = 2x + (3 + 5)$

This equation shows the sum of three terms. Pairs of terms are grouped in different ways.

$(2x + 3) + 5 = 2x + (3 + 5)$

The Associative Property of Addition is shown.

▶ **EXAMPLE 2**

Math Fact
The opposite of $-2n$ is $2n$.

Use a property to complete the equation. $-2n + ? = 0$

This equation shows a sum of 0. The sum of a number and its opposite is 0. Substitute $2n$ for ? in the equation.

$-2n + ? = 0$
$-2n + 2n = 0$

The Addition Property of Opposites is used.

▶ **EXAMPLE 3**

Use a property to complete. $x - ? = -10 + x$

This equation shows the sum of two terms. You can add two terms in any order. Substitute 10 for ? in the equation.

$x - ? = -10 + x$
$x - 10 = -10 + x$

The Commutative Property is used.

Try These

1. Name the property shown.

$0 + 8n = 8n$

> 0
> Adding ▪ does not change the value of a number.
>
> $0 + 8n = 8n$

$0 + 8n = 8n$ shows the ▪.
Identity Property of Addition

2. Use a property to complete.

$(b + 5) - 5 = b + (? - 5)$
Associative Property of Addition

> The ▪ says you can group pairs of terms in any way.
>
> 5
> $(b + 5) - 5 = b + (▪ - 5)$

The missing number is ▪. 5

Practice

Name the property shown.

1. $3x + 5x^2 = 5x^2 + 3x$
Commutative Property of Addition

2. $(-12 + 3) + 4 = -12 + (3 + 4)$
Associative Property of Addition

3. $7 + {}^-7 = 0$
Addition Property of Opposites

4. $2cd + 5 - 3cd = 2cd - 3cd + 5$
Commutative Property of Addition

5. $10 + 0 = 10$
Identity Property of Addition

6. $7x + (2x + 3) = (7x + 2x) + 3$
Associative Property of Addition

Use a property to complete.

7. $3d + 1 = 1 + ?$ Commutative; 3d

8. $4s + ? = 4s$ Identity; 0

9. $-6m + ? = 0$ Addition of Opposites; 6m

10. $(w^2 + 3w) + w = w^2 + (? + w)$
Associative; 3w

11. $x + 3k = 3k + ?$ Commutative; x

12. $(a + b) + c = a + (b + ?)$ Associative; c

13. $-n + 3 = ? - n$ Commutative; 3

14. $5k = ? + 0$ Identity; 5k

Cooperative Learning

15. Explain to a partner how to use a property to complete number **11** in **Practice.** Possible answer: The Commutative Property of Addition states that terms may be added in any order, so the missing variable is x.

16. Write a variable expression that shows one of the properties of addition. Have a partner name the property. Possible answer: $x + 0 = x$; Identity Property of Addition.

2·9 ▶ Properties of Multiplication

Getting Started
Have students evaluate
$-3 \bullet 7$ and $7 \bullet -3$. Help
them to recognize that the
order of the factors is
different but the product is
the same (-21).

There are multiplication properties that are always true.

Commutative Property of Multiplication
The order of two factors in multiplication does not matter.
$3 \bullet (-4) = (-4) \bullet 3$

Associative Property of Multiplication
The grouping of numbers in multiplication does not matter.
$(2 \bullet 4) \bullet 5 = 2 \bullet (4 \bullet 5)$

Identity Property of Multiplication
The product of any number and 1 is that number.
$21 \bullet 1 = 21$

Zero Property of Multiplication
The product of 0 and any number is 0.
$(-15) \bullet 0 = 0$

▶ **EXAMPLE 1**

Name the property shown. $2 \bullet (3 \bullet a) = (2 \bullet 3) \bullet a$

This equation shows the product $2 \bullet (3 \bullet a) = (2 \bullet 3) \bullet a$
of three factors. Pairs of terms are
grouped in different ways.

The Associative Property of Multiplication is shown.

▶ **EXAMPLE 2**

Use a property to complete the equation. $? \times c = c$

The value does not change. Multiplying by 1 $? \times c = c$
does not change a number. Substitute 1 $1 \times c = c$
for ? in the equation.

The Identity Property is used.

▶ **EXAMPLE 3**

Use a property to complete the equation. $a \bullet ? = 3a$

This equation shows the product of $a \bullet ? = 3a$
two factors. You can multiply two factors $a \bullet 3 = 3a$
in any order. Substitute 3 for ? in the equation.

The Commutative Property is used.

Try These

Name the property shown.

1. $8x \cdot 1 = 8x$

Multiplying by ■ does
not change the value
of a number.

$8x \cdot 1 = 8$ shows the ■.

$8x \cdot 1 = 8x$

Identity Property of
Multiplication

2. $0 \times x = 0$

The product of any
number and ■ is 0.

$0 \times x = 0$ shows the ■.

$0 \times x = 0$

Zero Property of
Multiplication

Use a property to complete.

3. $4 \cdot (5 \cdot b) = (4 \cdot ?) \cdot b$

The ■ says $4 \cdot (5 \cdot b)$
the grouping   Associ
does not matter   of Mult
when multiplying.

The missing factor is

$2) = -12b$

Practice

Name the property shown.

1. $(4x)(9x) = (9x)(4x)$
Commutative Property of Multiplication

4. $ba = ab$
Commutative Property of Multiplication

$(8 \cdot 5)$
y of Multiplication

...ative Property of
Multiplication

Use a property to complete.

7. $-8d \cdot 1 = 1 \cdot ?$
Commutative; $-8d$

10. $-6k \cdot ? = 0$
Zero; 0

8. $yx = ? \, y$
Commutative; x

11. $? \cdot 6 = 6$
Identity; 1

9. $(l \cdot w) \cdot h = l \cdot (w \cdot ?)$
Associative; h

12. $(3k)(2) = (?)(3k)$
Commutative; 2

Cooperative Learning

13. Explain to a partner how to use a property to complete number **8**
in **Practice**. Possible answer: The Commutative Property of Multiplication states that numbers
may be multiplied in any order, so the missing variable is x.

14. Write a variable expression that shows one of the properties of
multiplication. Have a partner name the property. Possible answer: $x \cdot 0 = 0$;
Zero Property of Multiplication.

2-10 ▶ Distributive Property

Getting Started

Have students simplify 5(7 − 2). Ask a volunteer to explain how this was done. (First subtract 7 and 2. Then multiply.)

Then ask students to simplify 5(a − 2). Elicit that the terms in the parentheses cannot be combined. Thus the need for the Distributive Property.

The **Distributive Property** uses multiplication with addition or subtraction. You can multiply a sum or difference by another number or term.

$$2(3 + 4) = 2 \bullet 3 + 2 \bullet 4$$
$$2(7) = \quad 6 \; + \; 8$$
$$14 = \quad\quad 14 \quad\quad \text{true}$$

Multiply each term of the sum or difference by the number. You can use this property with variables.

▶ **EXAMPLE 1**

Simplify. $6(x + 3)$

Multiply each term in the parentheses by 6. Simplify the expression.

$6(x + 3)$
$6 \bullet x + 6 \bullet 3$
$6x + 18$

▶ **EXAMPLE 2**

Simplify. $8(a - b)$

Multiply each term in the parentheses by 8. Simplify the expression.

$8(a - b)$
$8 \bullet a - 8 \bullet b$
$8a - 8b$

▶ **EXAMPLE 3**

Simplify. $-(6n + 5)$

Math Fact

$-(6n + 5)$ means $(-1)(6n + 5)$.

Multiply each term in the parentheses by −1. Simplify the expression.

$-(6n + 5)$
$-1(6n + 5)$
$(-1)6n + (-1)5$
$-6n - 5$

▶ **EXAMPLE 4**

Simplify. $-3(y - 4)$

Multiply each term in the parentheses by −3. Simplify the expression.

$-3(y - 4)$
$(-3)(y) - (-3)(4)$
$-3y - (-12)$
$-3y + 12$

Practice

Use the Distributive Property to simplify.

1. $7(2 - y)$ $14 - 7y$

2. $12(t + 2)$ $12t + 24$

3. $2(-12 + k)$ $-24 + 2k$

4. $5(r - 8)$ $5r - 40$

5. $-5(3 - x)$ $-15 + 5x$

6. $2(a + 4)$ $2a + 8$

7. $4(a - 7)$ $4a - 28$

8. $7(s + 3)$ $7s + 21$

9. $-6(3 - d)$ $-18 + 6d$

10. $2(l - 4)$ $2l - 8$

11. $2(3 - 2n)$ $6 - 4n$

12. $-(m - 7)$ $-m + 7$

13. $2(x + k)$ $2x + 2k$

14. $4(q + 4r)$ $4q + 16r$

15. $5(2w + 4)$ $10w + 20$

Cooperative Learning

16. Explain to a partner how to use the Distributive Property to simplify number **11** in **Practice.** Possible answer: Multiply 3 and 2n by 2. $2(3 - 2n) = 2 \cdot 3 - 2 \cdot 2n = 6 - 4n.$

17. Write a variable expression like one of the practice exercises. Have a partner use the Distributive Property to complete the equation. Possible answer: $2(x + 3) = 2x + 6.$

2·11 Simplifying Expressions

Getting Started
Have students identify like terms in the expression $2x - 3xy + 5x$.

Properties can help you simplify expressions. Use the Distributive Property to remove parentheses. Use the Commutative Property to rearrange terms.

▶ **EXAMPLE 1**

Simplify. $2x + 4y - x$

Math Fact
$-x$ means $(-1)x$.

Look for like terms. Change the order. $2x + 4y - x$

Combine like terms. $2x - 1x + 4y$

$x + 4y$

▶ **EXAMPLE 2**

Simplify. $5 + 2(x + 3)$

Use the Distributive Property. $5 + 2(x + 3)$

$5 + 2(x) + 2(3)$

Look for like terms. Change the order. $5 + 2x + 6$

Combine like terms. $5 + 6 + 2x$

$11 + 2x$

▶ **EXAMPLE 3**

Simplify. $-6x + 4(5 - x)$

Use the Distributive Property. $-6x + 4(5 - x)$

$-6x + 4(5) - 4(x)$

Look for like terms. Change the order. $-6x + 20 - 4x$

Combine like terms. $-6x - 4x + 20$

$-10x + 20$

▶ **EXAMPLE 4**

Simplify. $2xy^2 + 8 - xy^2 + 4$

Look for like terms. Change the order. $2xy^2 + 8 - xy^2 + 4$

Combine like terms. $2xy^2 - xy^2 + 8 + 4$

$xy^2 \quad + \quad 12$

Try These

Simplify the expressions.

1. $4(x - 3) + 5$

Use the ■. Distributive Property	$4(x - 3) + 5$ $\underset{4}{}$ $4\,■ \bullet x - \underset{12}{■} \bullet 3 + 5$
Combine like terms.	$4x - ■ + 5$ $4x - \underset{7}{■}$

$4(x - 3) + 5 = ■$
$4x - 7$

2. $8m - n - 3m + 12n$

Change the order.	$8m - n - 3m + 12n$ $8m - 3m - ■ + 12n$ n
Combine like terms.	$\underset{5}{■}m + \underset{11}{■}n$

$8m - n - 3m + 12n = ■$
$5m + 11n$

Practice

Simplify the expressions.

1. $a + a + 2$
$2a + 2$

2. $5(t + 8) - 6$
$5t + 34$

3. $-(r + 2)$
$-r - 2$

4. $3(x - 4) + 6$
$3x - 6$

5. $6(y - 8) - 10$
$6y - 58$

6. $7a + 3(a + 4)$
$10a + 12$

7. $5b + 2(b - 2)$
$7b - 4$

8. $10y + 4(1 + 3y)$
$4 + 22y$

9. $5t + 8 - (t + 2)$
$4t + 6$

10. $10 + 3(c + 4)$
$22 + 3c$

11. $2p + 2 + 9p - 2$
$11p$

12. $6(h + 2) + 3h$
$9h + 12$

13. $n + 3m - n$
$3m$

14. $2k + 3 - 7k + 4k$
$3 - k$

15. $x + 2(x - 4)$
$3x - 8$

16. $2b + 4(b - 5)$
$6b - 20$

17. $-5p + 2(p + 4)$
$-3p + 8$

18. $x - 3(x + 2)$
$-2x - 6$

19. $10 - (5 + m)$
$5 - m$

20. $-(2 - x) - 8$
$x - 10$

21. $-x + 4y - x + y$
$5y - 2x$

Cooperative Learning

22. Explain to a partner how to simplify the expression in number **12** in **Practice**. Possible answer: Multiply h and 2 by 6. Then, add the like terms 6h and 3h.

23. Write a variable expression containing parentheses. Have a partner simplify. Check the work. Possible answer: 3y + 2(y + 2), simplified as 5y + 4.

Getting Started
Review evaluating
expressions. Have
students evaluate
$2a - 3b$ when $a = 4$
and $b = 1$.

2·12

Calculator: Finding the Value of Expressions

You can use your calculator to evaluate expressions when the values of the variable are large numbers. Be sure to follow the Order of Operations.

► **EXAMPLE**

Use your calculator to find the value of the expression $7a + 3b - 21$ when a is 2.5 and b is .8.

Substitute 2.5 for a and .8 for b. $7a + 3b - 21$

$$7(2.5) + 3(.8) - 21$$

Display

Enter 7 by pressing: $\boxed{7}$ $\boxed{7}$

Multiply by 2.5 by pressing: $\boxed{\times}$ $\boxed{2}$ $\boxed{.}$ $\boxed{5}$ $\boxed{=}$ $\boxed{17.5}$

Write 17.5 on your paper.

Remember
Make sure you clear your calculator each time you start a calculation.

Enter 3 by pressing: $\boxed{3}$ $\boxed{3}$

Multiply by .8 by pressing: $\boxed{\times}$ $\boxed{.}$ $\boxed{8}$ $\boxed{=}$ $\boxed{2.4}$

Write 2.4 on your paper.

The expression becomes $17.5 + 2.4 - 21$. Now, find the value of the expression.

Enter 17.5 by pressing: $\boxed{1}$ $\boxed{7}$ $\boxed{.}$ $\boxed{5}$ $\boxed{17.5}$

Add 2.4 by pressing: $\boxed{+}$ $\boxed{2}$ $\boxed{.}$ $\boxed{4}$ $\boxed{19.9}$

Subtract 21 by pressing: $\boxed{-}$ $\boxed{2}$ $\boxed{1}$ $\boxed{=}$ $\boxed{-1.1}$

$7a + 3b - 21 = -1.1$ when $a = 2.5$ and $b = .8$.

Practice

Find the value of each expression.

1. $8x - 42$ when x is 32
214

2. $72(z - 12)$ when z is 22
720

3. $\frac{21y}{9}$ when y is 3.3
7.7

4. $\frac{32v}{15t}$ when v is 45 and t is 32
3

5. $\frac{n}{24} - 21$ when n is 1,248
31

6. $50y - 92 + 36y$ when y is 8.7
656.2

7. $3y^2$ when y is 1.5
6.75

8. $4a - 7b$ when a is .02 and b is 1.9
-13.22

On-the-Job Math

ASSEMBLY LINES

Large machines like cars and airplanes are made of many smaller parts. Together, the parts make the machine work. How do you think these machines are made?

Many machines are made on assembly lines. Here, parts are put together, or *assembled.* An assembly line has tools, parts, and workers. They are placed in an order. Each part is added to the machine in order. Workers have the tools they need right next to them. This keeps the line moving quickly. Sometimes, a robot will attach or adjust a part too.

An assembly line must follow steps in the correct order. You cannot put the wheels on before the axle. Workers need the right tools and skills to do their jobs. Building a car on an assembly line is a lot like doing algebra. You need to have the right tools and skills. Then, you follow the steps in the right order.

More practice is provided in Exercise 12 of the Workbook.

 ## 2·13 ▶ Problem Solving: Writing Equations

Getting Started
Have pairs of students find the perimeter of a textbook, a desk, and their classroom.

Math Fact
The order of the numbers in subtraction is important.

You can translate word statements into variable equations. Here are some words for the four operations.

Addition

sum of 3 and 5 $3 + 5$
3 increased by 5
5 more than 3

Subtraction

subtract 3 from 5 $5 - 3$
5 decreased by 3
3 less than 5

Multiplication

product of 3 and 5 $3 \cdot 5$
2 times 3 $2 \cdot 3$

Division

quotient of 10 and 2 $10 \div 2$

▶ **EXAMPLE**

The perimeter of a square is 4 times the length of a side. Write an equation for the perimeter of a square.

READ   **What do you need to find out?**
You need to find an equation for the perimeter of a square.

PLAN   **What do you need to do?**
Pick variables for perimeter and side. Then write an equation. Use the information given.

DO   **Follow the plan.**
Let P be the perimeter.
Let s be the side.
The perimeter is 4 times a side.

$$P \qquad \cdot \qquad s$$

You can write $P = 4s$ for the perimeter of the square.

CHECK   **Does your answer make sense?**
Compare the equation to the problem.
$P = 4s$ means perimeter is 4 times side. ✓

The equation for the perimeter of a square is $P = 4s$.

Try These

1. Maria's score is twice Jon's score.
Write a variable equation for Maria's score.

Pick variables for Maria's score and Jon's score.

Maria's score is twice Jon's score.
$$\downarrow \qquad\qquad\qquad \downarrow$$
$$m \qquad\qquad\qquad j$$

Translate "twice."

$$m = 2 \cdot j$$

You can write $m = 2 \cdot j$ for Maria's score.

2. The perimeter of a triangle is the sum of its 3 sides.
Write a variable equation for the perimeter of a triangle.

Pick variables for the perimeter and the sides. Use $a, b,$ and c for the 3 sides.

The perimeter of a triangle is the sum of its 3 sides.
$$\downarrow \qquad\qquad\qquad\qquad\qquad \downarrow$$
$$P \qquad\qquad\qquad\qquad\qquad a, b, c$$

Translate "sum."

$$P = a + b + c$$

You can write $P = a + b + c$.

Practice

Write a variable equation for each sentence.

1. The area of a rectangle is length times width. $A = lw$

2. Danika's new running route is 4 miles longer than her old route. $n = o + 4$

3. Today's temperature is 5 degrees less than yesterday's. $t = y - 5$

Cooperative Learning

4. Explain to a partner how to choose the variable in number **2** in **Practice.**   Possible answer: Since you must pick a variable for Danika's old route and new route, choose n for her new route and o for her old route.

5. Write three word sentences that can be translated into equations. Have a partner write an equation for each sentence. Answers will vary.

2·14 ▶ Application: Geometry Formulas

Getting Started
Review the formula $P = 4s$.
Draw a diagram.

You can use what you know about evaluating expressions to use a formula from geometry.

▶ **EXAMPLE 1**

The perimeter of a triangle is the sum of its three sides. Use the formula $P = a + b + c$. Find the perimeter of a triangle when a is 4 in., b is 3 in., and c is 5 in.

Write the formula for perimeter.	$P = a + b + c$
Substitute 4 for a, 3 for b, and 5 for c.	$P = 4 + 3 + 5$
Add.	$P = 12$

The perimeter of the triangle is 12 in.

▶ **EXAMPLE 2**

The area of a rectangle is its length times its width. Use the formula $A = lw$. Find the area of a rectangle when l is 6 cm and w is 3 cm.

Write the formula for area.	$A = lw$
Substitute 6 for l and 3 for w.	$A = 6 \bullet 3$
Multiply.	$A = 18$

The area of the rectangle is 18 square centimeters, or 18 cm^2.

▶ **EXAMPLE 3**

The volume of a box is its length times its width times its height. Use the formula $V = lwh$. Find the volume of a box when l is 5 cm, w is 2 cm, and h is 4 cm.

Write the formula for volume.	$V = lwh$
Substitute 5 for l, 4 for w, and 2 for h.	$V = 5 \bullet 2 \bullet 4$
Multiply.	$V = 40$

The volume of the box is 40 cubic centimeters, or 40 cm^3.

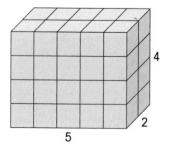

Try These

1. Use the formula $P = a + b + c$. Find the perimeter of a triangle when a is 23 ft, b is 17 ft, and c is 34 ft.

   Write the formula for ▪. perimeter $P = a + b + c$

   Substitute. $P = \underset{23}{▪} + \underset{17}{▪} + \underset{34}{▪}$

   Add. $P = ▪\ 74$

   The perimeter of the triangle is ▪.
   74 ft

2. Use the formula $A = lw$. Find the area of a rectangle when l is 24 yd and w is 14 yd.

   Write the formula for ▪. area $A = lw$

   Substitute. $A = 24 \cdot \underset{14}{▪}$

   Multiply. $A = ▪\ 336$

   The area of the rectangle is ▪.
   336 yd²

Practice

Use the formula $P = a + b + c$ to find the perimeter of each triangle.

1. a is 12 m, b is 13 m, c is 22 m
   47 m
2. a is 11 in., b is 9 in., c is 12 in.
   32 in.

Use the formula $A = lw$ to find the area of each rectangle.

3. l is 12 in., w is 6 in.
   72 in.²
4. l is 90 mm, w is 40 mm
   3,600 mm²
5. l is 8 yd, w is 2 yd
   16 yd²
6. l is 5 cm, w is 14 cm
   70 cm²

Use the formula $V = lwh$ to find the volume of each box.

7. l is 4 cm, w is 3 cm, h is 1 cm
   12 cm³
8. l is 2 yd, w is 10 yd, h is 8 yd
   160 yd³

Cooperative Learning

9. Explain to a partner how to find the perimeter of number **2** in **Practice**. Possible answer: Write the equation $P = a + b + c$. Substitute 11 for a, 9 for b, and 12 for c.
10. Write a length, width, and height for a box. Ask a partner to use the formula for volume to find the volume of the box. Check the work. Possible answer: Write 5 cm, 10 cm, and 2 cm. Formula is $V = l \cdot w \cdot h$; $5 \cdot 10 \cdot 2 = 100$ cm³.

Summary

The Order of Operations is used to find the value of an expression.
You can simplify expressions by combining like terms.
You can evaluate variable expressions by substituting numbers for variables.
Two expressions that have the same value are equivalent.
An equation is true if both sides of the equal sign have the same value.
Properties help you simplify expressions.
Words can be translated into variables, numbers, and signs.
You can evaluate geometry formulas.

More vocabulary review is provided in Exercise 11 of the Classroom Resource Binder.

variable

terms

coefficient

like terms

substitute

Commutative Property

Associative Property

Identity Property

Addition Property of Opposites

Distributive Property

Vocabulary Review

Complete the sentences with words from the box.

1. The _____ lets you add or multiply two numbers in any order. Commutative Property

2. Use the _____ to multiply a sum by a number. Distributive Property

3. A _____ is a letter that represents any number. variable

4. The _____ lets you add or multiply more than two numbers in groups of two in any order. Associative Property

5. The _____ of Multiplication tells you multiplying by 1 does not change the value of a number. Identity Property

6. To _____ means to replace a variable with a number. substitute

7. The _____ says the sum of any number and its opposite is zero. Addition Property of Opposites

8. A number that multiplies a variable is a _____. coefficient

9. Terms that have the same variables with the same exponents are _____. like terms

10. Parts of an expression separated by a + or − sign are called _____. terms

Chapter Quiz More assessment is provided in the Classroom Resource Binder.

Simplify.

1. $10 - 4 \div 2$
8

2. $3 \cdot 4 + 7$
19

3. $8 \div 2 - 6 \cdot 0$
4

4. $12 \div (3 + 3) \cdot 6$
12

5. $20 - 2(16 - 4)$
-4

6. $(5 + 8) \cdot 3 - 7$
32

Evaluate each variable expression.

7. $(15 \div a)a$ when a is 5   15

8. $s + 2s$ when s is 4   12

9. $-5s$ when s is 7 -35

10. $6 + c$ when c is 13   19

Tell whether the expressions form an equation. Write *yes* or *no*.

11. $3t + 8$ and 14 when t is 2
14, 14; yes

12. $3g - 3$ and $3(g - 1)$ when g is 2
3, 3; yes

Name the property shown.

13. $4(y + 2) = 4y + 8$
Distributive Property

14. $-3 + 3 = 0$
Addition Property of Opposites

15. $4x \cdot 2 = 2 \cdot 4x$
Commutative Property of Multiplication

16. $(t + 2) + 4 = t + (2 + 4)$
Associative Property of Addition

Simplify each expression.

17. $4x + x + 3$
$5x + 3$

18. $3w + 4x - 7x - w$
$2w - 3x$

19. $1 + 2b + 7b$
$1 + 9b$

20. $4(y + 3)$
$4y + 12$

21. $-(a + 9)$
$-a - 9$

22. $6(x - 8)$
$6x - 48$

23. $3x + 5(4 + x)$
$8x + 20$

24. $12 - (c + 8)$
$4 - c$

25. $16 - 4(n - 4)$
$32 - 4n$

Write a variable equation for the sentence.

26. Marie-José's time is 29 seconds less than Inger's. $M = I - 29$

Use the formula $A = lw$ to find the area of each rectangle.

27. $l = 4$ in. and $w = 8$ in.
32 in.²

28. $l = 10$ yd and $w = 5$ yd
50 yd²

Additional Practice for this chapter is provided on p. 414 of this text.

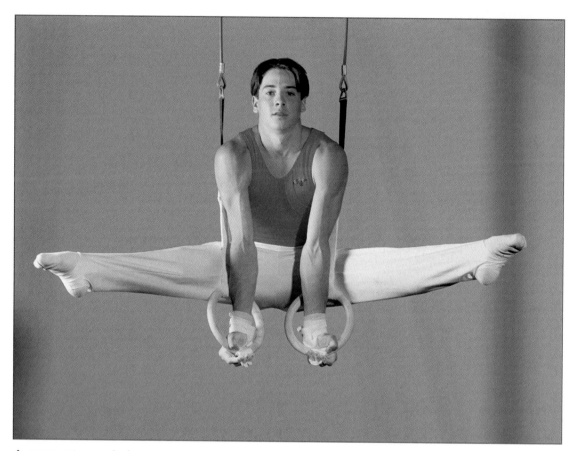

A gymnast uses balance to support himself. If his force on each side is not the same, he will fall. An equation also uses balance. How does the equation 9 + 6 = 15 show balance?

Learning Objectives

- Solve equations by adding, subtracting, multiplying, or dividing.
- Solve equations using more than one operation.
- Solve equations containing parentheses.
- Check solutions to equations by using a calculator.
- Solve problems about percents by writing and solving equations.
- Apply concepts and skills to find discounts and sale prices.

Words to Know

variable equation	an equation containing a variable
solution	a value of the variable that makes the equation true
check	substitute the solution for the variable
equivalent equations	equations with the same solutions
properties of equality	adding, subtracting, multiplying, or dividing both sides of an equation by the same number gives an equivalent equation
inverse operations	operations that "undo" each other; Addition and subtraction are inverse operations, and multiplication and division are inverse operations
solve	find the solution of an equation
discount	the amount you save when you buy an item on sale
sale price	the regular price minus the discount

Consumer Math Project

Choose four sale ads from the newspaper. The ads should show the regular price and the percent off. For each item, write and solve a percent equation to find the discount.

Item	Regular Price	Percent Off	Percent Equation	Discount
Watch	$40	10%	$d = 10\% \cdot 40$	$4.00
Shoes	$28	20%	$d = 20\% \cdot 28$	$5.60

How much will you spend if you buy all the items on sale? How much will you save?

Project See the Classroom Resource Binder for a scoring rubric to assess this project.

More practice is provided in Exercises 13, 14, and 16 of the Workbook.

3·1 Solution of an Equation

Getting Started
Write the following on the chalkboard:

☐ + 3 = 12

☐ − 2 = 8

☐ × 5 = 20

☐ ÷ 4 = 6

Ask for volunteers to write a number in each box to make the equation true.
(9; 10; 4; 24)

A **variable equation** is an equation that contains a variable. The equation $x = 8$ is a variable equation. If you substitute 8 for x, you get $8 = 8$. This is a true equation. The **solution** is the value of the variable that makes the equation true. The solution of $x = 8$ is 8.

This scale shows the equation $x + 4 = 10$.

It is balanced when x is 6. Other amounts will not balance the scale. So, 6 is the solution of $x + 4 = 10$.

Math Fact
≠ means *is not equal to.*

$x + 4 = 10$	$x + 4 = 10$	$x + 4 = 10$
$2 + 4 \neq 10$	$6 + 4 = 10$ true	$9 + 4 \neq 10$

The equation $x + 4 = 10$ is true when x is 6.

▶ **EXAMPLE 1**

Tell whether -9 is the solution of $-4 = 5 + w$.

Substitute -9 for w. $\qquad\qquad -4 = 5 + w$

Add. $\qquad\qquad\qquad\qquad -4 \ ? \ 5 + (-9)$

$\qquad\qquad\qquad\qquad\qquad -4 = -4 \quad$ true

-9 is the solution of $-4 = 5 + w$.

▶ **EXAMPLE 2**

Tell whether 20 is the solution of $15 = \frac{x}{2} - 5$.

Substitute 20 for x. $\qquad\qquad 15 = \frac{x}{2} - 5$

Remember
$\frac{x}{2}$ means $x \div 2$.

Divide. $\qquad\qquad\qquad 15 \ ? \ \frac{20}{2} - 5$

Subtract. $\qquad\qquad\qquad 15 \ ? \ 10 - 5$

$\qquad\qquad\qquad\qquad\quad 15 \neq 5$

20 is not the solution of $15 = \frac{x}{2} - 5$.

Practice

Tell whether the number is a solution of the equation.

1. 4; $a = 4$ yes

2. 5; $6 + w = 12$ no

3. -3; $11 + c = 8$ yes

4. -7; $c - 4 = 11$ no

5. 6; $2 - x = -4$ yes

6. 8; $11 = 3y$ no

7. 6; $5x = 30$ yes

8. -20; $\frac{n}{4} = -4$ no

9. -4; $2 - y = 6$ yes

10. -4; $2x = -8$ yes

11. 0; $12 = 3n + 9$ no

12. 1; $1 = -4 + 5s$ yes

13. 6; $3x + 2 = 17$ no

14. -3; $2a + 5 = -1$ yes

15. 4; $6 = -2 + 2y$ yes

16. 4; $-7 + 5y = 10$ no

17. 5; $6 = 16 - 2x$ yes

18. -3; $8 - 3x = 17$ yes

19. 0; $3x + 17 = 16$ no

20. 10; $8 - b = -2$ yes

21. 18; $\frac{w}{3} + 2 = 12$ no

Cooperative Learning

22. Explain to a partner how to tell whether 1 is the solution of the equation in number **12** in **Practice**. Possible answer: Substitute 1 for s. Then, multiply 5 by 1. Add 5 and -4. $1 = 1$ true.

23. Write the variable equation $3x + 5 = 11$. Then, write three integers that could be solutions to the equation. Ask a partner to check each integer to see if it is a solution of the equation.
Possible answer: Suppose the integers 2, 3, and 4 are chosen. The partner will substitute 2, 3, and then 4 for x. The partner will find that 2 is the solution.

3-2 ▶ Equivalent Equations

Getting Started

Write the following on the chalkboard:

$\square$ $+ 2 = 10$

$\square$ $- 5 = 3$

$\square$ $\times 3 = 24$

$\square$ $\div 4 = 2$

Ask for a volunteer to write a number in each box to make the equation true. (8; 8; 8; 8) Elicit that the solutions to each equation are the same.

You can look at the equation $x = 3$ to find the solution. The solution is 3. The solutions of $x - 1 = 2$ and $x + 1 = 4$ are not as easy to find. They also have 3 as a solution. You can **check** a solution. Substitute the solution for the variable in the equation. If the equation is true, the solution is correct.

$$x - 1 = 2 \qquad\qquad x + 1 = 4$$

Solution: 3   **Solution:** 3
Check: $x - 1 = 2$ **Check:** $x + 1 = 4$
       $3 - 1 ? 2$ $3 + 1 ? 4$
          $2 = 2$ true $4 = 4$ true

Equations with the same solution are **equivalent equations.** These are equivalent equations:

$$x = 3 \qquad x - 1 = 2 \qquad x + 1 = 4$$

▶ **EXAMPLE 1**

Show that $x = -3$ and $4 = x + 7$ are equivalent.

$$x = -3 \qquad\qquad\qquad 4 = x + 7$$

Solution: -3 →   Substitute -3 for x. $4 ? -3 + 7$
                                             $4 = 4$ true

$x = -3$ and $4 = x + 7$ are equivalent.

▶ **EXAMPLE 2**

Show that $12 = y$ and $1 = \frac{y}{4} - 2$ are equivalent.

$$12 = y \qquad\qquad\qquad 1 = \frac{y}{4} - 2$$

Solution: 12   →   Substitute 12 for y. $1 ? \frac{12}{4} - 2$
                                             $1 ? 3 - 2$
                                             $1 = 1$ true

$12 = y$ and $1 = \frac{y}{4} - 2$ are equivalent.

Show that each pair of equations is equivalent.

1. $x = -5$ and $2x + 6 = -4$

$$2x + 6 = -4$$

Substitute ■ $\quad 2(■) + 6 \; ? \; -4$
for x. $\quad -5 \qquad -5$

$$-10 \; ■ + 6 \; ? \; -4$$

$$-4 \; ■ = -4 \quad \text{true}$$

$x = -5$ and $2x + 6 = -4$
are equivalent.

2. $y = -4$ and $2 - 3y = 14$

$$2 - 3y = 14$$

Substitute ■ $\quad 2 - 3(■) \; ? \; 14$
for y. $\quad -4 \qquad\quad -4$

$$-12 \; 2 - ■ \; ? \; 14$$

$$14 \; ■ = ■14 \, \text{true}$$

$y = -4$ and $2 - 3y = 14$
are equivalent.

Practice

Show that each pair of equations is equivalent.

1. $a = 7$ and $10 - a = 3$
$7 = 7; \; 10 - 7 = 3$

2. $n = 4$ and $9 = n + 5$
$4 = 4; \; 9 = 4 + 5$

3. $x = -5$ and $7 = 12 + x$
$-5 = -5; \; 7 = 12 + (-5)$

4. $y = 11$ and $4 - y = -7$
$11 = 11; \; 4 - 11 = -7$

5. $c = 6$ and $2c = 12$
$6 = 6; \; (2)(6) = 12$

6. $x = 30$ and $\frac{x}{6} = 5$ $\quad 30 = 30; \; \frac{30}{6} = 5$

7. $y = 10$ and $-2y - 3 = -23$
$10 = 10; \; (-2)(10) - 3 = -23$

8. $n = -15$ and $\frac{n}{5} - 6 = -9$
$-15 = -15; \; \frac{-15}{5} - 6 = -9$

9. $b = 0$ and $8 + 6b = 8$
$0 = 0; \; 8 + 6(0) = 8$

10. $w = 5$ and $-2 = 8 - 2w$
$5 = 5; \; -2 = 8 - 2(5)$

11. $-2 = n$ and $-3n + 1 = 7$
$-2 = -2; \; -3(-2) + 1 = 7$

12. $x = -1$ and $1 + 5x = -4$
$-1 = -1; \; 1 + 5(-1) = -4$

Cooperative Learning

13. Explain to a partner how you show that the two equations are equivalent in number **5** in **Practice.** Possible answer: Show that by substituting 6 for c in $2c = 12$ you get $2(6) = 12$, which is true, so the equations are equivalent.

14. Write an equation equivalent to $d = 3$. Ask a partner to show the equations are equivalent. Possible answer: $2d + 3 = 9$; $2(3) + 3 = 9$

3·3 ▶ Properties of Equality

Getting Started

Place two known weights on each side of a balance scale. Add a different weight on only one side of the scale. Discuss what would have to be added to the other side of the scale to make it balance.

The equations $x + 4 = 7 + 4$ and $x - 2 = 7 - 2$ are both equivalent to $x = 7$. They all have 7 as a solution. These equations show the facts, or **properties of equality.**

$$x + 4 = 7 + 4 \qquad\qquad x - 2 = 7 - 2$$

Solution: 7

Check: $7 + 4 \ ? \ 7 + 4$

$11 = 11$

Solution: 7

Check: $7 - 2 \ ? \ 7 - 2$

$5 = 5$

Adding or subtracting the same number from both sides of an equation gives an equivalent equation. Later you will use these and other properties to solve equations.

▶ **EXAMPLE 1**

Complete to make equivalent equations.

$x - 6 = 9$ is equivalent to $x - 6 + 6 = 9 + ?$

6 is added to the left side. $\qquad\qquad x - 6 + 6 = 9 + ?$

Add 6 to the right side. $\qquad\qquad x - 6 + 6 = 9 + 6$

$x - 6 = 9$ is equivalent to $x - 6 + 6 = 9 + 6$.

The equations below are equivalent to $x = 6$. They all have 6 as a solution.

$$5 \cdot x = 5 \cdot 6 \qquad\qquad x \div 3 = 6 \div 3$$

Solution: 6

Check: $5 \cdot 6 \ ? \ 5 \cdot 6$

$30 = 30$

Solution: 6

Check: $6 \div 3 \ ? \ 6 \div 3$

$2 = 2$

Multiplying or dividing both sides of an equation by the same number gives an equivalent equation.

▶ **EXAMPLE 2**

Complete to make equivalent equations.

$-5x = 25$ is equivalent to $-5x \ ? \ -5 = 25 \div -5$

The right side is divided by −5. $\qquad -5x \ ? \ -5 = 25 \div -5$

Divide the left side by −5. $\qquad -5x \div -5 = 25 \div -5$

$-5x = 25$ is equivalent to $-5x \div -5 = 25 \div -5$.

Try These

Complete to make equivalent equations.

1. $x + 5 = -10$ and

$x + 5\ ?\ 5 = -10 - 5$

5 is ▇ from the subtracted

right side.
subtract

▇ 5 from the $x + 5 \underline{\blacksquare} 5 = -10 - 5$

left side.

$x + 5 = -10$ and

$x + 5 \underline{\blacksquare} 5 = -10 - 5$

are equivalent.

2. $-9 = \frac{y}{3}$ and $-9 \cdot\ ? = \frac{y}{3} \cdot 3$

The right side

is ▇ by 3. multiplied

multiply ▇ the left side $\quad -9 \cdot \overset{3}{\blacksquare} = \frac{y}{3} \cdot 3$

by 3.

$-9 = \frac{y}{3}$ and $-9 \cdot \underset{3}{\blacksquare} = \frac{y}{3} \cdot 3$

are equivalent.

Practice

Complete to make equivalent equations.

1. $a + 5 = 7$

$a + 5 - \underset{5}{?} = 7 - 5$

2. $6z = 24$

$6z \div \underset{6}{?} = 24 \div 6$

3. $\frac{x}{10} = 5$

$\frac{x}{10}\ \underset{\bullet}{?}\ 10 = 5 \cdot 10$

4. $t - 8 = 11$

$t - 8\ ?\ 8 = 11 + 8$
$\underset{+}{}$

5. $18 = -3b$

$18 \div \underset{-3}{?} = -3b \div -3$

6. $\frac{w}{9} = 2$

$\frac{w}{9}\ \underset{\bullet}{?}\ 9 = 2 \cdot 9$

7. $-16 = \frac{y}{4}$

$-16 \cdot 4 = \frac{y}{4} \cdot \underset{4}{?}$

8. $x + 25 = 25$

$x + 25\ ?\ 25 = 25 - 25$
$\underline{}$

9. $-6 = n - 2$

$-6 + \underset{2}{?} = n - 2 + 2$

Cooperative Learning

11. Explain to a partner how you complete the equation in number **5**
in **Practice.** Possible answer: Complete the equation by putting a -3 in place of the ?,
because the right side of the equation is divided by -3 so the same must be done on the left side.

12. Write the equation $a + 5 - 5 = -8 - 5$. Then, remove a number
or an operation from the equation. Ask a partner to fill in the
missing number or operation. Possible answer: Remove the $-$ from the left side.
$a + 5\ ?\ 5 = -8 - 5.$

More practice is provided in Exercises 13, 14, and 16 of the Workbook.

3·4 Inverse Operations

Getting Started
Draw four blocks in a row. Have a volunteer erase one block and write the mathematical expression. $(4 - 1 = 3)$. Discuss what happens when you now add one block. Write the expression. $(4 - 1 + 1 = 4)$

Adding and subtracting the same number from 8 does not change 8.

$$(8 - 3) + 3$$

$$5 + 3$$

$$8$$

$$(8 + 6) - 6$$

$$14 - 6$$

$$8$$

Addition "undoes" subtraction. Subtraction "undoes" addition. Addition and subtraction are **inverse operations**. Inverse operations also work with variables. You will use inverse operations to solve equations.

▶ **EXAMPLE 1**

Complete. $x + 2 \; ? \; 2 = x$

Undo addition. $x + 2 \; ? \; 2 = x$

Subtract 2. $x + 2 - 2 = x$

$x + 2 - 2 = x$

Multiplication and division are inverse operations. Division "undoes" multiplication. Multiplication "undoes" division.

$$8 \cdot 4 \div 4$$

$$32 \div 4$$

$$8$$

$$8 \div 2 \cdot 2$$

$$4 \cdot 2$$

$$8$$

▶ **EXAMPLE 2**

Remember
$-4y$ means $-4 \cdot y$.

Complete. $-4y \; ? \; (-4) = y$

Undo multiplication. $-4y \; ? \; (-4) = y$

Divide by -4. $-4y \div (-4) = y$

$-4y \div (-4) = y$

Practice

Complete each equation with the missing operation.

1. $a + 4 \; ? \; 4 = a \; -$

2. $z - 7 \; ? \; 7 = z \; +$

3. $2b \; ? \; 2 = b \div$

4. $\frac{v}{9} \; ? \; 9 = v \; \bullet$

5. $10 \; ? \; 10 + x = x \; -$

6. $y - 3 \; ? \; 3 = y \; +$

7. $-8x \; ? \, (-8) = x \div$

8. $\frac{s}{2} \; ? \, (2) = s \; \bullet$

9. $11 \; ? \; 11 + y = y \; -$

10. $\frac{r}{12} \; ? \; 12 = r \; \bullet$

11. $x - 25 \; ? \; 25 = x \; +$

12. $-15b \; ? \, (-15) = b \div$

Cooperative Learning

13. Explain to a partner how to complete the equation in number **7** in **Practice.** Possible answer: x is multiplied by -8. $-8x$ must be divided by -8 to undo multiplication.

14. Write an expression with a variable and one operation. Ask a partner to write an expression that undoes that operation.
Possible answer: $\frac{a}{5} \; ? \; = a$. The partner will fill in $\bullet$ 5.

More practice is provided in Exercises 15, 17, and 18 of the Workbook.

3-5 ▶ Solving Equations Using Subtraction

Getting Started
Show the equation
$x + 3 = 7$ on a balance
scale using an unknown
weight and known weights.
Discuss how to find x by
removing the same weight
from both sides of the scale.

You can find the solution of the equation $x = 4$ just by looking at it. It is not as easy to find the solution of the equation $x + 3 = 7$. It contains addition.

You **solve** an equation when you find its solution. You can solve this equation by using subtraction to undo addition. That will give you an equation that is easy to solve.

▶ **EXAMPLE 1**

Math Fact
Subtracting the same number
from both sides of an equation
gives an equivalent equation.

Solve. Then, check the solution. $x + 3 = 7$

Subtract to undo addition.
Subtract 3 from both sides.
Simplify each side.

$$x + 3 = 7$$
$$x + 3 - 3 = 7 - 3$$
$$x + 0 = 4$$
$$x = 4$$

Solution: 4

Check: Substitute 4 for x.

$$x + 3 = 7$$
$$4 + 3 \ ? \ 7$$
$$7 = 7 \quad \text{true}$$

The solution of $x + 3 = 7$ is 4.

The variable can also be on the right side of the equation. You still subtract to undo addition.

▶ **EXAMPLE 2**

Solve. Then, check the solution. $-9 = 4 + y$

Subtract to undo addition.
Subtract 4 from both sides.
Simplify each side.

$$-9 = 4 + y$$
$$-9 - 4 = 4 - 4 + y$$
$$-13 = 0 + y$$
$$-13 = y$$

Solution: -13

Check: Substitute -13 for y.

$$-9 = 4 + y$$
$$-9 \ ? \ 4 + (-13)$$
$$-9 = -9 \quad \text{true}$$

The solution of $-9 = 4 + y$ is -13.

Try These

Solve. Then, check the solution.

1. $n + 8 = -3$

Subtract ■ from both sides. $n + 8 - ■ = -3 - ■$

Simplify each side. $n + 0 = ■ -11$

$n = ■ -11$

Solution: ■ -11

Check. -11
Substitute ■ for n.

$n + 8 = -3$
$■ + 8 \ ? \ -3$ -11
$■ = ■$ true $-3 \ -3$

2. $24 = t + 6$

Subtract ■ from both sides. $24 - ■ = t + 6 - ■$

Simplify each side. $■ = t + ■$ $18 \quad 0$
$■ = t$ 18

Solution: ■ 18

Check. 18
Substitute ■ for t.

$24 = t + 6$
$24 \ ? \ ■ + 6$ 18
$■ = ■$ true
$24 \quad 24$

Practice

Solve. Then, check the solution.

1. $k + 0 = 6$ 6

2. $r + 2 = 10$ 8

3. $6 + n = 18$ 12

4. $10 = x + 9$ 1

5. $7 = s + 4$ 3

6. $3 = z + 7$ -4

7. $x + 4 = -11$ -15

8. $-10 = y + 5$ -15

9. $c + 12 = 4$ -8

10. $1 = y + 0$ 1

11. $7 + b = 3$ -4

12. $5 + a = -20$ -25

13. $-13 = b + 8$ -21

14. $x + 6 = -10$ -16

15. $y + 8 = 3$ -5

Cooperative Learning

16. Explain to a partner how you solve the equation in number 8 in **Practice**. Possible answer: Subtract 5 from both sides of the equation: $-10 - 5 = y + 5 - 5$; $-15 = y$. Check: $-10 = -15 + 5$; $-10 = -10$.

17. Write the equation $y = 10$. Then, write a new equation by adding a number less than 10 to the left side of the equation. Ask a partner to solve the new equation. Check the solution. Possible answer: Sample: $y + 2 = 10$. Solve by subtracting 2 from both sides of the equation: $y + 2 - 2 = 10 - 2$; $y = 8$. Check: $8 + 2 = 10$; $10 = 10$.

3·6 ▶ Solving Equations Using Addition

Getting Started
Write $9 - 5$ on the chalkboard. Discuss what can be added to get 9. (5)

You have solved equations containing addition. You subtracted to undo the addition. You can solve equations that contain subtraction by adding to undo the subtraction.

▶ **EXAMPLE 1**

Math Fact
Adding the same number to both sides of an equation gives an equivalent equation.

Solve. Then, check the solution. $x - 3 = 7$

Add to undo subtraction.
Add 3 to both sides.
Simplify each side.

$$x - 3 = 7$$
$$x - 3 + 3 = 7 + 3$$
$$x + 0 = 10$$
$$x = 10$$

Check: Substitute 10 for x.

$$x - 3 = 7$$
$$10 - 3 \ ? \ 7$$
$$7 = 7 \quad \text{true}$$

The solution of $x - 3 = 7$ is 10.

▶ **EXAMPLE 2**

Solve. Then, check the solution. $-5 = y - 9$

Add to undo subtraction.
Add 9 to both sides.
Simplify each side.

$$-5 = y - 9$$
$$-5 + 9 = y - 9 + 9$$
$$4 = y - 0$$
$$4 = y$$

Remember
$4 - 9$ means $4 + (-9)$.

Check: Substitute 4 for y.

$$-5 = y - 9$$
$$-5 \ ? \ 4 - 9$$
$$-5 = -5 \quad \text{true}$$

The solution of $-5 = y - 9$ is 4.

An equation can contain 0. Solve the equation the same way you solve other equations.

▶ **EXAMPLE 3**

Solve. Then, check the solution. $b - 6 = 0$

Add to undo subtraction.
Add 6 to both sides.
Simplify each side.

$$b - 6 = 0$$
$$b - 6 + 6 = 0 + 6$$
$$b + 0 = 6$$
$$b = 6$$

Check
$b - 6 = 0$
$6 - 6 \ ? \ 0$
$0 = 0$

The solution of $b - 6 = 0$ is 6.

Try These

Solve. Then, check the solution.

1. $n - 5 = -15$

Add ■ to both sides. $n - 5 + \underset{5}{■} = -15 + \underset{5}{■}$

Simplify each side. $n + \underset{0}{■} = \underset{-10}{■}$

$n = \underset{-10}{■}$

Check: $\underset{-10}{\ }$ $n - 5 = -15$

Substitute ■ for n. $\underset{-10}{■} - 5 \ ? \ -15$

$-15 \ ■ = -15$ true

2. $6 = t - 4$

Add ■ to both sides. $6 + \underset{4}{■} = t - 4 + \underset{4}{■}$

Simplify each side. $\underset{10}{■} = t + \underset{0}{■}$

$10 \ ■ = t$

Check: 10 $6 = t - 4$

Substitute ■ for t. $6 \ ? \ \underset{10}{■} - 4$

$6 = \underset{6}{■}$ true

Practice

Solve. Then, check the solution.

1. $k - 20 = 10$ 30

2. $r - 2 = 12$ 14

3. $21 = n - 6$ 27

4. $0 = x - 9$ 9

5. $16 = t - 4$ 20

6. $z - 3 = 0$ 3

7. $x - 4 = -15$ -11

8. $-3 = y - 15$ 12

9. $c - 2 = -8$ -6

10. $y - 0 = 8$ 8

11. $-13 = b - 7$ -6

12. $20 = v - 5$ 25

13. $k - 12 = 0$ 12

14. $-5 = m - 9$ 4

15. $x - 1 = -21$ -20

16. $-10 = a - 10$ 0

17. $x - 9 = -25$ -16

18. $y - 15 = -7$ 8

Cooperative Learning

19. Explain to a partner how to solve the equation in number 9 in **Practice.** Possible answer: Add 2 to both sides of the equation: $c - 2 + 2 = -8 + 2, c = -6.$

20. Write an equation that contains subtraction. Ask a partner to solve your equation. Check the solution. Possible answer: Sample: $x - 5 = -20.$ Add 5 to both sides: $x - 5 + 5 = -20 + 5, x = -15.$ Check: $-15 - 5 = -20, -20 = -20.$

More practice is provided in Exercises 15 to 17 of the Workbook.

3·7 Solving Equations Using Multiplication

Getting Started

Write $12 \div 3$ on the chalkboard. Discuss what can be done to get 12.

Remember

$\frac{x}{2}$ means $x \div 2$.

You have solved equations containing addition and subtraction by undoing the addition or the subtraction. The equation $\frac{x}{2} = -8$ contains division. You solve division equations by multiplying to undo the division.

 EXAMPLE 1

Solve. Then, check the solution. $\quad \frac{x}{2} = -8$

Multiply to undo division.

Multiply both sides by 2.

Simplify each side.

$$\frac{x}{2} = -8$$
$$\frac{2x}{2} = -8(2)$$
$$x = -16$$

Check

$$\frac{x}{2} = -8$$
$$\frac{-16}{2} \;?\; -8$$
$$-8 = -8 \text{ true}$$

The solution of $\frac{x}{2} = -8$ is -16.

 EXAMPLE 2

Solve. Then, check the solution. $\quad 9 = \frac{y}{-3}$

Multiply to undo division.

Multiply both sides by -3.

Simplify each side.

$$9 = \frac{y}{-3}$$
$$(-3)9 = \frac{-3y}{-3}$$
$$-27 = 1y$$
$$-27 = y$$

Check

$$9 = \frac{y}{-3}$$
$$9 \;?\; \frac{-27}{-3}$$
$$9 = 9 \quad \text{true}$$

The solution of $9 = \frac{y}{-3}$ is -27.

 EXAMPLE 3

Solve. Then, check the solution. $\quad \frac{c}{5} = 0$

Multiply to undo division.

Multiply both sides by 5.

Simplify each side.

$$\frac{c}{5} = 0$$
$$\frac{5c}{5} = 0(5)$$
$$1c = 0$$
$$c = 0$$

Check

$$\frac{c}{5} = 0$$
$$\frac{0}{5} \;?\; 0$$
$$0 = 0 \quad \text{true}$$

The solution of $\frac{c}{5} = 0$ is 0.

Try These

Solve. Then, check the solution.

1. $-7 = \dfrac{n}{-5}$

Multiply both sides by ■.

$\dfrac{-5}{■}(-7) = \dfrac{■n}{-5}$

Simplify.

$\dfrac{35}{■} = n$

Check.

$-7 = \dfrac{n}{-5}$

Substitute ■ for n.

$-7 \; ? \; \dfrac{■\,35}{-5}$

$-7 = \dfrac{■}{-7} \quad$ true

2. $\dfrac{t}{-4} = -6$

Multiply both sides by ■.

$\dfrac{■t}{-4} = -6(■)$

Simplify.

$t = \dfrac{24}{■}$

Check.

$\dfrac{t}{-4} = -6$

Substitute ■ for t.

$\dfrac{24■}{-4} \; ? \; -6$

$\dfrac{■}{-6} = -6 \quad$ true

Practice

Solve. Then, check the solution.

1. $\dfrac{k}{4} = 6$ 24

2. $\dfrac{b}{2} = 5$ 10

3. $3 = \dfrac{n}{6}$ 18

4. $9 = \dfrac{x}{3}$ 27

5. $-7 = \dfrac{s}{4}$ −28

6. $0 = \dfrac{z}{2}$ 0

7. $\dfrac{x}{4} = -5$ −20

8. $-5 = \dfrac{y}{8}$ −40

9. $\dfrac{c}{-12} = 2$ −24

10. $\dfrac{x}{3} = 4$ 12

11. $\dfrac{y}{5} = -10$ −50

12. $\dfrac{a}{2} = -3$ −6

13. $-8 = \dfrac{y}{-9}$ 72

14. $\dfrac{b}{-1} = -13$ 13

15. $-3 = \dfrac{a}{-5}$ 15

16. $\dfrac{x}{-3} = 8$ −24

17. $10 = \dfrac{n}{10}$ 100

18. $0 = \dfrac{c}{11}$ 0

Cooperative Learning

19. Explain to a partner how to solve the equation in number 9 in **Practice.**   Possible answer: Multiply both sides of the equation by −12. The solution is −24. To check, you will substitute −24 for c. −24 divided by −12 is 2.

20. Write an equation with $\dfrac{y}{3}$ on the left side. Use any number for the right side. Ask a partner to solve your equation. Check the solution.   Possible answers are: $\dfrac{y}{3} = 6$. Multiply both sides of the equation by 3; solution = 18. Check: $\dfrac{18}{3} = 6, 6 = 6$.

More practice is provided in Exercises 13, 15, and 17 of the Workbook.

3-8 ▶ Solving Equations Using Division

Getting Started
Write 6 • 5 on the chalkboard. Discuss what can be done to get 6.

You have solved equations that contain division. You multiplied to undo the division. You can also solve equations that contain multiplication. You divide to undo multiplication.

▶ **EXAMPLE 1**

Solve. Then, check the solution. $4x = -16$

Divide to undo multiplication.	$4x = -16$
Divide both sides by 4.	$\dfrac{4x}{4} = \dfrac{-16}{4}$
Simplify each side.	$1x = -4$
	$x = -4$
Check: Substitute -4 for x.	$4x = -16$
	$4(-4)\ ?\ -16$
	$-16 = -16$ true

The solution of $4x = -16$ is -4.

▶ **EXAMPLE 2**

Solve. Then, check the solution. $-y = 12$

Math Fact
$-y$ means $-1y$.

Check
$-y = 12$
$-(-12)\ ?\ 12$
$12 = 12$ true

Divide to undo multiplication.	$-y = 12$
Divide both sides by -1.	$\dfrac{-y}{-1} = \dfrac{12}{-1}$
Simplify each side.	$1y = -12$
	$y = -12$

The solution of $-y = 12$ is -12.

▶ **EXAMPLE 3**

Solve. Then, check the solution. $-20 = -5b$

Check
$-20 = -5b$
$-20\ ?\ -5(4)$
$-20 = -20$ true

Divide to undo multiplication.	$-20 = -5b$
Divide both sides by -5.	$\dfrac{-20}{-5} = \dfrac{-5b}{-5}$
Simplify each side.	$4 = 1b$
	$4 = b$

The solution of $-20 = -5b$ is 4.

Try These

Solve. Then, check the solution.

1. $-n = -30$

$-n$ means $-1 \cdot n$. $-1n = -30$

Divide both sides $\dfrac{-1n}{-1} = \dfrac{-30}{-1}$
by -1.

Simplify each side. $n = \blacksquare\!\!\!\!\!^{30}$

Check: $-n = -30$

Substitute $\blacksquare$ for n. $-(\blacksquare) \; ? \; -30$

$\blacksquare = -30$ true

2. $0 = 8y$

Divide both sides $\dfrac{0}{8} = \dfrac{8y}{8}$
by $\blacksquare$. 8

Simplify each side. $\blacksquare = y$

Check: $0 = 8y$

Substitute $\blacksquare$ for y. $0 \; ? \; 8(\blacksquare)$

$0 = \blacksquare$ true

Practice

Solve. Then, check the solution.

1. $3x = 21$ 7

2. $5r = 60$ 12

3. $32 = 4n$ 8

4. $49 = 7a$ 7

5. $48 = -8c$ -6

6. $0 = 2b$ 0

7. $-9x = 45$ -5

8. $-9b = -54$ 6

9. $-a = 24$ -24

10. $-80 = -y$ 80

11. $35 = -7y$ -5

12. $-4 = -4a$ 1

13. $5x = 50$ 10

14. $-12 = 4n$ -3

15. $-9b = 9$ -1

16. $-100 = -10x$ 10

17. $-64 = 8y$ -8

18. $56 = -7a$ -8

Cooperative Learning

19. Explain to a partner how to solve the equation in number 8
in **Practice.**   Possible answer: Divide both sides of the equation by -9; solution: 6.
Check: $-9(6) = -54$, $-54 = -54$.

20. Write an equation with $-2y$ on the left side. Use any even
number for the right side. Ask a partner to solve your equation.
Check the solution.   Possible answer: $-2y = 6$. Divide both sides of the equation by -2;
solution $= -3$. Check: $-2(-3) = 6$, $6 = 6$.

3·9 Solving Equations Using More Than One Operation

Getting Started

Write $8 \cdot 3 + 2$ on the chalkboard. Discuss what can be done to get 8.

Sometimes, you need more than one operation to solve equations. To solve these equations, first undo addition or subtraction. Then, undo multiplication or division.

▶ **EXAMPLE 1**

Solve. Then, check the solution. $5x - 3 = 7$

Add to undo subtraction.	$5x - 3 = 7$
Add 3 to both sides.	$5x - 3 + 3 = 7 + 3$
Simplify each side.	$5x = 10$
Divide to undo multiplication. Divide both sides by 5.	$\dfrac{5x}{5} = \dfrac{10}{5}$
Simplify each side.	$x = 2$

Check

$5x - 3 = 7$
$5(2) - 3 \ ? \ 7$
$10 - 3 \ ? \ 7$
$7 = 7$ true

The solution of $5x - 3 = 7$ is 2.

▶ **EXAMPLE 2**

Solve. Then, check the solution. $\dfrac{y}{3} + 2 = -7$

Subtract to undo addition.	$\dfrac{y}{3} + 2 = -7$
Subtract 2 from both sides.	$\dfrac{y}{3} + 2 - 2 = -7 - 2$
Simplify each side.	$\dfrac{y}{3} = -9$
Multiply to undo division. Multiply both sides by 3.	$\dfrac{3y}{3} = -9(3)$
Simplify each side.	$y = -27$

Check

$\dfrac{y}{3} + 2 = -7$
$\dfrac{-27}{3} + 2 \ ? \ -7$
$-9 + 2 \ ? \ -7$
$-7 = -7$ true

The solution of $\dfrac{y}{3} + 2 = -7$ is -27.

▶ **EXAMPLE 3**

Solve. Then, check the solution. $-5 = -x + 3$

Subtract to undo addition.	$-5 = -x + 3$
Subtract 3 from both sides.	$-5 - 3 = -x + 3 - 3$
Divide by -1.	$-8 = -1x$
Simplify each side.	$\dfrac{-8}{-1} = \dfrac{-1x}{-1}$
	$8 = x$

Check

$-5 = -x + 3$
$-5 \ ? \ -8 + 3$
$-5 = -5$ true

The solution of $-5 = -x + 3$ is 8.

Try These

Solve. Then, check the solution.

1. $5y - 8 = 12$

Add $\blacksquare$ to both sides. $\overset{8}{} \qquad 5y - 8 + \overset{8}{\blacksquare} = 12 + \overset{8}{\blacksquare}$

Simplify each side. $5y = \overset{20}{\blacksquare}$

Divide both sides by $\blacksquare$. $\;5$ $\dfrac{5y}{5\blacksquare} = \dfrac{20}{\blacksquare 5}$

Simplify each side. $y = \blacksquare\,4$

Check: $5y - 8 = 12$

Substitute $\blacksquare$ for y. $\;4$ $5(\overset{4}{\blacksquare}) - 8\;?\;12$

$20\blacksquare - 8\;?\;12$

$12\blacksquare = 12$ true

2. $14 = -\dfrac{v}{2} + 6$

subtract 6 from both sides. $\overset{6}{} \qquad 14 - \overset{6}{\blacksquare} = -\dfrac{v}{2} + 6 - \overset{6}{\blacksquare}$

Simplify each side. $\overset{8}{\blacksquare} = -\dfrac{v}{2}$

multiply both sides by -2. $\overset{-2}{} \qquad 8(\blacksquare) = \dfrac{\blacksquare v}{-2} \cdot -2$

Simplify each side. $\overset{-16}{\blacksquare} = v$

Check: $14 = -\dfrac{v}{2} + 6$

$14 = -\dfrac{-16}{2} + 6$

Substitute $\blacksquare$ for v. $\;-16$ $14\;?\;-(-8) + 6$

$8\,14\;?\;\blacksquare + 6$

$14 = \underset{14}{\blacksquare}$ true

Practice

Solve. Then, check the solution.

1. $10x - 4 = 16$ 2

2. $10x + 8 = 18$ 1

3. $7 = 2z - 7$ 7

4. $-8y + 2 = 26$ -3

5. $14 = -c - 14$ -28

6. $-1 = -4c - 9$ -2

7. $4u + 10 = 2$ -2

8. $-11 = \dfrac{y}{3} - 4$ -21

9. $\dfrac{x}{-5} + 3 = -2$ 25

10. $-n + 7 = 12$ -5

11. $\dfrac{m}{2} + 5 = -3$ -16

12. $26 = -5y + 6$ -4

Cooperative Learning

13. Explain to a partner how you chose the first step in solving number **6** in **Practice.** Possible answer: Since 9 is being subtracted, add 9 to both sides.

14. Write the equation $2b = 24$. Think of an even number. Subtract it from the left side of the equation. Ask a partner to solve your equation. Check the solution. Possible answer: $2b - 10 = 24$. Add 10 to both sides: $2b - 10 + 10 = 24 + 10$; $2b = 34$. Divide both sides by 2: $\dfrac{2b}{2} = \dfrac{34}{2}$; $b = 17$. Check: $2(17) - 10 = 24$; $34 - 10 = 24$; $24 = 24$.

More practice is provided in Exercises 16 and 17 of the Workbook.

3-10 Solving Equations Containing Parentheses

Getting Started

Ask for a volunteer to simplify
$-3(x - 4)$.
$-3(x - 4) = (-3)x - (-3)(4)$
$= -3x + 12$.

Some equations contain parentheses. Use the Distributive Property to remove the parentheses. Then, you will have an equation you know how to solve.

▶ **EXAMPLE 1**

Solve. Then, check the solution. $2(y + 6) = 18$

Use the Distributive Property.
$$2(y + 6) = 18$$
$$2 \cdot y + 2 \cdot 6 = 18$$

Simplify.
$$2y + 12 = 18$$

Subtract 12 from both sides.
$$2y + 12 - 12 = 18 - 12$$

Simplify each side.
$$2y = 6$$

Check

$2(y + 6) = 18$
$2(3 + 6) ? 18$
$2(9) ? 18$
$18 = 18$ true

Divide both sides by 2.
$$\frac{2y}{2} = \frac{6}{2}$$

Simplify each side.
$$y = 3$$

The solution of $2(y + 6) = 18$ is 3.

▶ **EXAMPLE 2**

Solve. Then, check the solution. $-4(b - 2) = -12$

Use the Distributive Property.
$$-4(b - 2) = -12$$
$$(-4)b - (-4)(2) = -12$$

Simplify.
$$-4b + 8 = -12$$

Subtract 8 from both sides.
$$-4b + 8 - 8 = -12 - 8$$

Simplify each side.
$$-4b = -20$$

Check

$-4(b - 2) = -12$
$-4(5 - 2) ? -12$
$-4(3) ? -12$
$-12 = -12$ true

Divide both sides by -4.
$$\frac{-4b}{-4} = \frac{-20}{-4}$$

Simplify each side.
$$b = 5$$

The solution of $-4(b - 2) = -12$ is 5.

▶ **EXAMPLE 3**

Solve. Then, check the solution. $15 = -(-x + 10)$

Use the Distributive Property.
Multiply by -1.
$$15 = -(-x + 10)$$
$$15 = (-1)(-x) + (-1)10$$

Check

$15 = -(-x + 10)$
$15 ? -(-25 + 10)$
$15 ? -(-15)$
$15 = 15$ true

Simplify.
$$15 = x - 10$$

Add 10 to both sides.
$$15 + 10 = x - 10 + 10$$

Simplify each side.
$$25 = x$$

The solution of $15 = -(-x + 10)$ is 25.

Try These

Solve. Then, check the solution.

1. $-5(s - 4) = 10$

	$-5(s - 4) = 10$
Use the	$-5(s) - (-5)(4) = 10$
Distributive	
Property.	$\underset{s}{\;}\;\;\underset{20}{\;}$
Simplify.	$-5\blacksquare + \blacksquare = 10$
subtract $\blacksquare$ 20 from	$-5s + \blacksquare - \blacksquare = 10 - \blacksquare$
both sides.	$\underset{20}{\;}\;\underset{20}{\;}\qquad\underset{20}{\;}$
Simplify.	$-5s = \blacksquare$
	$\qquad\quad -10$
Divide both	$\dfrac{-5s}{-5\blacksquare} = \dfrac{-10}{\blacksquare -5}$
sides by $\blacksquare$.-5	
Simplify.	$\underset{2}{\;}\qquad s = \blacksquare\;2$
Check:	$-5(\blacksquare - 4) \;?\; 10$
Substitute $\blacksquare$	$\underset{2}{\;}\quad -5(\blacksquare) \;?\; 10$
for s.	$\qquad\qquad -2$
	$10\;\blacksquare = 10$ true

2. $-8 = 4(n - 3)$

Distributive Property	$-8 = 4(n - 3)$
Use the $\blacksquare$.	
	$\underset{\;}{\;}\quad n-8 = 4\blacksquare - \blacksquare(3)\;4$
Simplify.	$-8 = \blacksquare - 12\;4n$
12 Add $\blacksquare$ to	$-8 + \blacksquare = 4n - 12 + \blacksquare$
both sides.	$\quad 12 \qquad\qquad\qquad 12$
Simplify.	$4\blacksquare = 4n$
Divide both	$\dfrac{4}{4\blacksquare} = \dfrac{4n}{\blacksquare 4}$
sides by $\blacksquare$.4	
Simplify.	$1\blacksquare = n\;1$
Check:	$-8 = 4(n - 3)$
	$-8 \;?\; 4(\blacksquare - 3)$
Substitute $\blacksquare$	$\qquad\qquad 1$
for n.	$-8 \;?\; 4(\blacksquare)$
	$\qquad\qquad -2$
	$-8 = \blacksquare$ true
	$\quad -8$

Practice

Solve. Then, check the solution.

1. $3(x + 3) = 18$ 3

2. $16 = 2(y + 7)$ 1

3. $5(b + 3) = -30$ -9

4. $2(s - 2) = 6$ 5

5. $-(x - 1) = -12$ 13

6. $16 = -4(r + 2)$ -6

7. $-5(a + 2) = 30$ -8

8. $27 = -9(z - 1)$ -2

9. $-5(y - 7) = -20$ 11

Cooperative Learning

10. Explain to a partner how you use the Distributive Property to remove the parentheses in number **7** in **Practice**.
Possible answer: Multiply -5 by a and -5 by 2. The equation will be $-5a - 10 = 30$.

11. Write an equation that contains parentheses. Ask a partner to solve your equation. Check the solution.
Possible answer: $4(t + 1) = -4$; solution: -2.

Getting Started
Review
combining like
terms. Ask
students to simplify
$5y + 7y$
$-8r + 3r$
$-4t - 6t$
$(12y; -5r; -10t)$

3·11 | **Solving Equations with Variables on Both Sides**

Sometimes equations have a variable on both sides of the equal sign. To solve these equations, get the variable on one side.

You can begin by subtracting the variable term with the smaller coefficient.

▶ **EXAMPLE 1**

Solve. Then, check the solution. $7x = 5x + 8$

Get the variable on one side. $7x = 5x + 8$

Subtract $5x$ from both sides. $7x - 5x = 5x - 5x + 8$

Combine like terms. $2x = 8$

Divide both sides by 2. $\dfrac{2x}{2} = \dfrac{8}{2}$

Simplify each side. $x = 4$

Solution: 4

The solution of $7x = 5x + 8$ is 4.

Check
$7x = 5x + 8$
$7(4) \; ? \; 5(4) + 8$
$28 \; ? \; 20 + 8$
$28 = 28$ true

When the smaller coefficient is negative, you can add the variable term to both sides.

▶ **EXAMPLE 2**

Solve. Then, check the solution. $4y + 4 = -2y - 8$

Get the variable on one side. $4y + 4 = -2y - 8$

Add $2y$ to both sides. $4y + 2y + 4 = -2y + 2y - 8$

Combine like terms. $6y + 4 = -8$

Subtract 4 from both sides. $6y + 4 - 4 = -8 - 4$

Simplify each side. $6y = -12$

Divide both sides by 6. $\dfrac{6y}{6} = \dfrac{-12}{6}$

Simplify each side. $y = -2$

Solution: -2

The solution of $4y + 4 = -2y - 8$ is -2.

Check
$4y + 4 = -2y - 8$
$4(-2) + 4 \; ? \; -2(-2) - 8$
$-8 + 4 \; ? \; 4 - 8$
$-4 = -4$ true

Try These

Solve.

1. $-6t = 14 + t$

Add ■ to both sides. $-6t + \underset{6t}{■} = 14 + t + \underset{6t}{■}$

Combine like terms. $0 = 14 + \underset{7t}{■}$

Subtract ■ 14 from both sides. $\underset{14}{0 - ■} = 14 - \underset{14}{■} + 7t$

Simplify each side. $-14 = \underset{7t}{■}$

Divide by $\underset{7}{■}$ on both sides. $\dfrac{-14}{■_7} = \dfrac{7t}{■_7}$

Simplify each side. $\underset{-2}{■} = t$

Solution: $\underset{-2}{■}$

2. $24 - 4k = -12k$

Add ■ to both sides. $24 - 4k + \underset{12k}{■} = -12k + \underset{12k}{■}$

Combine like ■. terms $24 + \underset{8k}{■} = 0$

Subtract 24 ■ from both sides. $24 - \underset{24}{■} + 8k = 0 - \underset{24}{■}$

Simplify each side. $8k = \underset{-24}{■}$

Divide by ■ 8 on both sides. $\dfrac{8k}{■_8} = \dfrac{-24}{■_8}$

Simplify each side. $k = \underset{-3}{■}$

Solution: ■ -3

13. Possible answer: You can subtract the smaller variable term (2a) from both sides. This will get both variable terms on the left. Then, you can add 9 to both sides to get $3a = 9$. Finally, you can divide **Practice** both sides by 3, and you are left with the solution $a = 3$.

Solve. Then, check the solution.

1. $2x = x + 3$ 3

2. $7x = 3x + 24$ 6

3. $30 + 6t = 11t$ 6

4. $5 - 2t = 3t$ 1

5. $z = 49 - 6z$ 7

6. $5a - 9 = 2a$ 3

7. $28 + 10r = 3r$ -4

8. $4x = 7x + 33$ -11

9. $-3y = -8y - 15$ -3

10. $10x + 9 = 4x - 9$ -3

11. $8x - 8 = -4x + 16$ 2

12. $7w + 5 = 3w - 15$ -5

Cooperative Learning

13. Explain to a partner how you solve the equation in number 6 in **Practice**. See above.

14. Take turns with a partner to solve $5x = x - 20$. $x = -5$

Getting Started
Have students
practice inputting
decimals on their
calculators. For example,
4.06, .5, and 20.4.

3-12 **Calculator: Checking Solutions**

Some equations have decimals. You can use a calculator to check the solutions to these equations.

▶ **EXAMPLE 1**

Is 17.04 the solution of $2.5(x - 16.4) = 1.6$?

Substitute 17.04 for x. $\qquad\qquad 2.5(x - 16.4) = 1.6$

$$2.5(17.04 - \overset{.}{1}6.4) \; ? \; 1.6$$

Use your calculator to simplify the left side.

Remember
Perform the operations in the parentheses first.

		Display
Enter 17.04 by pressing:	1 7 . 0 4	17.04
Subtract 16.4 by pressing:	− 1 6 . 4 =	.64
Multiply by 2.5 by pressing:	× 2 . 5 =	1.6

$1.6 = 1.6$ is true.
17.04 is the solution of $2.5(x - 16.4) = 1.6$.

▶ **EXAMPLE 2**

Check whether .56 is the solution of $11v + .456 = 19v$.

Substitute .56 for v. $\qquad\qquad 11v + .456 = 19v$

$$11(.56) + .456 \; ? \; 19(.56)$$

Use your calculator to simplify each side.

		Display
Enter 11 by pressing:	1 1	11
Multiply by .56 by pressing:	× . 5 6 =	6.16
Add .456 by pressing:	+ . 4 5 6 =	6.616
Enter 19 by pressing:	1 9	19
Multiply by .56 by pressing:	× . 5 6 =	10.64

The left side does not equal the right side.
.56 is not the solution of $11v + .456 = 19v$.

Practice

Tell whether the number is a solution of the equation.

1. $.28; .1998 = .27(x + .46)$ yes

2. $2.1; 12.2 = 11.5 + \frac{z}{3}$ yes

3. $58; .21y = .28y - 4.06$ yes

4. $20.4; 14(v - .89) = 162.4$ no

5. $6.2; .5(n + 4.9) = 5.55$ yes

6. $7; 9.5y - 8.8 = 5.39y$ no

Math Connection

KEEPING THINGS IN BALANCE

Scientists use an instrument called a balance scale to measure the weight of an object. When the scale is balanced, the object of unknown weight is equal to the known weight.

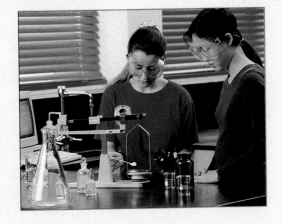

Chemists can use a small beam balance to measure the amount of a chemical they need for an experiment. They place the chemicals on a pan. Then they move a small weight along a beam until the scale is balanced. A mark on the beam tells the weight of the chemical.

Beam balance scales that chemists use need to be very accurate. It is important that the right amount of a chemical be used in an experiment or the experiment can go wrong.

Getting Started
Review changing a percent to a decimal by moving the decimal point two places to the left. Ask volunteers to write examples on the chalkboard.

3·13 Problem Solving: Writing Percent Equations

Many problems ask you to find the percent of a number. You can write an equation for the problem. Choose a variable for the missing number. Use "=" for "is" and "•" for "of."

Math Fact
25% = .25 = .25

What number is 25% of 60?

don't know = .25 • 60

Pick a letter to stand for the number. You can use n.

$n = .25 • 60$

$n = 15$

Solution: 15

15 is 25% of 60.

▶ **EXAMPLE**

85% of the 300 high school seniors are going to college. How many seniors are going to college?

READ   **What do you need to find out?**
You need to find how many seniors are going to college.

PLAN   **What do you need to do?**
You need to write an equation.

DO   **Follow the plan.**
            85% of seniors are going to college.

Math Facts
85% = .85 = .85

.85 • 300 = 255

Write an equation. $.85 • 300 = $ don't know

Use x for the variable. $.85 • 300 = x$

Solve for x. $255 = x$

CHECK   **Does your answer make sense?**
100% of the seniors is 300 seniors.
85% is close to 100%.
255 is close to 300. ✓

255 seniors are going to college.

Try These

Find the number.

1. What is 50% of 88?

Write an equation.   ? is 50% of 88

Use w as the variable. ■ $= .50 \cdot 88$ w

Solve for w. $w = $ ■ 44

Solution: ■ 44

44 is 50% of 88.

2. 15% of 40 computers have a virus. How many have a virus?

Write an equation. 15% of 40 have a virus.

Use n as the variable. $.15 \cdot 40 = $ ■ n

Solve for n.   ■ $= n$ 6

Solution: ■ 6

15% of 40 is 6.

6 computers have a virus.

Practice

Write an equation and solve each percent problem.

1. What is 55% of 80?
$n = .55 \cdot 80$; 44

2. What is 20% of 50?
$n = .20 \cdot 50$; 10

3. 25% of 100 is what number?
$.25 \cdot 100 = n$; 25

4. 40% of 65 is what number?
$.40 \cdot 65 = n$; 26

5. 5% of 160 teachers are retiring. How many teachers are retiring? $.05 \cdot 160 = n$; 8

6. Megan scored in 80% of 20 games this season. In how many games did Megan score? $.80 \cdot 20 = n$; 16

Cooperative Learning

7. Explain to a partner how you wrote the variable equation in number **6** in **Practice.** Possible answer: Pick a letter (n) to stand for the number of games Megan scored in. Then, write an equation using the variable ($.80 \cdot 20 = n$).

8. Write a word sentence. Have a partner write a variable equation for what you wrote. Check the work. Possible answer: 15% of 20 seventh graders will work this summer. How many seventh graders will work this summer? $.15 \cdot 20 = n$; 3.

More practice is provided in Exercise 18 of the Workbook.

3-14 ▶ Application: Consumer Math

Getting Started
Find ads in the newspaper that use the terms *regular price*, *discount*, and *sale price*. Discuss what these terms mean.

When you buy something on sale, you pay less than the regular price. The money you save is the **discount.** You can find the discount by multiplying by the percent of the discount.

discount = percent of discount × regular price

▶ **EXAMPLE 1**

A shirt costs $30.00. It is on sale for 20% off the regular price. Find the discount.

discount = percent of discount × regular price
discount = 20% • 30
discount = .2 • 30
discount = 6

Math Facts
20% = .20 = .2
```
   30
×  .2
  6.0
```

The discount is $6.00.

Once you know the discount you can find the **sale price.** Subtract the discount from the regular price.

sale price = regular price − discount

▶ **EXAMPLE 2**

A CD costs $15.00. It is on sale for 5% off the regular price. Find the sale price.

Find the discount.

discount = percent of discount × regular price
discount = 5% • 15
discount = .05 • 15
discount = .75

Math Fact
5% = .05

The discount is $.75.

Find the sale price.

sale price = regular price − discount
sale price = 15 − .75
sale price = 14.25

Math Fact
```
 $15.00
−   .75
 $14.25
```

The sale price is $14.25.

Try These

Solve.

1. Find the discount on a $24 shirt that is on sale for 25% off.

discount =
  percent of discount × regular price

discount = ■ • 24 .25

discount = ■ 6

The discount is ■. $6.00

2. Find the sale price of the $24 shirt.

sale price = ■ − discount Regular price

sale price = ■ − 6 24

sale price = ■ 18

The sale price is ■. $18.00

Practice

Find the discount or the sale price.

1. Find the discount on a $15 T-shirt. It is on sale for 10% off. $1.50

2. Find the sale price of a $50 bookshelf that is on sale for 15% off. $42.50

3. A train set costs $120.00. Find the discount if it is on sale for 30% off. $36.00

4. What is the sale price of a $300 mountain bike that is on sale for 50% off? $150.00

5. Find the discount for a stereo that is on sale for 12% off. The original price is $200.00. $24.00

Cooperative Learning

6. Explain to a partner how you find the discount and the sale price for the item in number **2** in **Practice.** Possible answer: First multiply (50)(0.15); Then, subtract that from $50; this is the sale price.

7. Work with a partner. Think of the cost of an item. The item is on sale for 10% off. Ask your partner to find the amount that would be saved with the discount. Then have your partner find the sale price of the item. Possible answer: An item cost $40.00; 10% of 40 = (.1)(40); The discount is $4.00. The sale price is $40 − $4 = $36.00.

Chapter **3** Review

Summary

The solution of an equation is the value of the variable that makes the equation true.
Adding, subtracting, multiplying, or dividing both sides of an equation by the same number gives an equivalent equation.
When you add, subtract, multiply, or divide both sides of an equation by the same number, you are using properties of equality.
You can use inverse operations to solve an equation.
You can use the Distributive Property to remove parentheses in equations.
To solve an equation with variables on both sides, you can add or subtract the variable term from one side.
To write a percent equation, use "=" for "is," " • " for "of," and a variable for the number you do not know. Write the percent as a decimal.
You can find the sale price by subtracting the amount of the discount. You can find the discount by multiplying the regular price by the percent of the discount.

More vocabulary review is provided in Exercise 21 of the Classroom Resource Binder.

variable equation

solution

equivalent equations

properties of equality

inverse operations

solve

check

discount

sale price

Vocabulary Review

Complete the sentences with words from the box.

1. The regular price minus the discount is the ____. sale price

2. Operations that "undo" other operations are ____. inverse operations

3. You can ____ a solution when you substitute the solution for the variable. check

4. The amount you save when you buy an item on sale is the ____. discount

5. Equations that have the same solution are ____. equivalent equations

6. A ____ is an equation that contains a variable. variable equation

7. The ____ is the value of the variable that makes a variable equation true. solution

8. An example of one of the ____ is adding the same amount to both sides of an equation. properties of equality

9. To ____ an equation is to find its solution. solve

Chapter Quiz   More assessment is provided in the Classroom Resource Binder.

Tell whether the number is the solution of the equation.

1. $-15; x + 35 = 20$
yes

2. $3; 2y + 4 = 12$
no

3. $-2; 8 = 10 + x$
yes

Show that each pair of equations is equivalent.

4. $b = 9$ and $3b = 27$
$3(9) = 27; 27 = 27$

5. $w = -14$ and $w + 8 = -6$
$-14 + 8 = -6; -6 = -6$

6. $2 = b$ and $6b - 3 = 9$
$6(2) - 3 = 9; 12 - 3 = 9; 9 = 9$

Complete to make equivalent equations.

7. $\frac{x}{4} = 3$
$\frac{x}{4} ? 4 = 3 \bullet 4 \bullet$

8. $6 + x = -11$
$6 - ? + x = -11 - 6$ 6

9. $-2y = 14$
$-2y ? (-2) = 14 \div (-2) \div$

Complete each equation with the missing operation.

10. $x + 3 ? 3 = x$ $-$

11. $-5y ? (-5) = y$ $\div$

12. $\frac{v}{10} ? 10 = v$ $\bullet$

Solve. Then check the solution.

13. $x - 4 = 20$ 24

14. $a - 13 = -20$ -7

15. $0 = t - 7$ 7

16. $4t = -20$ -5

17. $2 = 3x - 13$ 5

18. $\frac{y}{3} + 6 = -1$ -21

19. $4(y + 2) = 28$ 5

20. $-(w + 3) = -15$ 12

21. $4x = 2x + 6$ 3

Find the number.

22. What is 30% of 150? 45

23. 40% of 250 students have part-time jobs. How many students have part-time jobs? 100

Find the discount or the sale price.

24. Find the discount for a \$40.00 jacket that is on sale at 20% off. \$8.00

25. Find the sale price of a \$10.00 T-shirt. It is discounted 15%. \$8.50

Additional Practice for this chapter is provided on p. 415 of this text.

Unit 1 **Review**

Choose the letter for the correct answer.

Use the broken-line graph to answer Questions 1 and 2.

Average Temperature

1. What was the average temperature on Monday? A
   A. $-10°$
   B. $0°$
   C. $10°$
   D. $20°$

2. Which day had the highest temperature? C
   A. Tuesday
   B. Wednesday
   C. Thursday
   D. Friday

3. A refrigerator box measures 4 ft long, 5 ft wide, and 6 ft tall. What is the volume of the box? D
   A. 72 ft^3
   B. 13 ft^3
   C. 30 ft^3
   D. 120 ft^3

Critical Thinking See the Classroom Resource Binder for a scoring rubric to assess this Critical Thinking question.

4. Al and Joe are waiters. One night Al earned $22 less than Joe in tips. Which equation shows how much Al earned? B
   A. $j = a - 22$
   B. $a = j - 22$
   C. $a = j + 22$
   D. None of the above

5. The regular price of a pair of shoes is $60. They are on sale for 20% off. What is the sale price? A
   A. $48
   B. $12
   C. $20
   D. $72

6. 80% of 210 students took Algebra. How many students took Algebra? D
   A. 29 students
   B. 200 students
   C. 32 students
   D. 168 students

Critical Thinking
A $50 blue jacket is on sale at 20% off. A $60 red jacket is on sale at 30% off. Find the sale price of each jacket. Which is cheaper? See below.
CHALLENGE Which of these pairs of gloves is the cheapest: a pair that costs $20; a $25 pair that is on sale at 10% off; or a $30 pair that is on sale at 30% off? the $20 pair that is not on sale

$40, $42; The blue jacket is cheaper.

Unit Two

A grid system is used on maps to show the location of a place. A grid system is used in algebra to show the location of a function. How would you locate Terra on the map of Venus above?

Learning Objectives

- Graph ordered pairs.
- Find ordered pairs from tables and equations.
- Identify a function.
- Use a calculator to find ordered pairs.
- Use a function shown as a table or equation to solve problems.
- Apply concepts and skills to use information in tables and bar graphs.

Words to Know

coordinate plane	plane with two perpendicular number lines
coordinate axes	perpendicular number lines
origin	the point where coordinate axes cross
ordered pairs	two numbers in a special order; Ordered pairs give the locations of points
graph of an ordered pair	a dot that shows the location of an ordered pair
function	a group of ordered pairs where no two ordered pairs have the same first number
vertical line test	a test you use on a graph to tell if the graph is a function
function notation	a way to write an equation that is a function
bar graph	a graph that uses bars to represent information

Function Project

Measure the height and arm span of each student in your class. Write each measurement as an ordered pair (height, arm span). Then graph the ordered pairs. Describe the relationship between height and arm span.

> Susan
> height: 64 in.
> arm span: 64 in.

Project See the Classroom Resource Binder for a scoring rubric to assess this project.

More practice is provided in Exercise 19 of the Workbook.

4·1 The Coordinate Plane

A **coordinate plane** has two perpendicular number lines called **coordinate axes.** The axis that goes left and right is the horizontal axis. It is called the *x*-axis. The axis that goes up and down is the vertical axis. It is called the *y*-axis. The axes cross at the **origin.**

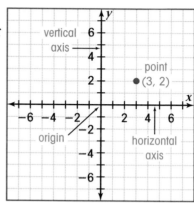

Ordered pairs give the locations of points on the coordinate plane. The first number tells the location in the horizontal direction. The second number gives the location in the vertical direction. The ordered pair for the origin is (0, 0). When you use the variables *x* and *y*, the ordered pair is (*x*, *y*).

▶ **EXAMPLE 1**

Math Facts
Positive numbers are right or up from the origin.
Negative numbers are left or down from the origin.

Give the location of *A* at (4, −2).

Begin at the origin.

Move right 4 units.

Move down 2 units.

The location of *A* is right 4 units, down 2.

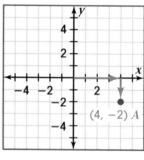

Sometimes, other letters are used to label the axes.

▶ **EXAMPLE 2**

Give the location of *B* at (−3, −1).

Begin at the origin.

Move left 3 units.

Move down 1 unit.

The location of *B* is left 3 units, down 1 unit.

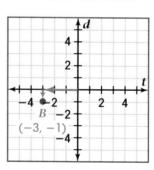

Try These

Give the location of each point.

1. A (2, 5)
   right 2 units, up **5** units

2. B (−2, −3)
   left **2** units, down 3 units

3. C (−4, 2)
   left 4 units, up **2** units

4. D (0, 3)
   up **3** units from the origin

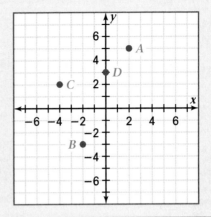

Practice

Give the location of each point.

1. A (1, 3)
   right 1 unit, up 3 units
2. B (−3, 3)
   left 3 units, up 3 units
3. C (0, 2)
   up 2 units from the origin
4. D (2, −1)
   right 2 units, down 1 unit
5. E (−4, 0)
   left 4 units from the origin
6. F (3, 1)
   right 3 units, up 1 unit
7. G (−2, −5)
   left 2 units, down 5 units
8. H (0, −3)
   down 3 units from the origin
9. I (−5, −4)
   left 5 units, down 4 units
10. J (3, −4)
    right 3 units, down 4 units

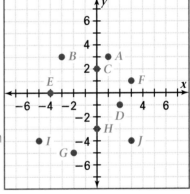

Cooperative Learning

11. Explain to a partner how to give the location of the point in
    number **5** in **Practice.** Start at the origin; move 4 units left.

12. Ask a partner to tell why A (1, 3) and F (3, 1) are not at the
    same location. The location of A is right 1 unit, up 3 units, but the location of F
    is right 3 units, up 1 unit.

4·2 Graphing Ordered Pairs

Getting Started

Place the point $(-1, 2)$ on a graph on an overhead projector slide. Ask a volunteer to locate the point.

You have used an ordered pair to find the location of a point. Now, you will graph an ordered pair on a coordinate plane. The **graph of an ordered pair** is a point.

▶ **EXAMPLE 1**

Remember

In $(3, -2)$, 3 means right 3 units. -2 means down 2 units.

Graph point A at $(3, -2)$

Begin at the origin.

Move right 3 units.

Move down 2 units.

Draw a dot at this location.

Label it A $(3, -2)$.

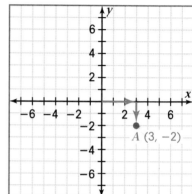

▶ **EXAMPLE 2**

Remember

In $(-4, 0)$, -4 means left 4 units. 0 means no units up or down.

Graph point B at $(-4, 0)$

Begin at the origin.

Move left 4 units.

Do not move up or down.

Draw a dot at this location.

Label it B $(-4, 0)$.

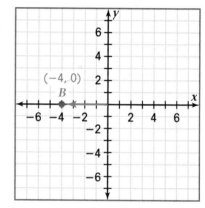

▶ **EXAMPLE 3**

Remember

In $(0, 3)$, 0 means no units left or right. 3 means up 3 units.

Graph point C at $(0, 3)$

Begin at the origin.

Do not move left or right.

Move up 3 units.

Draw a dot at this location.

Label it C $(0, 3)$.

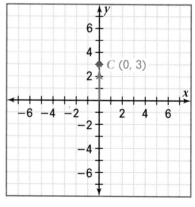

Try These

Graph and label each point.

1. P at $(-2, 1)$

Begin at the origin.
Move left ▧ units.
Move ▧ 1 unit.
Draw a dot.
Label it P $(-2, 1)$.

2. Q at $(-4, -3)$

Begin at the origin.
Move ▧ 4 units.
Move down ▧ units.
Draw a dot.
Label it Q $(-4, -3)$.

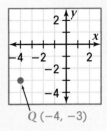

Practice

Use graph paper. Draw coordinate axes. Graph and label each point on the same pair of axes.

1. A at $(4, 4)$ **2.** B at $(-2, 2)$ **3.** C at $(-2, -4)$

4. D at $(3, -2)$ **5.** E at $(2, 4)$ **6.** F at $(0, 3)$

7. G at $(-3, 1)$ **8.** H at $(1, -3)$ **9.** I at $(2, 2)$

10. J at $(-3, -3)$ **11.** K at $(-2, 0)$ **12.** L at $(5, 2)$

13. M at $(2, -1)$ **14.** N at $(-4, 3)$ **15.** O at $(-1, -1)$

Cooperative Learning

16. Explain to a partner how to graph and label the point in number **8** in **Practice**.

17. Write four ordered pairs. Ask a partner to graph each point on coordinate axes. Check the work.

More practice is provided in Exercise 20 of the Workbook.

4·3 ▶ Tables and Ordered Pairs

Getting Started
Have students read tables from newspapers in order to help them interpret information in tables.

You can show ordered pairs in tables. The first column of the table contains the first number of an ordered pair. The second column of the table contains the second number.

▶ **EXAMPLE 1**

Write the ordered pairs from the table.

Write each row as an ordered pair.
(1, 2), (2, 4), (3, 6)

Time	Distance
1 second	2 feet
2 seconds	4 feet
3 seconds	6 feet

The ordered pairs are (1, 2), (2, 4), and (3, 6)

You can graph the ordered pairs. Use the heading of the first column for the horizontal axis. Use the heading of the second column for the vertical axis.

▶ **EXAMPLE 2**

Write the ordered pairs from the table. Label the coordinate axes. Then, graph the ordered pairs.

Minutes	°Celsius
4	−4
5	−2
6	0

Write each row as an ordered pair.
(4, −4), (5, −2), (6, 0)

Label the horizontal axis with the heading from the first column.

Label the vertical axis with the heading from the second column.

Graph the ordered pairs.

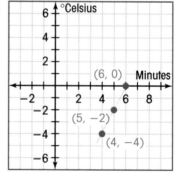

Try These

1. Write the ordered pairs from the table.

Write the rows as ordered pairs.

(1, ■)

(2, ■)

(■, ■)

The ordered pairs are (1, ■), (2, ■),

and ■, ■).

Hours	Feet
1	2
2	−2
3	−6

2. Label the axes. Graph the ordered pairs.

Label the horizontal axis with the heading from the first column.

Label horizontal axis: Hours.

Label the vertical axis with the heading from the second column.

Label vertical axis: ■. Feet

Graph the ordered pairs.

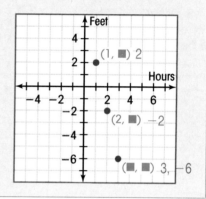

Practice

Write the ordered pairs from each table. Use graph paper.
Label the axes. Then, graph the ordered pairs.

1.

Day	Temperature	
1	−5	(1, −5)
2	0	(2, 0)
3	5	(3, 5)

See Additional Answers, p. 471.

2.

Quarts	Pints	
2	4	(2, 4)
4	8	(4, 8)
6	12	(6, 12)

See Additional Answers, p. 471.

Cooperative Learning

3. Explain to a partner how to write the ordered pairs in number **2** in **Practice**. Possible answer: Use the first column to write the first number in the ordered pair. The second column is for the second number in the ordered pair.

4. Make a table containing three pairs of numbers. Ask a partner to write the ordered pairs. Be sure to put labels in the table. Answers will vary.

Getting Started
On the chalkboard, write (1,2), (2,4), (3,6). Ask a student to follow the pattern and write the next ordered pair. (4,8) Have volunteers continue the pattern.

4·4 ▶ Equations and Ordered Pairs

One way to find ordered pairs is from equations that have two variables. Substitute a value for one variable into the equation, and find the corresponding value for the other variable. Each pair of values forms an ordered pair.

▶ **EXAMPLE 1**

Remember
The x-value is the first number in the ordered pair.
The y-value is the second number in the ordered pair.

Find four ordered pairs for $y = x - 3$.

Let $x = -1$. Then, $y = (-1) - 3 = -4$. $(-1, -4)$

Let $x = 0$. Then, $y = (0) - 3 = -3$. $(0, -3)$

Let $x = 1$. Then, $y = (1) - 3 = -2$. $(1, -2)$

Let $x = 2$. Then, $y = (2) - 3 = -1$. $(2, -1)$

Four ordered pairs for $y = x - 3$ are $(-1, -4)$, $(0, -3)$, $(1, -2)$, and $(2, -1)$.

You can use a table to show the ordered pairs. The columns show the values of each number in an ordered pair.

▶ **EXAMPLE 2**

Math Fact
Choose values for the variables that are easy to use.

Make a table of values for $d = a^2 - 1$.

Write column headings from the equation.

a	$a^2 - 1$	d
-1	$(-1)^2 - 1$	0
0	$(0)^2 - 1$	-1
1	$(1)^2 - 1$	0
2	$(2)^2 - 1$	3

Let $a = -1$. Substitute -1 for a. Simplify.

Let $a = 0$. Substitute 0 for a. Simplify.

Let $a = 1$. Substitute 1 for a. Simplify.

Let $a = 2$. Substitute 2 for a. Simplify.

Write the ordered pairs.

Four ordered pairs for $d = a^2 - 1$ are $(-1, 0)$, $(0, -1)$, $(1, 0)$, and $(2, 3)$.

Try These

1. Find three ordered pairs for the equation $y = 3(x + 1)$.

Let $x = -1$.

Then,
$y = 3(-1 + 1) = $ ■ $\rightarrow (-1,$ ■$)$.

Let $x = 0$.

Then, $y = 3(0 + 1) = $ ■ $\rightarrow (0,$ ■$)$.

Let $x = 1$.

Then, $y = 3($■$ + 1) = $ ■ $\rightarrow ($■$,$ ■$)$.

Three ordered pairs for $y = 3(x + 1)$ are $(-1,$ ■$)$, $(0,$ ■$)$, and $($■$,$ ■$)$.

2. Make a table of values for $y = 2x + 4$.

Write column headings from the equation.

Let $x = -1$.
Let $x = 0$.
Let $x = 1$.

x	■	y
-1	$2(-1) + 4$	■
■	$2($■$) + 4$	4
■	$2($■$) + 4$	■

Three ordered pairs for $y = 2x + 4$ are $(-1,$ ■$)$, $($■$, 4)$, and $($■$,$ ■$)$.

Practice

Find three ordered pairs for each equation.

1. $y = 5x + 1$
Possible answer: $(-1, -4)$, $(0, 1)$, $(1, 6)$

2. $y = 10 - x$
Possible answer: $(-1, 11)$, $(0, 10)$, $(1, 9)$

3. $y = 2x$
Possible answer: $(-1, -2)$, $(0, 0)$, $(1, 2)$

Complete each table to show four ordered pairs for the equation.

4.

x	x^2	y
-1	$(-1)^2$	■
0	■	■
1	■	■
2	■	■

5.

x	$2(x - 1)$	y
-1	$2(-1 - 1)$	■
0	■	■
1	■	■
2	■	■

Cooperative Learning

6. Explain to a partner how to find the last row in number **4** in **Practice**. Substitute 2 for x. Simplify the expression 2^2 to get $y = 4$.

7. Write a simple equation. Ask a partner to find an ordered pair for your equation. Possible answer: student writes $y = x + 2$. Partner chooses $x = 0$ and gets the ordered pair $(0, 2)$.

More practice is provided in Exercise 21 of the Workbook.

4-5 ▶ Functions

Getting Started
Have students graph the
points $(-1, 2)$, $(-1, 3)$, and
$(-1, 4)$. Discuss what the
graph shows. (The points
form a vertical line.)

Some groups of ordered pairs are called **functions**. In a function, each value of x has only one value of y.

$(2, 3)$, $(4, 5)$, $(6, 7)$, $(8, 9)$	$(5, 8)$, $(5, 9)$, $(6, 10)$, $(7, 11)$
x-values: 2, 4, 6, and 8	x-values: 5, 5, 6, and 7
Each x-value has only one y-value.	5 has two y-values, 8 and 9
This is a function.	This is not a function.

▶ **EXAMPLE 1**

Tell whether $(2, -1)$, $(3, -2)$, $(4, 0)$, $(3, 1)$ is a function.

List each x-value.   2, 3, 4, 3

Look for repeated numbers.   3 has two y-values, -2 and 1.

This group of ordered pairs is not a function.

You can look at a graph to see if the ordered pairs form a function. If a vertical line can cross the graph more than once, it is not a function. This is the **vertical line test.**

Function

Function

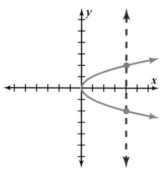

Not a Function

▶ **EXAMPLE 2**

Tell whether the graph is a function.

Draw a vertical line.

The line crosses the graph exactly once.

The graph is a function.

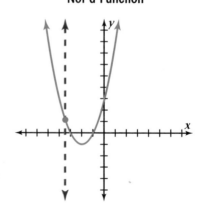

Try These

1. Tell without graphing whether (0, 2), (1, 3), (2, 4), (3, 4) is a function.

List each *x*-value.   0, 1, 2, ■ 3

Look for repeated numbers.   Each *x*-value has ■ *y*-value.
                       only one

This set of ordered pairs ■ a function.
                   is

2. Tell whether the graph is a function.
      crosses

A vertical line ■ this graph
more than one time.

This graph ■ a function.
   is not

Practice

Tell without graphing whether each group of ordered
pairs is a function.

1. (5, 1), (10, 2), (15, 3), (15, 4) no   **2.** (2, 5), (3, 9), (4, 12), (5, 15) yes

Tell by using the vertical line test whether each graph
is a function.

3.
yes

4.
yes

5.
no

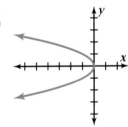

Cooperative Learning

6. Explain to a partner how to tell whether the group of ordered
pairs is a function in number **2** in **Practice**. Look for duplicate *x*-values.
There are not any, so it must be a function.

7. Draw two graphs. Make one a function. Make the other not a
function. Ask a partner to tell which one is the function.
Answers will vary. Check students' drawings.

More practice is provided in Exercise 21 of the Workbook.

Getting Started

On the chalkboard, write the equation $y = 2x + 1$ and the ordered pair (2, 5). Ask a volunteer to show that (2, 5) is a solution to the equation.

Math Fact

You can say "f of x" for f(x).

Some equations are functions. Ordered pairs from these equations have only one y-value for each x-value. You can use **function notation** for an equation that is a function. The symbol $f(x)$ means "the function of x."

$$y = 2x + 4 \rightarrow f(x) = 2x + 4$$

A function is a rule for finding ordered pairs. It tells you how to find y when you know x.

$f(3)$ means the value of $f(x)$ when x is 3.

$$f(x) = 2x + 4$$
$$f(3) = 2(3) + 4$$
$$f(3) = 6 + 4$$
$$f(3) = 10 \rightarrow (3, 10) \text{ is an ordered pair for } f(x) = 2x + 4.$$

▶ **EXAMPLE 1**

Find $f(4)$ when $f(x) = -3x$.

$$f(x) = -3x$$

Substitute 4 for x.

$$f(4) = -3 \cdot 4$$

Simplify.

$$f(4) = -12$$

$f(4) = -12$ when $f(x) = -3x$.

▶ **EXAMPLE 2**

Find $f(-1)$ when $f(x) = x^2$.

Math Fact

$(-1)^2 = (-1)(-1)$

$$f(x) = x^2$$

Substitute −1 for x.

$$f(-1) = (-1)^2$$

Simplify.

$$f(-1) = 1$$

$f(-1) = 1$ when $f(x) = x^2$.

▶ **EXAMPLE 3**

Find $f(0)$ when $f(x) = 2(x + 4)$.

$$f(x) = 2(x + 4)$$

Substitute 0 for x.

$$f(0) = 2(0 + 4)$$

Simplify.

$$f(0) = 8$$

$f(0) = 8$ when $f(x) = 2(x + 4)$.

Try These

Write using function notation.

1. $y = x + 2$

$$y = x + 2$$

Use $f(x)$ for y. $\blacksquare = x + 2$
                         $\underset{f(x)}{}$

2. $y = 6(x + x^2)$

$$y = 6(x + x^2)$$

Use $\blacksquare$ for y. $f(x) = \underset{6(x+x^2)}{\blacksquare}$
       $\underset{f(x)}{}$

Find the value of each function.

3. $f(-2)$ when $f(x) = 3 - x$

$$f(x) = 3 - x$$

Substitute -2 for x. $f(\underset{-2}{\blacksquare}) = 3 - (-2)$

Simplify. $f(-2) = 3 + \blacksquare\,2$

$$f(-2) = \blacksquare\,5$$

$f(-2) = \underset{5}{\blacksquare}$ when $f(x) = 3 - x$.

4. $f(0)$ when $f(x) = 5(x + 4)$

$$f(x) = 5(x + 4)$$

Substitute $\blacksquare$ for x. $f(0) = 5(\underset{0}{\blacksquare} + 4)$

Simplify. $^0f(\blacksquare) = 5(\blacksquare)\,4$

$$f(0) = \blacksquare\,20$$

$f(0) = \underset{20}{\blacksquare}$ when $f(x) = 5(x + 4)$.

Practice

Each equation below is a function. Write in function notation.

1. $y = 4 + x$
$f(x) = 4 + x$

2. $y = -x - 9$
$f(x) = -x - 9$

3. $y = 3(x - 5)$
$f(x) = 3(x - 5)$

Find the value of each function.

4. $f(5)$ when $f(x) = 5 + x$ $f(5) = 10$

5. $f(0)$ when $f(x) = x - 9$ $f(0) = -9$

6. $f(-2)$ when $f(x) = 6x$ $f(-2) = -12$

7. $f(8)$ when $f(x) = 4(x - 2)$ $f(8) = 24$

8. $f(3)$ when $f(x) = x^2 - 2$ $f(3) = 7$

9. $f(-3)$ when $f(x) = x + 2$ $f(-3) = -1$

Cooperative Learning

10. Explain to a partner how to find the value in number **5** in **Practice**. Substitute 0 for x. Simplify. $f(0) = -9$

11. Write the function $f(x) = 6x - 10$. Think of an even number between 2 and 10. Ask a partner to find the value of the function for the number you chose. Possible answer: 4; $f(4) = 14$.

Calculator: Finding Ordered Pairs

Some equations have large numbers. You can use a calculator to find ordered pairs for these equations.

► EXAMPLE 1

Getting Started
Model for students how to use a calculator to compute
$1.3 + .4$, $1.3 - .4$, $1.3 \times .4$, and $1.3 \div .4$.

Complete this table of ordered pairs for the equation $y = 25(x + 3)$.

x	$25(x + 3)$	y
.2	$25(.2 + 3)$	?
1.4	$25(1.4 + 3)$	?
.06	$25(.06 + 3)$	?

Remember
Do the work in the parentheses first.

Use .2 for x.

PRESS: `.` `2` `+` `3` `=` **Display** `3.2`

Then multiply.

PRESS: `×` `2` `5` `=` `80`

The first ordered pair is (.2, 80).

Use 1.4 for x.

PRESS: `1` `.` `4` `+` `3` `=` `4.4`

Then multiply.

PRESS: `×` `2` `5` `=` `110`

The second ordered pair is (1.4, 110).

Use .06 for x.

PRESS: `.` `0` `6` `+` `3` `=` `3.06`

Then multiply.

PRESS: `×` `2` `5` `=` `76.5`

The third ordered pair is (.06, 76.5)

Practice

Complete each table of ordered pairs.

1. $y = 0.5x + 18$

x	$0.5x + 18$	y
2	$0.5(2) + 18$	?
4	?	?
6	?	?
8	?	?

1. $0.5(4) + 18$
$0.5(6) + 18$
$0.5(8) + 18$

19
20
21
22

2. $y = 10(x + 6)$

x	$10(x + 6)$	y
2	$10(2 + 6)$	?
4	?	?
6	?	?
8	?	?

2. $10(4 + 6)$
$10(6 + 6)$
$10(8 + 6)$

80
100
120
140

On-the-Job Math

MAKING MAPS

There are many kinds of maps. Some maps show natural places, like rivers and deserts. Others show things like streets and cities. Maps can show large areas, such as continents. They can also show small places, like a town or even your school.

One thing maps have in common is how they are made. Mapmakers, also called *cartographers,* start with a photograph of the place they are mapping. The photograph may be taken from an airplane or even a

satellite. They study the photograph carefully so they don't make mistakes. From the air, many things can look alike. A park and a forest need to be labeled correctly.

Labels make reading a map easier. Some maps are labeled with a special coordinate plane. One axis is numbered, and the other axis is lettered. A grid divides the map into squares. Each square on the map is located by its number and letter. This is like finding a point on a graph by its ordered pair.

More practice is provided in Exercise 22 of the Workbook.

4-8 Problem Solving: Choosing the Best Method

▶ **EXAMPLE**

You can choose to use an equation or a table to solve a problem that is a function.

Brian plans to order CDs from a catalog. Each CD is $12. There is a $4 shipping charge. How much will it cost Brian to order 3 CDs from the catalog?

READ **What do you need to find out?**

You need to find the cost of 3 CDs.

PLAN **What do you need to do?**

Is this a function? Yes, the total cost is a function of the number of CDs you buy. You can use a table or an equation to find the total cost of 3 CDs.

DO **Follow the plan.**

Write an equation to represent the function.
Let t be the total cost.
Let c be the number of CDs you buy.

t is $12 for each c plus $4
$$t = 12c + 4$$

Use a table or equation to find the cost of 3 CDs.

c	$12c + 4$	t
1	$12(1) + 4$	16
2	$12(2) + 4$	28
3	$12(3) + 4$	40

$t = 12c + 4$
$t = 12(3) + 4$
$t = 40$

CHECK **Does your answer make sense?**

The cost of 3 CDs alone is $3 \times \$12$ or $36. $40 is greater than $36. This makes sense because it includes the shipping charge. ✓

It costs $40.00 to order 3 CDs.

Try These

Answer each question using the table or equation.

1. How much do 100 CDs cost?

Use the ■. equation $t = 12c + 4$

Substitute 100 for c. $t = 12 (■) + 4$
$$\overset{100}{}$$

Simplify. $t = ■ + 4$
$$\overset{1,200}{}$$
$$t = ■ \; 1,204$$

100 CDs cost ■. $1,204

2. How much do 2 CDs cost?

Use the ■. table

c	$12c + 4$	t
1	$12(1) + 4$	16
2	$12(2) + 4$	28
3	$12(3) + 4$	40

2 CDs cost ■. $28

Practice

Tell whether you would use the table or equation. Then, answer the question.

1. How much does 1 CD cost? table; $16

2. How much do 8 CDs cost? equation; $100

3. How much do 5 CDs cost? equation; $64

4. How much do 50 CDs cost? equation; $604

5. As the number of CDs you buy increases, what happens to the cost? The cost increases.

Cooperative Learning

6. Explain to a partner how to decide which method to use in number **3** in **Practice**. Use the equation because the value for $C = 5$ is not in the table

7. Choose a number between 6 and 20. Ask a partner to find the cost to order that many CDs. Possible answer. Choose 9 CDs; cost $112.

4·9 ► Application: Tables and Graphs

Getting Started
Draw a line graph that shows changes over time. Ask students to determine the changes.

The table shows what kinds of music the students in a class like best. You can show the information from the table in a **bar graph**.

You can use either the table or the bar graph to answer questions about the information.

Kinds of Music	Number of Students
Alternative	5
Classical	2
Country	4
Rap	2
Oldies	4
Rock	6
Tejano	3

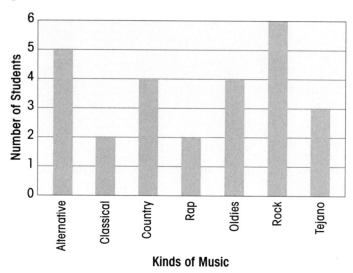

► **EXAMPLE 1**

How many students chose Rock?

Use the table.

Rock	6

Find "Rock" in the table, and read the number to the right.

The number is 6.

Six students like Rock best.

► **EXAMPLE 2**

What kinds of music were the least liked? How many students chose each of these kinds of music?

The shortest bars represent the music students liked the least.

The Rap and Classical bars are the shortest.

Find the height by looking across to the vertical axis.

The height of the bars is 2.

Rap and Classical music were liked the least. Two students chose Rap, and two chose Classical.

Try These

Use the bar graph or table to answer each question.

1. What kind of music was the second favorite? How many students chose this kind of music?

| Find the second highest bar. | The second highest bar represents Alternative. |

| Find the height by looking across to the vertical axis. | The height of the bar is ■.5 |

Alternative was the second favorite. ■ students chose Alternative.
5

2. How many more students chose Rock than Oldies?

| Use the table to find Rock. | 6
■ students chose Rock. |

| Use the table to find Oldies. | 4
■ students chose Oldies. |

| Find the difference. | ■ − 4 = 2
6 |

2 ■ more students chose Rock than Oldies.

Practice

Use the bar graph or table to answer each question.

1. How many students chose Tejano? 3 students

2. How many students chose Country? 4 students

3. How many more students chose Alternative than Classical? 3 more students

4. List the types of music from least liked to most liked. Classical and Rap (2), Tejano (3), Oldies and Country (4), Alternative (5), Rock (6)

Cooperative Learning

5. Explain to a partner how you find the number of students in number 1 in **Practice.** Look at the bar for Tejano. Read the height of the bar from the vertical axis. Three students chose Tejano.

6. Think of a question you can answer using the bar graph. Ask a partner your question. Accept any reasonable answer. Possible answer: Which kind of music was chosen the most? (Answer: Rock)

Summary

Coordinate axes can be used to graph the locations of ordered pairs.
Tables can be used to show ordered pairs.
You can find ordered pairs from equations that have two variables.
You can use the vertical line test on a graph to tell if a set of ordered pairs is a function.
To answer questions about a function, you can use an equation or a table of ordered pairs.
A bar graph shows information from a table.

More vocabulary review is provided in Exercise 31 of the Classroom Resource Binder.

coordinate axes

coordinate plane

origin

ordered pairs

graph of an ordered pair

function

vertical line test

function notation

bar graph

Vocabulary Review

Complete the sentences with words from the box.

1. A dot that shows the location of a point is called a _____. graph of an ordered pair

2. Perpendicular number lines are called _____. coordinate axes

3. Coordinate axes cross at the _____. origin

4. You can use _____ to give the location of points on the coordinate plane. ordered pairs

5. A _____ is a group of ordered pairs for which no two pairs have the same first number. function

6. You use the _____ to tell if the graph is a function. vertical line test

7. A plane with two perpendicular number lines is called a _____. coordinate plane

8. You can use _____ for an equation that is a function. function notation

9. A graph that uses bars to show information is called a _____. bar graph

Chapter Quiz   More assessment is provided in the Classroom Resource Binder.

Use graph paper. Draw coordinate axes. Graph and label each point.

1. A at $(3, -2)$ **2.** B at $(0, -5)$ **3.** C at $(-1, 3)$

See Additional Answers, p. 471

4. Write the ordered pairs. Graph. **5.** Copy and complete the table.

Seconds	°Celsius
1	−3
2	−1
3	1

(1, −3)
(2, −1)
(3, 1)

See graph on p. 471.

x	$3(x - 2)$	y	
−1	$3(-1 - 2)$	?	−9
0	?$3(0 - 2)$?		−6
1	?$3(1 - 2)$?		−3

Tell whether each group of ordered pairs is a function.

6. $(-1, 1)$, $(0, 1)$, $(1, 1)$, $(2, 4)$ yes **7.** $(-1, 2)$, $(0, 0)$, $(0, 5)$, $(2, 7)$ no

8.
no

9.
yes

Find the value of each function.

10. $f(2)$ when $f(x) = 15 + x$ $f(2) = 17$ **11.** $f(0)$ when $f(x) = 2(x + 6)$ $f(0) = 12$

Use the table or $d = 55t + 20$

12. What is the distance when the time is 6 hours? 350 miles

Time	Distance
1 hour	75 miles
2 hours	130 miles
3 hours	185 miles

Use the bar graph.

13. How many were employed in 1997? 300 employees

Additional Practice for this chapter
is provided on p. 416 of this text.

Linear Equations and Functions

In a race, time varies with speed. You can use a linear equation to find speed. You need to know the distance and time. What is used to measure time in a race?

Learning Objectives

- Graph linear equations using ordered pairs.
- Find the slope of a line.
- Find the intercepts of a line.
- Graph a line using the slope and a point.
- Use a calculator to find intercepts.
- Use slope to solve problems.
- Apply concepts and skills to using direct variation.

Words to Know

linear equation	an equation whose graph is a straight line
slope	a measure of the steepness of a straight line; tells how fast one variable changes compared with the other
rise	the change between two points on a line in an up-and-down direction
run	the change between two points on a line in a left-to-right direction
x-intercept	the *x*-value of the ordered pair at the point where a line crosses the *x*-axis
y-intercept	the *y*-value of the ordered pair at the point where a line crosses the *y*-axis
slope-intercept form	$y = mx + b$; m is the slope and b is the *y*-intercept
standard form	$Ax + By = C$
direct variation	$y = kx$; k is a positive number; as one variable increases, the other increases.

Speed Limit Project

In the equation $d = 45t$, 45 is a speed limit. Find three speed limits: one on a highway, one in your town, and one in front of your school. Write an equation for each speed limit. Graph the equations. Then find the slope. Explain what happens to the slope of the line as the speed limit increases.

Project See the Classroom Resource Binder for a scoring rubric to assess this project.

5-1 ▶ Equations with Two Variables

Getting Started
Have students find three ordered pairs for the equation $y = 3x - 2$. See Lesson 4.4.

Math Fact
The order of the variables is always (x, y).

Some equations have two variables. The solutions are ordered pairs. You can substitute the first number of the ordered pair for x and the second number for y. If the ordered pair makes a true equation, the ordered pair is a solution.

$$y = 2x + 1 \text{ has 2 variables } x \text{ and } y$$

$(1, 3)$ is one solution of $y = 2x + 1$.

$$3 = 2 \bullet 1 + 1$$
$$3 = 3 \text{ true}$$

The equation $y = 2x + 1$ has other solutions.

▶ **EXAMPLE 1**

Tell whether $(1, -1)$ is a solution of $y = 2x - 3$.

Substitute 1 for x and -1 for y. $y = 2x - 3$

Simplify. $-1 = 2(1) - 3$
$$-1 = 2 - 3$$
$$-1 = -1 \text{ true}$$

$(1, -1)$ is a solution of $y = 2x - 3$.

▶ **EXAMPLE 2**

Tell whether $(-2, 1)$ is a solution of $y = 2x - 3$.

$$y = 2x - 3$$

Substitute -2 for x and 1 for y. $1 = 2(-2) - 3$

Simplify. $1 = -4 - 3$
$$1 = -7 \text{ false}$$

$(-2, 1)$ is not a solution of $y = 2x - 3$.

▶ **EXAMPLE 3**

Tell whether $(6, -2)$ is a solution of $y + x = 4$.

$$y + x = 4$$

Substitute 6 for x and -2 for y. $-2 + 6 = 4$

Simplify. $4 = 4 \text{ true}$

$(6, -2)$ is a solution of $y + x = 4$.

Try These

Tell whether each ordered pair is a solution of $y = 1 - 4x$.

1. $(0, 2)$

Substitute $\blacksquare$ for x and $\blacksquare$ for y.

$$y = 1 - 4x$$
$$\blacksquare = 1 - 4(\blacksquare)$$

Simplify.

$$2\,\blacksquare = 1 - \blacksquare\,0$$
$$2\,\blacksquare \neq \blacksquare\,1$$

$(0, 2)$ $\blacksquare$ a solution of $y = 1 - 4x$.
is not

2. $(-3, 13)$

Substitute $\blacksquare$ for x and $\blacksquare$ for y. 13

$$y = 1 - 4x$$
$$\blacksquare = 1 - 4(\blacksquare)$$

Simplify.

$$13\,\blacksquare = 1 + \blacksquare\,12$$
$$13\,\blacksquare = \blacksquare\,\text{true } 13$$
is

$(-3, 13)$ $\blacksquare$ a solution of $y = 1 - 4x$.

Practice

Tell whether each ordered pair is a solution of $y = 2 - 3x$.

1. $(0, 2)$ yes

2. $(1, -5)$ no

3. $(3, -7)$ yes

4. $(-1, 5)$ yes

5. $(-2, 8)$ yes

6. $(-3, -3)$ no

Tell whether each ordered pair is a solution of $y = -\dfrac{x}{3} - 2$.

7. $(3, -4)$ no

8. $(2, -6)$ no

9. $(-3, 4)$ no

10. $(0, -1)$ no

11. $(-6, 0)$ yes

12. $(9, -4)$ no

Tell whether each ordered pair is a solution of $y = 2x$.

13. $(0, 2)$ no

14. $(2, 4)$ yes

15. $(15, 30)$ yes

Cooperative Learning

16. Explain to a partner how you tell whether the ordered pair is a solution in number **5** in **Practice.**   Possible answer: Substitute -2 for x and 8 for y. Since the equation simplifies to a true statement, $(-2, 8)$ is a solution.

17. Write an equation containing x and y. Think of an ordered pair. Have a partner tell whether the ordered pair is a solution. Check the work.   Answers will vary. Possible answer: Equation: $x + y = 1$. Ordered pair: $(1, 1)$. $1 + 1 = 2$; $2 \neq 1$ false. $(1, 1)$ is not a solution to $x + y = 1$.

More practice is provided in Exercises 24, 25, and 26 of the Workbook.

5·2 ▶ Graphing Linear Equations

Remind students that the first number in an ordered pair tells the location in the horizontal, or *x*, direction. The second number in an ordered pair gives the location in the vertical, or *y*, direction. Positive numbers are above and to the right of (0, 0). Negative numbers are to the left and below (0, 0).

The equation $y = 3x - 1$ is a **linear equation.** Solutions to the equation are ordered pairs. You can graph the ordered pairs. The graph is a straight line. It is a picture of the solutions of the equation. $(-1, -4)$, $(\frac{1}{3}, 0)$, and $(2, 5)$ are points on the line. So, they are solutions.

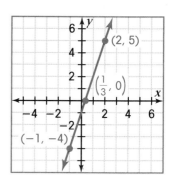

$$-4 = 3(-1) - 1 \qquad 0 = 3(\tfrac{1}{3}) - 1 \qquad 5 = 3(2) - 1$$
$$-4 = -3 - 1 \qquad\quad 0 = 1 - 1 \qquad\qquad 5 = 6 - 1$$
$$-4 = -4 \text{ true} \qquad 0 = 0 \text{ true} \qquad\quad 5 = 5 \text{ true}$$

To graph a linear equation, start by finding at least three ordered pairs. Choose values for *x*, then find *y*.

▶ **EXAMPLE 1**

Graph. $y = 2x - 2$

x	2*x* − 2	*y*
−1	2(−1) − 2	−4
0	2(0) − 2	−2
2	2(2) − 2	2

Graph the ordered pairs.
Draw a line through the points.

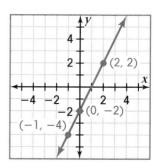

▶ **EXAMPLE 2**

Graph. $y = 3 - 3x$

x	3 − 3*x*	*y*
−1	3 − 3(−1)	6
0	3 − 3(0)	3
1	3 − 3(1)	0

Graph the ordered pairs.
Draw a line through the points.

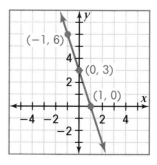

Try These

Graph each equation.

1. $y = 3 - x$

x	3 - x	y
-1	3 - (-1)	4
0	3 - 0	3
1	3 - 1	2

Graph the ordered pairs $(-1, \blacksquare)$, 4
$(0, \blacksquare)$, and $(1, \blacksquare)$. Draw a line 2
through the points.

2. $y = \dfrac{x}{-2}$

x	$\dfrac{x}{-2}$	y
-2	$\dfrac{-2}{-2}$	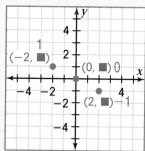 1
0	$\dfrac{0}{-2}$	0
2	$\dfrac{2}{-2}$	-1

Graph the ordered pairs $(-2, \blacksquare)$, 1
$(0, \blacksquare)$, and $(2, \blacksquare)$. Draw a line -1
through the points.

Practice

Graph each equation.   See Additional Answers, p. 471.

1. $y = x + 3$ **2.** $y = 3x - 1$ **3.** $y = 2x$

4. $y = 2 - x$ **5.** $y = \dfrac{x}{2}$ **6.** $y = \dfrac{x}{-1}$

Cooperative Learning

7. Explain to a partner how to graph the equation in number **3**
in **Practice.**   Possible answer: Let $x = -1$: $y = 2(-1)$; $y = -2$. Let $x = 0$: $y = 2(0)$; $y = 0$.
Let $x = 1$: $y = 2(1)$; $y = 2$. Graph the points $(-1, -2)$, $(0, 0)$, and $(1, 2)$. Connect the points with a line.

8. Write an equation containing x and y. Work with a partner to
graph the equation. Take turns finding points. Check each
other's work. Answers will vary. Check the coordinates with the equation.

5·3 ▶ Slope of a Line

Getting Started

Invite students to describe the slant they have observed in playground slides, ski runs, and skateboard ramps. Point out that each of these slanted items has a *slope*.

Slope describes the steepness of a line. It also tells how fast the value of y is changing compared with x. The change in the y direction is called the **rise**. The change in the x direction is called the **run**.

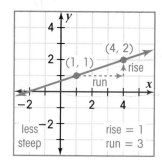

Math Fact

slope $= \frac{\text{rise}}{\text{run}}$

Pick two points on the line. To find the rise, subtract the y-values. To find the run, subtract the x-values in the same order. The slope is the rise divided by the run.

Slope can be positive or negative.

▶ **EXAMPLE 1**

Math Facts

A positive slope means that as x increases, y also increases.

A negative slope means that as x increases, y decreases.

Find the slope of the line that contains $(1, 0)$ and $(3, 1)$.

Find the rise. Subtract the y-values. $(1, 0), (3, 1)$ $0 - 1 = -1$.

Find the run. Subtract the x-values. $(1, 0), (3, 1)$ $1 - 3 = -2$

Divide rise by run.

$$\frac{\text{rise}}{\text{run}} = \frac{-1}{-2} = \frac{1}{2}$$

The slope of the line is $\frac{1}{2}$.

▶ **EXAMPLE 2**

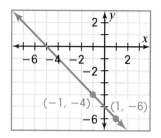

Find the slope of the line that contains $(1, -6)$ and $(-1, -4)$.

Find the rise. Subtract the y-values. $-6 - (-4) = -2$
$(1, -6), (-1, -4)$

Find the run. Subtract the x-values. $1 - (-1) = 2$
$(1, -6), (-1, -4)$

Divide rise by run.

$$\frac{\text{rise}}{\text{run}} = \frac{-2}{2} = -1$$

The slope of the line is -1.

Try These

Find the slope of the line that contains each pair of points.

1. $(-2, 5)$ and $(3, -3)$

Find the rise. Subtract the ■ values. y $5 - \overset{-3}{\blacksquare} = \overset{8}{\blacksquare}$

Find the run. Subtract the ■ values. x $-2 - \overset{3}{\blacksquare} = \overset{-5}{\blacksquare}$

Divide rise by run. $\dfrac{\text{rise}}{\text{run}} = \dfrac{\blacksquare}{\blacksquare} \overset{8}{\underset{-5}{}}$

The slope of the line is ■. $\dfrac{8}{-5}$

2. $(0, -4)$ and $(3, 2)$

Find the rise. Subtract the ■ values. y $-4 - \overset{2}{\blacksquare} = \overset{-6}{\blacksquare}$

Find the run. Subtract the ■ values. x $0 - \overset{3}{\blacksquare} = \overset{-3}{\blacksquare}$

Divide rise by run. $\dfrac{\text{rise}}{\text{run}} = \dfrac{\blacksquare}{-3} \overset{-6}{\underset{}{}} = \overset{2}{\blacksquare}$

The slope of the line is ■. 2

Practice

Find the slope of the line that contains each pair of points.

1. $(5, 7)$ and $(3, 4)$ $\dfrac{3}{2}$

2. $(7, 6)$ and $(4, 3)$ 1

3. $(-1, 3)$ and $(2, -2)$ $\dfrac{5}{-3}$

4. $(0, -2)$ and $(4, 3)$ $\dfrac{5}{4}$

5. $(6, 0)$ and $(-3, 5)$ $\dfrac{-5}{9}$

6. $(-4, -1)$ and $(1, 3)$ $\dfrac{4}{5}$

7. $(1, 3)$ and $(-4, -5)$ $\dfrac{8}{5}$

8. $(-5, -6)$ and $(-1, -5)$ $\dfrac{1}{4}$

9. $(4, 3)$ and $(6, 4)$ $\dfrac{1}{2}$

10. $(1, 4)$ and $(-2, 2)$ $\dfrac{2}{3}$

11. $(2, 3)$ and $(-4, 3)$ 0

12. $(4, 5)$ and $(1, 6)$ $\dfrac{-1}{3}$

13. $(4, 4)$ and $(7, 7)$ 1

14. $(-4, 5)$ and $(5, -4)$ -1

Cooperative Learning

15. Possible answer: Find the rise; subtract the y-values: $-1 - 3 = -4$. Find the run; subtract the x-values: $-4 - 1 = -5$. Write $\dfrac{\text{rise}}{\text{run}}$: $\dfrac{-4}{-5} = \dfrac{4}{5}$.

15. Explain to a partner how you find the slope of the line in number **6** in **Practice.** See above.

16. Write two points. Have a partner find the slope of the line that contains the two points. Check the work. Answers will vary. Make sure students subtract coordinates in the same order and divide rise by run.

$\dfrac{\text{rise}}{\text{Run}}$

More practice is provided in Exercise 26 of the Workbook.

5·4 ▶ More About Slopes

Getting Started
Encourage students to
describe the slope of flat
surfaces. Prompt responses
by asking students to
describe the slope of a table.
Ask for other examples.

Look at the lines below.

Vertical Line

Horizontal Line

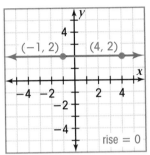

Remember
You cannot divide by 0.

The *x*-values do not change. So, run = 0.

$$\text{Slope} = \frac{\text{rise}}{\text{run}} = \frac{\text{rise}}{0}$$

All vertical lines have no slope.

The *y*-values do not change. So, rise = 0.

$$\text{Slope} = \frac{\text{rise}}{\text{run}} = \frac{0}{\text{run}} = 0$$

All horizontal lines have 0 slope.

▶ **EXAMPLE 1**

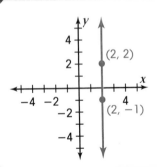

Find the slope of the line that contains (2, 2) and (2, −1).

Find the rise. $2 - (-1) = 3$

Find the run. $2 - 2 = 0$

Divide rise by run. $\dfrac{\text{rise}}{\text{run}} = \dfrac{3}{0}$

You cannot divide by 0.   No slope

The line has no slope. The line is vertical.

▶ **EXAMPLE 2**

Find the slope of the graph.

The line is flat right and left.

The line is horizontal.

Horizontal lines have a slope of 0.

The slope is 0.

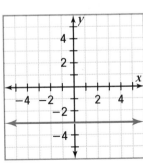

Try These

1. Find the slope of the line that contains the points $(-1, 8)$ and $(9, 8)$.

Find the rise.

$$\overset{8}{\blacksquare} - 8 = \blacksquare$$
$$\underset{-1 \quad 9}{} \qquad -10$$

Find the run.

$$\blacksquare - \blacksquare = \blacksquare$$

Divide rise by run.

$$\frac{0}{-10} \frac{\blacksquare}{\blacksquare} = \blacksquare \; 0$$

The slope of the line is $\blacksquare.0$

2. Find the slope of the line from the graph.

The line runs straight up and down.

vertical

The line is $\blacksquare$.

vertical   no

$\blacksquare$ lines have $\blacksquare$ slope.

no

The line has $\blacksquare$ slope.

Practice

Find the slope of each line from its graph.

1.

0

2.

no slope

3.

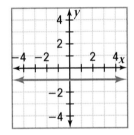

0

Find the slope of the line that contains each pair of points.

4. $(3, 5)$ and $(4, 5)$ 0

5. $(4, 3)$ and $(4, 7)$ no slope

6. $(-3, -2)$ and $(-3, 8)$
no slope

7. $(0, 4)$ and $(0, -7)$
no slope

8. $(-1, -2)$ and $(-9, -2)$ 0

9. $(6, 6)$ and $(-4, 6)$ 0

Cooperative Learning

10. Explain to a partner how you use the graph to find the slope of the line in number **2** in **Practice**. Possible answer: The x-values are all the same. The line is vertical. Vertical lines have no slope.

11. Draw a graph of a horizontal or vertical line. Have a partner find the slope of the line. Check the work. Answers will vary. Check that horizontal lines have zero slope and vertical lines have no slope.

5·5 ▶ Parallel and Perpendicular Lines

Getting Started

Review parallel lines as lines that never meet and perpendicular lines as lines that form right angles. Invite volunteers to point out pairs of parallel and perpendicular lines in the classroom, such as the ceiling and the floor (parallel), the wall and the floor (perpendicular).

Use slope to find parallel and perpendicular lines.

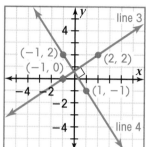

slope of line 1: $\dfrac{1}{2}$ slope of line 3: $\dfrac{2}{3}$

slope of line 2: $\dfrac{1}{2}$ slope of line 4: $-\dfrac{3}{2}$

Math Facts

$\dfrac{2}{3}$ and $\dfrac{3}{2}$ are reciprocals.

$\dfrac{2}{3}$ and $-\dfrac{3}{2}$ are negative reciprocals.

Lines 1 and 2 are parallel. They have the same slope.

Lines 3 and 4 are perpendicular. Their slopes are negative reciprocals of each other.

▶ **EXAMPLE 1**

Show that the line that contains $(-2, -3)$ and $(1, 3)$ and the line that contains $(0, -4)$ and $(2, 0)$ are parallel.

Find the slope of the first line.
Divide rise by run. $\dfrac{-3 - 3}{-2 - 1} = \dfrac{-6}{-3} = 2$

Find the slope of the second line.
Divide rise by run. $\dfrac{-4 - 0}{0 - 2} = \dfrac{-4}{-2} = 2$

The slopes are equal. So, the lines are parallel.

▶ **EXAMPLE 2**

Show that the line that contains $(1, -1)$ and $(0, 2)$ and the line that contains $(-1, 0)$ and $(2, 1)$ are perpendicular.

Find the slope of the first line.
Divide rise by run. $\dfrac{-1 - 2}{1 - 0} = \dfrac{-3}{1} = -3$

Find the slope of the second line.
Divide rise by run. $\dfrac{0 - 1}{-1 - 2} = \dfrac{-1}{-3} = \dfrac{1}{3}$

-3 and $\dfrac{1}{3}$ are negative reciprocals. So, the lines are perpendicular.

Try These

1. Tell whether the line containing $(-1, -2)$ and $(4, 4)$ and the line containing $(6, 3)$ and $(-1, -3)$ are parallel.

Find the slope of the first line. $(-1, -2)$ and $(4, 4)$

Divide rise by run. $\dfrac{-2\,\blacksquare - \blacksquare\,4}{-1\,\blacksquare - \blacksquare\,4} = \blacksquare\,\dfrac{6}{5}$

Find the slope of $(6, 3)$ and $(-1, -3)$ the second line.

Divide rise by run. $\dfrac{3\,\blacksquare - \blacksquare\,-3}{6\,\blacksquare - \blacksquare\,-1} = \blacksquare\,\dfrac{6}{7}$

$\dfrac{6}{5}, \dfrac{6}{7}\,\blacksquare$ and $\blacksquare$ are not the same slope.

The lines $\blacksquare$ parallel. are not

2. Tell whether the line containing $(-1, -2)$ and $(2, 7)$ and the line containing $(-1, 5)$ and $(-4, 4)$ are perpendicular.

Find the slope of the first line. $(-1, -2)$ and $(2, 7)$

Divide rise by run. $\dfrac{-2\,\blacksquare - \blacksquare\,7}{-1\,\blacksquare - \blacksquare\,2} = \blacksquare\,3$

Find the slope of $(-1, 5)$ and $(-4, 4)$ the second line.

Divide rise by run. $\dfrac{5\,\blacksquare - \blacksquare\,4}{-1\,\blacksquare - \blacksquare\,-4} = \blacksquare\,\dfrac{1}{3}$

$3\,\blacksquare$ and $\blacksquare$ are not negative $\dfrac{1}{3}$ reciprocals.

The lines $\blacksquare$ perpendicular. are not

Practice

Tell whether the lines containing each pair of points are parallel.

1. $(1, 3)(2, 4)$ and $(-2, 1)(-3, 0)$ yes

2. $(-4, -3)(2, 4)$ and $(0, 2)(5, 9)$ no

3. $(3, 4)(1, 0)$ and $(6, 8)(4, 4)$ yes

4. $(5, -2)(3, 2)$ and $(6, -1)(4, -3)$ no

Tell whether the lines containing each pair of points are perpendicular.

5. $(4, 5)(1, 3)$ and $(3, 7)(5, 4)$ yes

6. $(-2, -3)(2, 5)$ and $(-4, -4)(-6, -3)$ yes

7. Possible answer: Find the slope between $(-2, -3)$ and $(2, 5)$: $\frac{-8}{-4} = 2$; find the slope between $(-4, -4)$ $(-6, -3)$: $\frac{-1}{2}$. Since 2 and $\frac{-1}{2}$ are negative reciprocals the lines are perpendicular.

Cooperative Learning

7. Explain to a partner how to tell whether the lines are perpendicular in number **6** in **Practice**. See above.

8. Pick two points. Have a partner pick two points. Show whether the lines that connect the points are parallel or perpendicular. They may be neither. Answers will vary. Make sure students find the slope correctly.

5·6 ▶ Intercepts

The ***x*-intercept** is the value of x at the point where a line crosses the x-axis. This happens when $y = 0$.

The ***y*-intercept** is the value of y at the point where a line crosses the y-axis. This happens when $x = 0$.

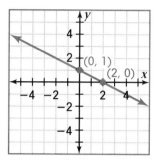

x-intercept → 2

y-intercept → 1

At the point where the line crosses the x-axis, $y = 0$. So, you can find the x-intercept of an equation without a graph. Substitute 0 for y. Then, solve for x.

▶ **EXAMPLE 1**

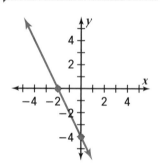

Find the x-intercept. $y = -2x - 4$

$$y = -2x - 4$$

Substitute 0 for y. $0 = -2x - 4$

Solve for x. $4 = -2x$

$$-2 = x$$

The x-intercept of $y = -2x - 4$ is -2.

You can also solve for the y-intercept. At the point of the y-intercept, $x = 0$. So, substitute 0 for x and solve for y.

▶ **EXAMPLE 2**

Find the y-intercept. $y = -2x - 4$

$$y = -2x - 4$$

Substitute 0 for x. $y = -2(0) - 4$

Simplify. $y = 0 - 4$

$$y = -4$$

The y-intercept of $y = -2x - 4$ is -4.

Try These

1. Find the *x*-intercept. $y = 3x + 3.$

$$y = 3x + 3$$

Substitute ▓ for *y*. $0\ \blacksquare = 3x + 3$

Subtract ▓ from $-3\ \blacksquare = 3x$
both sides.

Divide both sides by ▓. $\blacksquare = x$

The *x*-intercept of $y = 3x + 3$ is ▓.

2. Find the *y*-intercept. $y = 3x + 3.$

$$y = 3x + 3$$

Substitute ▓ for *x*. $y = 3(\blacksquare) + 3$

Simplify. $y = \blacksquare + 3$

$$y = \blacksquare\ 3$$

The *y*-intercept of $y = 3x + 3$ is ▓. 3

Practice

13. Answers will vary. Make sure the *x*-intercept is labeled on the *x*-axis as (*a*, 0), and the *y*-intercept is labeled on the *y*-axis as (0, *b*).

Use the graph to find the *x*-intercept and *y*-intercept of each line.

1.

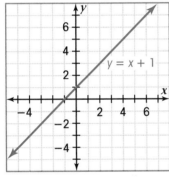

$y = x + 1$

x-intercept: −1;
y-intercept: 1

2.

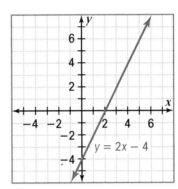

$y = 2x − 4$

x-intercept: 2;
y-intercept: −4

Find the *x*-intercept and *y*-intercept of each line.

3. $y = x - 2$
x-intercept: 2; y-intercept: −2

4. $y = -3x + 3$
x-intercept: 1; y-intercept: 3

5. $y = 5x + 10$
x-intercept: −2; y-intercept: 10

6. $y = -4x - 4$
x-intercept: −1; y-intercept: −4

7. $y = \frac{1}{2}x - 3$
x-intercept: 6; y-intercept: −3

8. $y = \frac{-1}{4}x + 1$
x-intercept: 4; y-intercept: 1

9. $y = \frac{1}{5}x$
x-intercept: 0; y-intercept: 0

10. $y = -6x - 12$
x-intercept: −2; y-intercept: −12

11. $y = 3x + 9$
x-intercept: −3; y-intercept: 9

Cooperative Learning

12. Explain to a partner how you find the *y*-intercept in number **8** in **Practice.**   Possible answer: To find the *y*-intercept, let $x = 0$: $y = \frac{-1}{4}(0) + 1$; $y = 1$. So the *y*-intercept is 1.

13. Draw a line. Have a partner label the *x*-intercept and the *y*-intercept. Check the work. See above.

More practice is provided in Exercise 29 of the Workbook.

Getting Started
Ask students to describe *slope* in their own words. Then, have them describe the relationship between a point and an ordered pair.

You can graph a line using one point on the line and the slope. First, graph the point. Then, start at that point and use the slope to find another point.

▶ **EXAMPLE 1**

Graph the line that contains (1, 3) and has a slope of $\frac{2}{3}$.

Remember
Slope is $\frac{\text{rise}}{\text{run}}$.
$\frac{2}{3}$ means up 2, right 3.

Graph (1, 3).

Move up 2 units.

Move right 3 units.

Draw a dot at (4, 5).

Draw a line through the points.

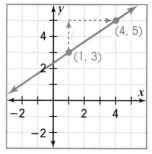

▶ **EXAMPLE 2**

Graph the line that contains (−2, −1) and has a slope of −3.

Math Facts
−3 means $\frac{-3}{1}$.
$\frac{-3}{1}$ means down 3, right 1.

Graph (−2, −1).

Move down 3 units.

Move right 1 unit.

Draw a dot at (−1, −4).

Draw a line through the points.

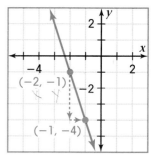

Sometimes, you are given an intercept for the point.

▶ **EXAMPLE 3**

Graph the line with a *y*-intercept of 3 and slope of $-\frac{1}{2}$.

Graph (0, 3).

Move down 1 unit.

Math Facts
A *y*-intercept of 3 means the ordered pair (0,3).
$-\frac{1}{2}$ means down 1, right 2.

Move right 2 units.

Draw a dot at (2, 2).

Draw a line through the points.

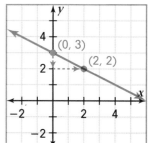

Try These

Graph each line.

1. y-intercept: -2; slope: 2
0,−2

Graph (■, ■).
2

Move up ■ units.
1

Move right ■ unit.

Draw a dot at

(■, ■).
1 0

Draw a line
through the points.

2. $(1, 1)$; slope: $-\dfrac{4}{3}$

Graph (■, ■).
1 1

Move down ■ 4
units.
3

Move right ■ units.

Draw a point at

(■, ■).
4 −3

Draw a line through the points.

Practice   See Additional Answers, p. 472.

Graph the line that contains the point and has the given slope.

1. point: $(2, 2)$; slope: $\dfrac{1}{2}$

2. point: $(-1, 3)$; slope: 3

3. point: $(3, -2)$; slope: $-\dfrac{3}{2}$

4. point: $(-2, -3)$; slope: -2

Graph the line that contains the y-intercept and has the given slope.

5. y-intercept: 1; slope: 2

6. y-intercept: 4; slope: $\dfrac{1}{3}$

7. y-intercept: -3; slope: $\dfrac{2}{5}$

8. y-intercept: -2; slope: -4

Cooperative Learning

9. Explain to a partner how to graph the line in number **5**
in **Practice.** Possible answer: Graph y-intercept: (0, 1). Move up 2 units. Move right 1 unit.
Plot (1, 3). Connect the points.

10. Write an ordered pair and a slope. Have a partner graph the line.
Check the work. Answers will vary. Make sure students do not reverse x and y and rise and run.

More practice is provided in Exercise 29 of the Workbook.

5·8 ▶ Slope-Intercept Form

Sometimes, you write equations so you can find
the slope and *y*-intercept of a line just by looking at
the equation.

Look at the equation of the line
$$y = \frac{1}{2}x + 2$$

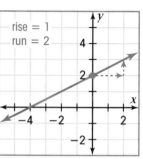

slope   *y*-intercept

This is called the **slope-
intercept form** of an equation.

Sometimes, the slope-intercept
form is written: $y = mx + b$. *m* is the coefficient of the
x-term. It tells you the slope *b* is a constant. It tells you
the *y*-intercept.

▶ **EXAMPLE 1**

Remember
−*x* means −1*x*.
−*x* − 2 means −*x* + (−2).

Find the slope and *y*-intercept.	$y = -x - 2$
Write the slope-intercept form.	$y = mx + b$
Write the equation.	$y = -x - 2$
Find *m* and *b*.	*m* is −1 and *b* is −2.

The slope is −1 and the *y*-intercept is −2.

▶ **EXAMPLE 2**

Math Fact
$\frac{x}{2}$ is the same as $\frac{1x}{2}$ or $\frac{1}{2}x$.

Find the slope and *y*-intercept.	$y = 4 - \frac{x}{2}$
Rearrange the terms.	$y = -\frac{1}{2}x + 4$
Write the slope-intercept form.	$y = mx + b$
Find *m* and *b*.	*m* is $-\frac{1}{2}$ and *b* is 4.

The slope is $-\frac{1}{2}$ and the *y*-intercept is 4.

▶ **EXAMPLE 3**

Math Fact
If there is no *b*-term, the
y-intercept is 0.

Find the slope and *y*-intercept.	$y = 2x$
Write the slope-intercept form.	$y = mx + b$
Write the equation.	$y = 2x + 0$
Find *m* and *b*.	*m* is 2 and *b* is 0.

The slope is 2 and the *y*-intercept is 0.

Try These

Find the slope and y-intercept of each line.

1. $y = x + 5$

$y = mx + b$
$y = x + 5$

Find m and b. m is 1 and b is 5.

The slope is ▇ and the y-intercept
is ▇.   1   5

2. $y = \frac{3}{2}x - 1$

$y = mx + b$
$y = \frac{3}{2}x - 1$

Find m and b. $\frac{3}{2}$ m is ▇ and b is ▇. −1

The slope is ▇ and the y-intercept
is ▇. −1 $\frac{3}{2}$

3. $y = 4x$

$y = mx + b$
$y = 4x + $ ▇ 0

Find m and b. m is ▇ and b is ▇.
4   0

The slope is ▇ and the y-intercept
is ▇. 0   4

4. $y = 3 - x$

Rearrange the terms. $y = -x + 3$
$y = mx + b$
−1

Find m and b. m is ▇ and b
is ▇. 3

The slope is ▇ and the y-intercept −1
is ▇. 3

Practice

Find the slope and y-intercept of each line.

1. $y = \frac{1}{2}x + 3$
slope: $\frac{1}{2}$; y-intercept: 3

2. $y = 4x - 1$
slope: 4; y-intercept: −1

3. $y = -\frac{2}{3}x + 6$
slope: $-\frac{2}{3}$; y-intercept: 6

4. $y = -5x - 3$
slope: −5; y-intercept: −3

5. $y = \frac{3}{4}x$
slope: $\frac{3}{4}$; y-intercept: 0

6. $y = 5x - 2$
slope: 5; y-intercept: −2

7. $y = -4 - 2x$
slope: −2; y-intercept: −4

8. $y = x - 4$
slope: 1; y-intercept: −4

9. $y = 1 + \frac{x}{3}$
slope: $\frac{1}{3}$; y-intercept: 1

10. $y = 5x + 3$
slope: 5; y-intercept: 3

11. $y = 3x + 6$
slope: 3; y-intercept: 6

12. $y = -x$
slope: −1; y-intercept: 0

Cooperative Learning

13. Possible answer: Pick $y = \frac{3}{4}x$. New equation $y = x$. First equation has a slope of $\frac{3}{4}$ and a y-intercept of 0. The second equation has a slope of 1 and a y-intercept of 0.

13. Pick a problem from practice. Write an equation with the same y-intercept and a different slope. Explain your work to a partner. See above.

14. Write an equation in slope-intercept form. Ask a partner to find the slope and y-intercept. Answers will vary. Make sure students do not confuse slope and intercept.

More practice is provided in Exercises 24 and 29 of the Workbook.

5·9 ▶ The Standard Form

Getting Started
Point out that in the equation $Ax + By = C$, x and y are the variables. A, B, and C are the constants for any given equation.

Linear equations can be written in many ways. The **standard form** is one way.

$$\text{Standard form} \rightarrow Ax + By = C$$

You can rewrite an equation in standard form as an equation in slope-intercept form. Solve the equation for y.

▶ **EXAMPLE 1**

Write in slope-intercept form. $4x + 2y = -8$
$$4x + 2y = -8$$

Subtract 4x from both sides. $4x - 4x + 2y = -8 - 4x$
$$2y = -8 - 4x$$

Math Fact
To divide both sides of the equation, divide all terms by 2.

Divide both sides by 2. $\dfrac{2y}{2} = \dfrac{-8}{2} - \dfrac{4x}{2}$
$$y = -4 - 2x$$

Rearrange the terms. $y = -2x - 4$

You can write $4x + 2y = -8$ as $y = -2x - 4$.

▶ **EXAMPLE 2**

Write in slope-intercept form. $3x - 2y = -6$
$$3x - 2y = -6$$

Subtract 3x from both sides. $3x - 3x - 2y = -6 - 3x$
$$-2y = -6 - 3x$$

Math Fact
$\dfrac{3x}{2}$ means $\dfrac{3}{2}x$.

Divide both sides by -2. $\dfrac{-2y}{-2} = \dfrac{-6}{-2} - \dfrac{3x}{-2}$
$$y = 3 + \dfrac{3}{2}x$$

Rearrange the terms. $y = \dfrac{3}{2}x + 3$

You can write $3x - 2y = -6$ as $y = \dfrac{3}{2}x + 3$.

▶ **EXAMPLE 3**

Write in slope-intercept form. $x + y = 0$
$$x + y = 0$$

Subtract x from both sides. $x - x + y = 0 - x$
$$y = -x$$

You can write $x + y = 0$ as $y = -x$.

Write each equation in slope-intercept form.

1. $3x - 4y = 0$

$$3x - 4y = 0$$

Subtract $\blacksquare$ $3x$ from both sides. $3x$

$3x - \blacksquare - 4y = 0 - \blacksquare$ $3x$

$-4y = -3x$

Divide both sides by $\blacksquare$. -4

$\dfrac{-4y}{-4} = \dfrac{-3x}{-4}$

$$y = \blacksquare \dfrac{3}{4}x$$

2. $4x - y = 4$

$$4x - y = 4$$

Subtract $\blacksquare$ $4x$ from both sides.

$4x - \blacksquare - y = 4 - \blacksquare 4x$ $4x$

$-y = 4 - 4x$

Divide both sides by $\blacksquare$. -1

$\dfrac{-y}{-1\blacksquare} = \dfrac{4}{-1\blacksquare} - \dfrac{4x}{-1\blacksquare}$

$y = \blacksquare + \blacksquare$ -4 $4x$

$y = \blacksquare - \blacksquare$ $4x$ 4

Practice

Write each equation in slope-intercept form.

1. $6x + 2y = 2$ $\quad y = -3x + 1$

2. $x - y = 0$ $\quad y = x$

3. $-5x - y = -10$ $\quad y = -5x + 10$

4. $-2x + 5y = -5$ $\quad y = \dfrac{2x}{5} - 1$

5. $6x + y = 6$ $\quad y = -6x + 6$

6. $x - y = 4$ $\quad y = x - 4$

7. $-3x - y = -10$ $\quad y = -3x + 10$

8. $3x - 3y = 9$ $\quad y = x - 3$

9. $2x + 3y = 0$ $\quad y = \dfrac{-2x}{3}$

10. $x - 4y = -8$ $\quad y = \dfrac{x}{4} + 2$

11. $2x + y = 3$ $\quad y = -2x + 3$

12. $2y - 6x = 0$ $\quad y = 3x$

Cooperative Learning

13. Explain to a partner how you write the equation in number **2** in **Practice** in slope-intercept form. Possible answer: Subtract x from both sides; divide both sides by -1 so the equation is solved for y.

14. Write an equation in standard form. Ask a partner to write it in slope-intercept form. Answers will vary. Make sure students divide both the coefficient of x and the constant by the coefficient of y.

Getting Started
Review the keys
on a calculator for
operations. Contrast them
with keys used to designate
positive or negative numbers.

5·10 ▶ # Calculator: Finding Intercepts

You can use your calculator to find the intercept of a line.

▶ **EXAMPLE 1**

Find the x-intercept.　　$y = 17x + 119$

$$y = 17x + 119$$

Remember
The x-intercept is the value of x when $y = 0$.

Let $y = 0$.　　　　　　　　$0 = 17x + 119$

Subtract 119 from both sides.　　$-119 = 17x$

Divide both sides by 17.　　$\dfrac{-119}{17} = \dfrac{17x}{17}$

Use your calculator to simplify the left side.

Display

Remember
Make sure to clear your
calculator before you start.

Enter 119 by pressing:　　1 1 9　　| 119 |

Divide by 17 by pressing:　　÷ 1 7 =　　| 7 |

Find the sign of a negative number divided
by a positive number.　　　　　　　　-7

The x-intercept of $y = 17x + 119$ is -7.

▶ **EXAMPLE 2**

Find the y-intercept.　　$9x - 4y = -96$

$$9x - 4y = -96$$

Remember
The y-intercept is the value of y when $x = 0$.

Let $x = 0$.　　　　　　　　$9(0) - 4y = -96$

Divide both sides by -4.　　$\dfrac{-4y}{-4} = \dfrac{-96}{-4}$

Use your calculator to simplify the right side.

Display

Enter 96 by pressing:　　9 6　　| 96 |

Divide by 4 by pressing:　　÷ 4 =　　| 24 |

Find the sign of a negative number divided
by a negative number.　　　　　　　　$+24$

The y-intercept of $9x - 4y = -96$ is 24.

Practice

Find the *x*-intercept of each line.

1. $5y = 8x + 104$ −13   **2.** $-3y = -19x + 114$ 6   **3.** $-13x + 36y = -91$ 7

Find the *y*-intercept of each line.

4. $63x + 12y = 168$ 14   **5.** $-15x - 3y = -72$ 24   **6.** $27x + 15y = -75$ −5

7. $12y - 24x = 21.6$ 1.8   **8.** $28.2y - 282 = 42.3x$ 10 **9.** $5y - 9x = 160$ 32

People in Math

EVELYN BOYD GRANVILLE

Evelyn Boyd Granville was born in 1924. As a child, she liked both math and science. After high school, she studied math in college. There, she got her first degree in math. Then she went on to study at Yale University. In 1949, she became the first African American woman to get a Ph.D. in math from Yale.

Dr. Granville's first job was with the space program. Her knowledge of math and science was a great combination. She studied the orbits for space probes, and she worked on Project Mercury. She also worked for IBM as a math and computer expert.

Later, Dr. Granville became a professor at a California university. Her goal was to improve the way math is taught. Teaching young students was part of her plan. She also ran an after-school enrichment program.

Although she retired and moved to Texas, Dr. Granville still stays involved in teaching. She tutors young people and helps adults learn to read.

More practice is provided in Exercise 30 of the Workbook.

5·11 ▶ Problem Solving: Using Slope

The distance you travel changes with the amount of time you travel. You can describe the change in distance compared with the change in time with slope.

▶ **EXAMPLE**

Alison walks 4 miles by 9:00 A.M. She walks 8 miles by 11:00 A.M. If she continues at this rate, how far will she walk by 12:00 noon?

READ   **What do you need to find out?**
You need to find how many miles Alison will walk by 12:00 noon.

PLAN   **What do you need to do?**
Write the information as ordered pairs. Find the slope. Then use the slope to find how many miles Alison will walk by 12:00 noon.

DO   **Follow the plan.**

Write the information as ordered pairs.

(time, miles)   (time, miles)
   (9, 4)   (11, 8)

Graph the ordered pairs.

Find the slope.

$$\frac{\text{rise}}{\text{run}} = \frac{\text{difference in miles}}{\text{difference in time}} = \frac{4 - 8}{9 - 11} = 2$$

Use the slope to find the distance at 12:00 noon.

Start at (11, 8). Move up 2, right 1. Graph (12,10).

CHECK   **Does your answer make sense?**
Alison walks 2 miles in 1 hour. By 11:00 A.M. she walks 8 miles. So, between 11:00 and 12:00 she walks 2 more miles. 8 + 2 = 10

By 12:00 noon, Alison will walk 10 miles. ✓

Try These

1. During a race, Carolina passed the 3 mile mark at 24 minutes. She passed the 5 mile mark at 40 minutes. Find the slope to describe her rate.

Write the information as ordered pairs.

(time, miles)   (time, miles)

(■, 3) 24   (40, ■) 5

Graph the ordered pairs. Find the slope.

$$\frac{rise}{run} = \frac{difference\ in\ miles}{difference\ in\ time} = \frac{3 - 5}{24 - 40} = \frac{■}{■\ 8}\ \frac{1}{8}$$

Her rate is 1 mile in ■ minutes. 8

2. If Carolina continues at the same rate, where will she be at 48 minutes?

Use the slope to find another point.
Start at (40, 5).
Move up ■ and right 8.   Point is (48, ■).
       1   6

At 48 minutes, Carolina will be at the ■ mile mark.
                                        6

Practice

Use slope to solve each problem.

1. Gracie earns $15 by 12:00 P.M. She earns $25 by 2:00 P.M. How much will she earn if she continues at the same rate until 5:00 P.M.?
   Gracie will earn $40.
2. Michael fixes computers. By 1:00 P.M., he has fixed 5 computers. By 3:00 P.M., 7 computers are fixed. How many will he fix by 6:00 P.M.?
   Michael can fix 10 computers.
3. A bus leaves a city at 6:00 A.M. It travels 150 miles by 9:00 A.M. How far will it travel by 12:00 noon?   The bus could travel 300 miles.

Cooperative Learning

4. Explain to a partner how to use slope to solve the problem in number 2 in **Practice**. Possible answer: Use slope to find how many computers Michael fixes in an hour. Once you have this slope, you can use the graphs of the points and the slopes to find the answer.
5. Write a problem that can be solved using slope. Write the information as ordered pairs. Ask a partner to graph the ordered pairs and find the slope. Check the work. Answers will vary.

5·12 ▶ Application: Direct Variation

Look at the graphs of lines 1, 2, and 3.

line 1: $y = 3x$ slope = 3

line 2: $y = x$ slope = 1

line 3: $y = \dfrac{x}{2}$ slope = $\dfrac{1}{2}$

$\quad\quad y = kx$ slope = k

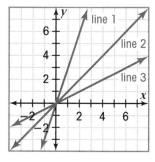

These equations are examples of **direct variation.** In direct variation, the slope, k, is always positive. Also, all the lines go through the point (0, 0).

When an equation shows direct variation, you can say y varies directly with x. The equation is $y = kx$.

You can use a graph of direct variation to find equations. Then, you can use the equation to solve problems.

▶ **EXAMPLE 1**

Corey earned $20.00 in 4 hours. His pay varies directly with his hours. Find the equation for his pay.

Graph (0, 0) to show the money when he starts work.

Graph (4, 20) for 4 hours and $20.00.

Find the slope. $\dfrac{\text{rise}}{\text{run}} = \dfrac{20 - 0}{4 - 0} = 5$

Write the equation.
Use P for pay and h for hours. $P = kh$

Substitute the slope for k. $P = 5h$

The equation for the graph is $P = 5h$.

▶ **EXAMPLE 2**

Use the equation to find Corey's pay for 40 hours of work.

Write the equation. $P = 5h$

Substitute 40 for h. $P = 5(40)$

Simplify. $P = 200$

Corey earns $200.00 for 40 hours of work.

Try These

The cost of notebooks varies directly with the number of notebooks you buy. Three notebooks cost $9.00.

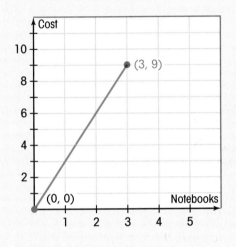

1. Find the equation for the cost of notebooks.

   Graph the cost of 3 notebooks. $(3, \blacksquare^{9})$

   Graph $(0, 0)$.

   Find the slope. $\dfrac{\text{rise}}{\text{run}} = \dfrac{9-0}{3-0} = \dfrac{3}{\blacksquare}$

   Write the equation.

   Use C for cost and n for notebooks. $C = kn$

   Substitute the slope for k. $C = \blacksquare^{3}n$

2. Find the cost of 15 notebooks.

   Write the equation. $C = \blacksquare^{3}n$

   Substitute 15 for $\blacksquare.n$ $C = 3(\blacksquare)15$

   Simplify. $C = \blacksquare\ 45$

   Fifteen notebooks cost $\$\blacksquare^{45}$.

Practice

The cost of pens varies directly with the number of pens. One pen costs $2.00.

1. Find k in the equation for the cost of pens. Use $C = kp$. 2

2. Find the total cost of 12 pens. $24.00

Jasmine's pay varies directly with the hours she works. She earns $40.00 in 5 hours.

3. Find k in the equation for Jasmine's pay. Use $P = kh$. 8

4. Find her pay for 30 hours. $240.00

Cooperative Learning

5. Explain to a partner how to find the total cost in number **2** in **Practice**. Possible answer: Use the equation $C = 2p$. Replace p with 12. Then multiply 2 times 12 to get $24.

6. Draw the graph of a line that goes through the origin. Have a partner solve for k and write the equation. Check the work. Answers will vary. Make sure the equation is in the form $y = mx$, and that the slope is correct.

Chapter 5 • Linear Equations and Functions   141

Summary

Equations with two variables have solutions that are ordered pairs. A graph of the ordered pairs in a linear equation makes a straight line.

The slope of a line is the change in the *y*-values divided by the change in the *x*-values.

Horizontal lines have a slope of 0. Vertical lines have no slope.

You can use slope to find parallel and perpendicular lines.

Substituting 0 for *y* will give you the *x*-intercept. Substituting 0 for *x* will give you the *y*-intercept.

You can graph a line when you have a point and the slope.

The slope-intercept form of a linear equation lets you find the slope and *y*-intercept by looking at the equation.

Using the slope as rate of change can help you solve problems.

Direct variation is a linear equation with positive slope that goes through the point (0, 0).

More vocabulary review is provided in Exercise 41 of the Classroom Resource Binder.

linear equation

slope

rise

run

x-intercept

y-intercept

slope-intercept form

standard form

direct variation

Vocabulary Review

Complete the sentences with words from the box.

1. The change in the left-to-right direction between two points is ____. run

2. $Ax + By = C$ is a linear equation in ____. standard form

3. $y = mx + b$ is the ____ of a linear equation.
slope-intercept form

4. An equation whose graph is a straight line is a ____.
linear equation

5. A linear equation in the form $y = kx$ shows ____.
direct variation

6. The *y*-value of the point where a line crosses the *y*-axis is called the ____. *y*-intercept

7. The change in the up-and-down direction between two points is ____. rise

8. The point where a line crosses the *x*-axis is the ____.
x-intercept

9. The steepness of a straight line is ____. slope

Chapter Quiz   More **assessment** is provided in the Classroom Resource Binder.

Tell whether each ordered pair is a solution of the equation.

1. $(1, 5); y = 2 + 3x$ yes **2.** $(0, -2); y = 1 - 4x$ no   **3.** $(-4, 4); y = 2 - \frac{x}{2}$ yes

Find three ordered pairs for each equation. Then, graph the equation. See Additional Answers, p. 472.

4. $y = 2x + 3$
$(-1, 1); (0,3); (1,5)$

5. $y = 4 - x$
$(-1, 5); (0, 4); (1, 3)$

6. $x + y = 0$
$(-1, 1); (0, 0); (1, -1)$

Find the slope of each line that contains the given pair of points.

7. $(2, 4)$ and $(1, 0)$ 4   **8.** $(-2, 3)$ and $(4, -4)$ $-\frac{7}{6}$ **9.** $(-1, -3)$ and $(-2, -5)$ 2

10. $(2, 3)$ and $(1, 3)$ 0   **11.** $(-1, -5)$ and $(2, -5)$ 0   **12.** $(-1, 4)$ and $(-1, 3)$ no slope

Tell whether the lines containing each pair of points are parallel or perpendicular.

13. $(1, 3)(-1, 0)$ and $(5, 0)(3, -3)$
parallel

14. $(-2, -4)(1, 5)$ and $(6, 2)(3, 3)$
perpendicular

Find the x-intercept and y-intercept of each line.

15. $5x + y = 10$
x-intercept: 2; y-intercept: 10

16. $4x - 4y = 12$
x-intercept: 3; y-intercept: -3

17. $10x - 5y = 15$
x-intercept: $\frac{3}{2}$; y-intercept: -3

Graph each line. See Additional Answers, p. 472.

18. point: $(0, 3)$; slope: $-\frac{1}{4}$

19. y-intercept: 2; slope: $\frac{2}{3}$

20. $y = 2x - 6$

21. $y = x - 4$

22. $y = -2x + 10$

Write each equation in slope-intercept form.

23. $3x + 2y = 12$
$y = \frac{-3x}{2} + 6$

24. $y - x = 0$
$y = x$

25. $3x - y = 7$
$y = 3x - 7$

Find the slope to solve each problem.

26. Sue drives 200 miles by 1:00 P.M. She drives 350 miles by 4:00 P.M. If she continues at the same rate, how far will she drive by 5:00 P.M.? 400 miles

27. Manny's pay varies directly with the number of lawns he mows. He earns $100 for mowing 4 lawns. Find k in the equation for Manny's pay. Use $P = kl$. 25

Additional Practice for this chapter is provided on p. 417 of this text.

Writing Linear Equations

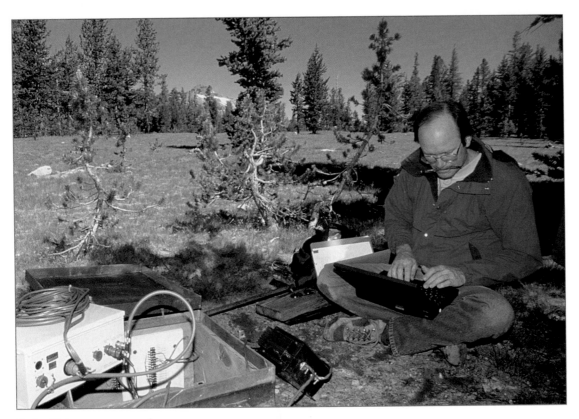

Scientists use measuring tools to look for patterns in nature. They write equations to describe the patterns they find. What is the equation for direct variation?

Learning Objectives

- Write an equation using the slope and *y*-intercept.
- Write an equation using a point and the slope.
- Write an equation using two points.
- Write equations of horizontal and vertical lines.
- Write equations of parallel and perpendicular lines.
- Use a calculator to check that a point is on a line.
- Solve problems by writing equations from patterns.
- Apply concepts and skills to writing equations in science.

Words to Know

slope-intercept form	$y = mx + b$
horizontal lines	lines with slope $= 0$
vertical lines	lines with no slope
perpendicular lines	two lines with slopes that are negative reciprocals
parallel lines	lines that have the same slope

Temperature Project

First, measure the outdoor temperature at 9:00 A.M. and at 12:00 noon. Graph the two points. Draw a straight line between the points. Then find the slope of the line. Assume the rate of the change in temperature stays the same. Calculate what the temperature will be at 3:00 P.M. After you have completed Lesson 6.8, write an equation for the line.

Project See the Classroom Resource Binder for a scoring rubric to assess this project.

Outdoor Temperature	
9:00 A.M.	12:00 noon
10° F	30° F

More practice is provided in Exercises 31, 33, and 34 of the Workbook.

6·1 Using the Slope and y-Intercept

Getting Started
Write $y = mx + b$
directly below the equation
$7 = 2x + 3$. Ask a volunteer
to identify the slope and
y-intercept in each equation.

You have worked with the **slope-intercept form** of an equation. It is $y = mx + b$. Now you will use the slope and y-intercept to write an equation.

▶ **EXAMPLE 1**

Write the equation of the line with slope $= \frac{3}{2}$ and y-intercept $= -2$.

Remember
m is the slope and b is the y-intercept.

Write the slope-intercept form.	$y = mx + b$
Substitute $\frac{3}{2}$ for m.	$y = \frac{3}{2}x + b$
Substitute -2 for b.	$y = \frac{3}{2}x + (-2)$
Simplify.	$y = \frac{3}{2}x - 2$

The equation of the line is $y = \frac{3}{2}x - 2$.

▶ **EXAMPLE 2**

Write the equation of the line with slope $= -2$ and y-intercept $= 0$.

Write the slope-intercept form.	$y = mx + b$
Substitute -2 for m.	$y = -2x + b$
Substitute 0 for b.	$y = -2x + 0$
Simplify.	$y = -2x$

The equation of the line is $y = -2x$.

You can find the slope and y-intercept of a line from its graph.

▶ **EXAMPLE 3**

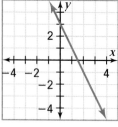

Use the graph to write the equation of the line.

Find the slope by looking at rise over run.	$m = -\frac{2}{1} = -2$
Look at the graph to find the y-intercept.	$b = 3$
Write the slope-intercept form.	$y = mx + b$
Substitute -2 for m and 3 for b.	$y = -2x + 3$
Check: Pick a point on the line.	$(1, 1)$
Substitute 1 for x and 1 for y.	$1 = -2(1) + 3$
	$1 = 1$ true

The equation of the line is $y = -2x + 3$.

Try These

Write the equation of each line.

1. Slope $= \frac{1}{2}$ and y-intercept $= 1$

Write the slope-intercept $\quad y = mx + b$
form. $\quad \frac{1}{2}$

Substitute ■ for m. $\quad y = \blacksquare x + \blacksquare$
$\quad\quad\quad\quad\quad\quad\quad\quad\quad \frac{1}{2} \quad 1$

Substitute ■ for b. $1 \quad \frac{1}{2}$

The equation is $y = \blacksquare x + \blacksquare$.
$\quad\quad\quad\quad\quad\quad\quad\quad\quad \frac{1}{2} \quad 1$

2. Slope $= 3$ and y-intercept $= 0$

Write the slope-intercept $\quad y = mx + b$
form.

Substitute ■ for m. $\quad y = \blacksquare x + \blacksquare$
$\quad\quad\quad\quad\quad\quad \frac{3}{} \quad\quad\quad\quad\quad\quad\quad 3 \quad 0$

Substitute ■ for b.
$\quad\quad\quad\quad\quad\quad \frac{0}{}$

The equation is $y = \blacksquare x$.
$\quad\quad\quad\quad\quad\quad\quad\quad\quad 3$

3.

Find the slope. $\quad\quad\quad\quad\quad\quad\quad m = \blacksquare \; 1$

Find the y-intercept. $\quad\quad\quad\quad b = \blacksquare \; 3$
$\quad\quad\quad\quad\quad\quad\quad\quad\quad\quad\quad\quad m \quad b$

Write the slope-intercept form. $\quad y = \blacksquare x + \blacksquare$
$\quad\quad\quad\quad\quad\quad\quad\quad\quad\quad\quad\quad\quad 1 \quad 3$

Substitute ■ for m and ■ for b. $\quad y = \blacksquare x + \blacksquare$
$\quad\quad\quad\quad\quad\quad 1 \quad\quad\quad\quad\quad 3$

The equation is $y = x + \blacksquare$. 3

Practice

Write the equation of each line.

1. slope $= -4$ and y-intercept $= -3$
$y = -4x - 3$

2. slope $= \frac{1}{2}$ and y-intercept $= 0$ $\quad y = \frac{1}{2}x$

Use the graph to write the equation of each line. Then, check by using a point.

3.

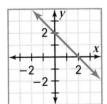

$y = -x + 2$;
Possible check:
Use $(1, 1)$; $1 = -1 + 2$.

4.

$y = 3x - 2$;
Possible check:
Use $(1, 1)$; $1 = 3 - 2$.

Cooperative Learning

5. Explain to a partner how to write the equation for number **3**
in **Practice**. Write the equation $y = mx + b$. Find $m = -1$ and $b = 2$. Substitute. $y = -x + 2$.

6. Graph the line that passes through the points $(0, -2)$ and
$(-4, 0)$. Have a partner write the equation of this line. Partner should write
$y = -\frac{1}{2}x - 2$. See graph in Additional Answers, p. 473.

6·2 Using a Point and the Slope

Getting Started
Write the ordered pair (4, 3) on the chalkboard. Ask a volunteer to describe how to plot the ordered pair on a coordinate grid.

You can write the equation of a line when you know any point on the line and the slope. Use the form of the equation $y = mx + b$. Substitute the slope for m. Use the ordered pair to substitute for x and y. Then, solve for b.

▶ **EXAMPLE 1**

Write the equation of the line that passes through the point (3, 0) and has slope $= -2$. Then, check the equation.

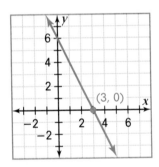

Write the slope-intercept form.	$y = mx + b$
Substitute -2 for m.	$y = -2x + b$
Substitute 3 for x and 0 for y.	$0 = -2(3) + b$
Solve for b.	$6 = b$
Write the equation. Use -2 for m and 6 for b.	$y = -2x + 6$
Check: Substitute 3 for x and 0 for y.	$y = -2x + 6$
	$0 = -2(3) + 6$
	$0 = 0$ true

The equation of the line is $y = -2x + 6$.

▶ **EXAMPLE 2**

Write the equation of the line that passes through the point (6, 4) and has slope $= \frac{2}{3}$.

Write the slope-intercept form.	$y = mx + b$
Substitute $\frac{2}{3}$ for m.	$y = \frac{2}{3}x + b$
Substitute 6 for x and 4 for y.	$4 = \frac{2}{3}(6) + b$
Solve for b.	$4 = \frac{12}{3} + b$
	$4 = 4 + b$
	$0 = b$

Check
Use (6, 4).

$y = \frac{2}{3}x$

$4 = \frac{2}{3}(6)$

$4 = \frac{12}{3}$

$4 = 4$ true

Write the equation. Use $\frac{2}{3}$ for m and 0 for b. $y = \frac{2}{3}x + 0$

The equation of the line is $y = \frac{2}{3}x$.

Try These

Find the equation of each line.

1. through (2, 3) and with slope $= \frac{1}{2}$

Write the slope-intercept $y = mx + b$
form.

Substitute $\frac{1}{2}$ for m.　　　$y = \frac{1}{2}x + b$

Substitute $\frac{2}{2}$ for x　　　$3 = \frac{1}{2}(2) + b$
and $\frac{3}{}$ for y.

Solve for b.　　　　　$2\ \blacksquare = b$

Write the slope-intercept $y = mx + b$
form.

Substitute $\frac{1}{2}$ for m　　$y = \frac{1}{2}x +\blacksquare\ 2$
and $\frac{2}{}$ for b.

　　　　　　　　　　$y = \frac{1}{2}x + 2$

The equation of the line is $\blacksquare$.

2. through (2, 0) and with slope $= -3$

Write the slope-intercept $y = mx + b$
form.

Substitute $\frac{-3}{}$ for m.　　$y = \blacksquare x + b$

Substitute $\frac{2}{}$ for x　　$0 = \blacksquare(2) + b$
and $\frac{0}{}$ for y.　　　　　　-3

Solve for b.　　　　　$\overset{6}{\blacksquare} = b$

Write the slope-intercept $y = mx + b$
form.

Substitute $\frac{-3}{}$ for m　　$y = -3x + \overset{6}{\blacksquare}$
and $\frac{6}{}$ for b.

　　　　　　　　　　$y = -3x + 6$

The equation of the line is $\blacksquare$.

Practice

3. $y = \frac{3}{2}x + 1$　　　**5.** $y = \frac{1}{4}x + 2$

Find the equation of each line.

$y = \frac{3}{2}x - 4$

1. through (1, 1) and with slope $= -2$
$y = -2x + 3$

2. through (2, −1) and with slope $= \frac{3}{2}$

3. through (2, 4) and with slope $= \frac{3}{2}$
See above.

4. through (2, 5) and with slope $= 5$
$y = 5x - 5$

5. through (4, 3) and with slope $= \frac{1}{4}$
See above.

6. through (−3, 0) and with slope $= -2$
$y = -2x - 6$

7. through (4, 4) and with slope $= 1$
$y = x$

8. through (3, 3) and with slope $= -1$
$y = -x + 6$

Cooperative Learning

9. Explain to a partner how to write the equation for number **4**
in **Practice**. First, write the slope-intercept form: $y = mx + b$; substitute 5 for m, 2 for x,
and 5 for y; solve for b.

10. Graph number **1** in **Practice**. Find a point on the graph other
than the one given. Ask a partner to use that point to check your
equation. Possible answer: (0, 3); $y = -2x + 3$, $3 = -2(0) + 3$, $3 = 3$, true. See graph in
Additional Answers, p. 473.

Getting Started
Ask students for descriptions of slope in addition to $\frac{rise}{run}$. Elicit from students that slope is (change in y values) ÷ (change in x values).

6-3 Using Two Points

You can write the equation of a line if you know two points. Use the ordered pairs to find the slope. Then, use one of the ordered pairs and the slope to find b in the $y = mx + b$ equation.

▶ **EXAMPLE 1**

Find the equation of a line through points $(2, 4)$ and $(1, 1)$.

Remember
slope = $\frac{rise}{run}$

Find the slope. $\qquad$ $m = \dfrac{4 - 1}{2 - 1} = \dfrac{3}{1} = 3$

Substitute 3 for m in $y = mx + b$. $\qquad y = 3x + b$

Use $(2, 4)$. Substitute 2 for x and 4 for y. $\quad 4 = 3(2) + b$

Solve for b. $\qquad -2 = b$

Write the slope-intercept form. $\qquad y = mx + b$

Substitute 3 for m and -2 for b. $\qquad y = 3x - 2$

Check: Use the other point, $(1, 1)$.

Substitute 1 for x and 1 for y. $\qquad 1 = 3(1) - 2$

$\qquad 1 = 1$ true

The equation of the line is $y = 3x - 2$.

▶ **EXAMPLE 2**

Find the equation of a line through points $(3, 7)$ and $(2, 7)$.

Find the slope. $\qquad$ $m = \dfrac{7 - 7}{3 - 2} = \dfrac{0}{1} = 0$

Substitute 0 for m in $y = mx + b$. $\qquad y = 0x + b$

Use $(3, 7)$. Substitute 3 for x and 7 for y. $\quad 7 = 0(3) + b$

Solve for b. $\qquad 7 = b$

Write the slope-intercept form. $\qquad y = mx + b$

Substitute 0 for m and 7 for b. $\qquad y = 0x + 7$

Simplify. $\qquad y = 7$

Check: Use the other point, $(2, 7)$. $\qquad 7 = 0(2) + 7$

$\qquad 7 = 7$ true

The equation of the line is $y = 7$.

Try These

Find the equation for each line through the two points. Then, check the equation.

1. (2, 5) and (−1, −4)

Find the slope.	$m = \dfrac{5 - (-4)}{2 - (-1)} = \blacksquare\, 3$

$\overset{3}{}$

Substitute $\blacksquare$ for m. $y = \blacksquare x + b$

$\overset{3}{}$

Substitute 2 for x $\blacksquare = 3(2) + b$
and $\blacksquare$ for y. $\overset{5}{}$

$\overset{5}{}$

Solve for b. $-1\blacksquare = b$

Write the equation $y = 3x + \blacksquare^{-1}$
in slope-intercept $y = 3x - \blacksquare\,1$
form.

Check with the other point.

Substitute −1 for x $\overset{-4}{\blacksquare} = 3(\overset{-1}{\blacksquare}) - 1$
and −4 for y. $\blacksquare = \blacksquare$ true
$\overset{-4}{}\quad\overset{-4}{}$

The equation of the line is $\blacksquare$. $y = 3x - 1$

2. (0, 4) and (2, 3)

Find the slope.	$m = \dfrac{4 - 3}{0 - 2} = \blacksquare\, -\dfrac{1}{2}$

$-\dfrac{1}{2}$ Substitute $\blacksquare$ for m. $y = \blacksquare x + b\;\; -\dfrac{1}{2}$

Substitute 0 for x $4\blacksquare = -\dfrac{1}{2}(0) + b$
and $\blacksquare$ for y. $\overset{4}{}$

Solve for b. $4\blacksquare = b$

Write the equation $y = \blacksquare x + \blacksquare$
in slope-intercept $-\dfrac{1}{2}\quad 4$
form.

Check with the other point.

Substitute 2 for x $\overset{3}{\blacksquare} = -\dfrac{1}{2}(\overset{2}{\blacksquare}) + 4$
and 3 for y. $3 = \blacksquare$ true
$\overset{3}{}$

The equation of the line is $\blacksquare$. $y = -\dfrac{1}{2}x + 4$

1. $y = -\dfrac{1}{2}x + 5$ **2.** $y = -2x + 2$ **3.** $y = -x + 10$ **4.** $y = \dfrac{1}{2}x - 6$

5. $y = 6$ **6.** $y = 2x - 1$ **7.** $y = \dfrac{1}{2}x$ **8.** $y = -\dfrac{3}{2}x + 6$

Practice

9. $y = x$

Find the equation for each line through the two points. Then, check the equation. See above.

1. (4, 3) and (2, 4)   **2.** (5, −8) and (2, −2)   **3.** (1, 9) and (7, 3)

4. (6, −3) and (8, −2)   **5.** (2, 6) and (3, 6)   **6.** (4, 7) and (3, 5)

7. (0, 0) and (4, 2)   **8.** (2, 3) and (0, 6)   **9.** (−1, −1) and (2, 2)

11. Possible answer: Start at (5, −8), count up to find the rise: 6. Count left to find the run: −3. Write the rise over the run: $\dfrac{6}{-3} = -2$. See graph in Additional Answers, p. 473.

Cooperative Learning

10. Explain to a partner how to write the equation for number **6** in **Practice**. Find the slope $m = \dfrac{7 - 5}{4 - 3} = 2$. Substitute 2 for m. Substitute the coordinates of one point to find b.

11. Graph the two points in number **2** in **Practice**. Have a partner explain how to find the slope using the graph. See above.

6·4 Equations of Horizontal and Vertical Lines

Getting Started
Review the meaning of *horizontal* and *vertical*. Ask volunteers to draw horizontal and vertical lines on the chalkboard.

You can write the equations of **horizontal lines** and **vertical lines** by looking at their graphs.

 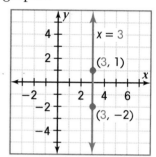

horizontal line   vertical line

In horizontal lines all of the ordered pairs have the same value for y. In vertical lines, all of the ordered pairs have the same value for x.

EXAMPLE 1

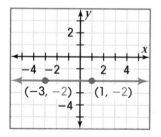

Write the equation of the line from the graph.

Find two ordered pairs on the line. $(-3, -2)$ and $(1, -2)$

Find the y-value in the ordered pairs. -2

Check: Pick another point on the line. $(2, -2)$

Substitute. $y = -2$

$-2 = -2$ true

The equation of the line is $y = -2$.

EXAMPLE 2

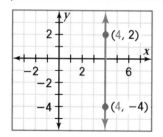

Write the equation of the line from the graph.

Find two ordered pairs on the line. $(4, 2)$ and $(4, -4)$

Find the x-value of the ordered pairs. 4

The equation of the line is $x = 4$.

Try These

Write the equation for each line described.

1. through the point (4, 1) and perpendicular to $y = -4x - 1$

 Find the slope of $y = -4x - 1$. ■-4

 Find the negative reciprocal of -4. ■$\frac{1}{4}$

 Write the slope-intercept form. $y = mx + b$

 Substitute $\frac{1}{4}$ for m. $y = \blacksquare x + b \; \frac{1}{4}$

 Substitute 4 for x and 1 for y. $\blacksquare = \frac{1}{4}(\blacksquare) + b \; \frac{1}{1} \; \frac{4}{4}$

 Solve for b. $1 = 1 + b$

  $0\blacksquare = b$

The equation of the line is $y = \blacksquare. \; \frac{1}{4}x$

2. y-intercept $= -5$ and parallel to $y = -2x + 4$

 Find the slope of $y = -2x + 4$. ■-2

 Write the slope-intercept form. $y = mx + b$

 Parallel lines have the same slope.

 Substitute -2 for m and -5 for b. $y = \blacksquare x + (\blacksquare) \; \frac{-2 \quad -5}{}$
  $y = -2x - \blacksquare 5$

 The equation of the line is $y = \blacksquare.$
  $-2x - 5$

Practice

Write the equation for each line.

1. y-intercept $= 1$ and parallel to $y = 4x - 3$ $y = 4x + 1$

2. through $(-1, 5)$ and parallel to $y = -x + 1$ $y = -x + 4$

3. y-intercept $= -3$ and parallel to $y = -\frac{1}{2}x + 2$ $y = -\frac{1}{2}x - 3$

4. y-intercept $= 9$ and perpendicular to $y = \frac{1}{5}x + 4$ $y = -5x + 9$

5. y-intercept $= -6$ and perpendicular to $y = -2x - 3$ $y = \frac{1}{2}x - 6$

6. through $(2, 8)$ and perpendicular to $y = -\frac{1}{3}x - 8$ $y = 3x + 2$

Cooperative Learning

7. Work with a partner to check number **1** in **Practice** by graphing both lines. See Additional Answers, p. 473.

8. Pick any point. Have a partner write the equation of the line through that point and perpendicular to the line $y = \frac{1}{3}x - 2$. Check by graphing the equations. Answers will vary. Make sure new equations have a slope of -3.

Calculator: Is the Equation Correct?

You can write the equations of lines from their graphs. You can check whether the equation is correct with a calculator. Pick a point that you know is on the line. Substitute the x- and y-values into the equation.

▶ **EXAMPLE 1**

Check that the graph of the equation $y = 4x - 9$ goes through the point (3.5, 5).

Substitute 3.5 for x and 5 for y. $5 = 4(3.5) - 9$

Use the calculator to simplify.   **Display**

Enter 4 by pressing:	**4**	4
Multiply by 3.5 by pressing:	**×** **3** **.** **5** **=**	14
Subtract 9 by pressing:	**−** **9** **=**	5

$5 = 5$ is true. The equation is correct.

▶ **EXAMPLE 2**

Check that the graph of the equation $y = 7x + 80$ goes through the point (1.8, 91).

Substitute 1.8 for x and 91 for y. $91 = 7(1.8) + 80$

Use the calculator to simplify.   **Display**

Enter 7 by pressing:	**7**	7
Multiply by 1.8 by pressing:	**×** **1** **.** **8** **=**	12.6
Add 80 by pressing:	**+** **8** **0** **=**	92.6

$91 = 92.6$ is not true. The equation is not correct.

▶ **EXAMPLE 3**

Check that the graph of the equation $y = 5.3x$ goes through the point (2, 10.6).

Substitute x with 2 and y with 10.6. $10.6 = 5.3(2)$

Use the calculator to simplify.   **Display**

Enter 5.3 by pressing:	**5** **.** **3**	5.3
Multiply by 2 by pressing:	**×** **2** **=**	10.6

$10.6 = 10.6$ is true. The equation is correct.

Practice

Check the equation using the given point.

1. $y = 4.2x$
given the point (9, 37.8) true

2. $y = 1.9x + 2.3$
given the point (3, 8) true

3. $y = 56x - 39$
given the point (1.2, 29) false

4. $y = 38x + 5$
given the point (.7, 31.6) true

5. $y = 60x + 9.1$
given the point (4, 359.1) false

6. $y = 4.2x - 13$
given the point (5, 8) true

People in Math

LUIS ALVAREZ

Luis Alvarez was born in San Francisco, California. In 1936, he received his Ph.D. degree in physics. He used his physics and math skills in scientific research.

First, he worked on microwaves and radar. He made a special radar beam. It helped planes to land safely, even in very thick fog.

He was awarded the Nobel Prize in Physics in 1968. His work helped build the "bubble chamber." This is used to find very tiny subatomic particles. He found many previously unknown particles with his research.

In 1980, he wrote an article with his son who is a geologist. They said that a giant asteroid struck the Earth 65 million years ago. It forced a thick cloud of dust up into the sky. This blocked out the sun for a very long time. They think this is what killed the dinosaurs. This theory has caused a lot of debate. As Dr. Alvarez said, "Only time will tell the real story."

More practice is provided in Exercises 35 and 36 of the Workbook.

Problem Solving: Looking for Number Patterns

6·7

Sometimes you can see a pattern in a table of ordered pairs. You can write an equation to show the pattern.

▶ **EXAMPLE**

Getting Started
Write the numbers 2, 4, 6, and 8 on the chalkboard. Invite a volunteer to explain how to find the next number in the pattern. Challenge a second volunteer to write an equation that matches the pattern.

Find the pattern. Then write the equation.

Time	Distance
1	2
2	4
3	6

READ   **What do you need to find out?**
You need to find the pattern in the table. Then, you need to write the equation to show the pattern.

PLAN   **What do you need to do?**
Look at each pair of numbers. (Time, Distance) Find how you use the first number to get the second number. Then, write an equation.

DO   **Follow the plan.**

Look at the first pair of numbers. $1 \rightarrow 2$
How do you use 1 to find 2?   multiply by 2 or add 1

Look at the next pair of numbers. $2 \rightarrow 4$
How do you use 2 to find 4?   multiply by 2 or add 2

Look at the third pair of numbers. $3 \rightarrow 6$
How do you use 3 to find 6?   multiply by 2 or add 3

What is the common pattern?   multiply by 2
Write the equation. Use
t for time and d for distance. $2t = d$

CHECK   **Does your answer make sense?**
Check each pair of numbers in the equation. ✓

The equation for the pattern in the table is $2t = d$.

Try These

Find the pattern. Then, write the equation.

1.

x	y
$50	$10
40	8
30	6

First pair.   50 ■ → 10   divide by 5 or subtract ■ 40

Second pair.   40 → 8   5   divide by ■ or subtract 32

Third pair.   30 → 6   5   divide by ■ or subtract 24

The common pattern is ■. divide by 5
The equation is $y = x$ ■ 5. ÷

2.

Gallons (g)	Miles (m)
1	30
2	60
3	90

First pair.   1 ■ → 30   multiply by 30 or add ■ 29

Second pair.   2 → 60   30   multiply by ■ or add 58

Third pair.   3 → 90   30   multiply by ■ or add ■ 87

multiply by 30
The common pattern is ■.
The equation is $m =$ ■ g. 30

Practice

Find the pattern. Then, write the equation.

1.

x	y
28	25
30	27
32	29

$y = x - 3$

2.

Quarts	Gallons
1	4
2	8
3	12

$g = 4q$

3.

Jo's Age	Mia's Age
3	9
4	10
5	11

$m = j + 6$

Cooperative Learning

4. Explain to a partner how to find the pattern in number **3** in **Practice.** In all three pairs, the difference is 6.

5. Write a table using an addition pattern. Ask a partner to describe the pattern in your table and write an equation that gives the pattern. Answers will vary.

More practice is provided in Exercise 36 of the Workbook.

6·8 ▶ Application: Writing Formulas

Getting Started
Remind students they are already familiar with formulas. For example, Area = length × width. Have students supply additional examples of formulas.

This graph shows how volumes of a gas change with its temperature. You can use this graph to write an equation or formula that describes this.

t	V
0	450
30	500
60	550
90	600
120	650
150	700

Math Fact
The broken line means a break in the vertical axis.

▶ **EXAMPLE 1**

Write an equation to show how volume changes with temperature.

Pick variables for volume and temperature. Use V for volume and t for temperature.

Find the slope. Use (90, 600) and (30, 500). $\dfrac{\text{rise}}{\text{run}} = \dfrac{600 - 500}{90 - 30} = \dfrac{100}{60} = \dfrac{5}{3}$

Find the y-intercept 450

Substitute $\dfrac{5}{3}$ for m and 450 for b in $V = mt + b$. $V = \dfrac{5}{3}t + 450$

The formula for the volume of a gas is $V = \dfrac{5}{3}t + 450$.

▶ **EXAMPLE 2**

Use the formula to find the volume of a gas when its temperature is 75°C.

Write the formula. $V = \dfrac{5}{3}t + 450$

Substitute 75 for t. $V = \dfrac{5}{3}(75) + 450$

Simplify. $V = 125 + 450$

Math Fact
cc means *cubic centimeters*. It is a measure of volume.

$V = 575$

The volume of the gas is 575 cc at 75°C.

Try These

A spring stretches and gets longer as you put more mass on it. The graph shows how the length of the spring changes with the mass.

1. Write a formula to describe how length changes with mass.

Length of a Spring

| Pick variables for length and mass. | Use l for length and g for mass. |

Find the slope. Use (75, 81) and (50, 79).

$$\frac{rise}{run} = \frac{81-79}{75-50} = \frac{2}{25}$$

Find the y-intercept. $\blacksquare$ $\frac{2}{25}$ $\frac{75}{}$

Substitute $\blacksquare$ for m and $\blacksquare$ for b in $l = mg + b$. $\frac{2}{25}$ $\frac{75}{}$

$$l = \blacksquare g + \blacksquare 75$$

The formula is $l = \blacksquare g + \blacksquare.75$ $\frac{2}{25}$

2. Use the formula to find the length of the spring when the mass is 100 grams.

Write the formula. $\qquad l = \frac{2}{25}g + 75$

Substitute 100 for g. $\qquad l = \frac{2}{25}\blacksquare + 75$ 100

Simplify. $\qquad l = \blacksquare$ 83

The length is $\blacksquare$ 83 millimeters when the mass is 100 grams.

Practice

Use the formula $V = \frac{5}{3}t + 450$ to find the volume of a gas at each temperature.

1. 21°C? 485 cc **2.** 45°C? 525 cc **3.** 150°C? 700 cc **4.** 180°C? 750 cc

Cooperative Learning

5. Explain to a partner how to find the volume in number **1** of **Practice.** Substitute 21 for t in the equation.

6. Pick a mass in grams. Have a partner use the formula $l = \frac{2}{25}g + 75$ to find the length of a spring. Answers will vary. Make sure there are no negative numbers.

Summary

You can write the equation of a line if you know the slope and the *y*-intercept.
To write the equation of a line when you know a point and the slope, substitute the coordinates for *x* and *y* and solve for *b*.
To write the equation of a line when you know two points, first find the slope. Then, use a point on the line to find *b*.
The ordered pairs for points on a vertical line have the same value for *x*.
The ordered pairs for points on a horizontal line have the same value for *y*.
The slopes of perpendicular lines are negative reciprocals.
Parallel lines have the same slope.
You can describe a pattern with an equation.
You can write formulas from graphs.

More vocabulary review is provided in Exercise 51 of the Classroom Resource Binder.

slope-intercept form

horizontal line

vertical line

perpendicular lines

parallel lines

Vocabulary Review

Complete the sentences with words from the box.

1. Lines that have the same slope are _____. parallel lines

2. An equation written in $y = mx + b$ form is in _____. slope-intercept form

3. A line with slope = 0 is a _____. horizontal line

4. Two lines with slopes that are negative reciprocals are _____. perpendicular lines

5. A line with no slope is a _____. vertical line

Chapter Quiz   More **assessment** is provided in the Classroom Resource Binder.

Write the equation of each line.

1. with slope = −1 and y-intercept = 3
$y = -x + 3$

2. with slope = $\frac{1}{2}$ and y-intercept = 7
$y = \frac{1}{2}x + 7$

3. with slope = 2 and y-intercept = −6
$y = 2x - 6$

4. through (1, 1) and with slope = 4
$y = 4x - 3$

5. through (−4, 3) and with slope = 0
$y = 3$

6. through (1, 6) and (3, 16)
$y = 5x + 1$

7. through (1, 2) and (2, 0)
$y = -2x + 4$

8. through (3, 5) and parallel to
$y = x + 5$ $y = x + 2$

9. with y-intercept = −6 and perpendicular to $y = 2x + 1$ $y = -\frac{1}{2}x - 6$

Write the equation of each line.

10.
$y = -2x + 3$

11.
$y = x$

12.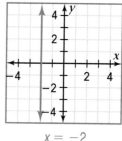
$x = -2$

Find the pattern. Then, write the equation.

13.

Time	Distance
3	12
4	16
5	20

Multiply Time by 4 to find Distance. $d = 4t$

14.

x	y
15	11
16	12
17	13

Subtract 4 from x to find y. $y = x - 4$.

Use the formula $l = \frac{2}{25}g + 75$ to answer the question. Use *l* for length and *g* for mass.

15. What is the length of a spring when the mass is 250 grams? $l = 95$ mm

Additional Practice for this chapter
is provided on p. 418 of this text.

Unit 2 Review

Choose the letter for the correct answer.

Use the graph to answer Questions 1 and 2.

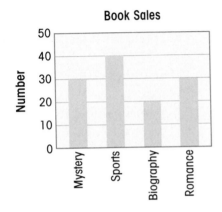

Book Sales

1. How many Biographies were sold? A
   A. 20
   B. 30
   C. 40
   D. 50

2. Which kind of books were most popular? B
   A. Mysteries
   B. Sports
   C. Biographies
   D. Romance

3. Which set of ordered pairs is NOT a function? D
   A. (1, 3), (−2, 0), (4, 3), (2, 0)
   B. (−1, 0), (0, 1), (1, 2), (2, 3)
   C. (1, 2), (2, 4), (3, 6), (4, 8)
   D. (1, 3), (1, −3), (0, 2), (0, −2)

4. Al earned $30.00 in 5 hours. His pay varies directly with his hours. Which is the equation for his pay? B
   A. $P = 5h$
   B. $P = 6h$
   C. $P = 10h$
   D. $P = 15h$

5. A train leaves a city at 7:00 A.M. It travels 120 miles by 9:00 A.M. How far will it travel by 11:00 A.M.? A
   A. 240 miles
   B. 280 miles
   C. 300 miles
   D. 320 miles

6. Which is the length of a spring when the mass is 125 grams? Use $l = \frac{2}{25} g + 75$. C
   A. 13 millimeters
   B. 25 millimeters
   C. 85 millimeters
   D. 125 millimeters

Critical Thinking

You can order CDs from a catalog. Each CD costs $15. For each order, you have to pay $8.00 for shipping. Write an equation for this function. How much does an order of 30 CDs cost? $t = 15c + 8$; $458

CHALLENGE Sam spent $98 on an order of CDs from the catalog. How many CDS did he order? 6 CDs

Critical Thinking See the Classroom Resource Binder for a scoring rubric to assess this Critical Thinking question.

Unit Three

Chapter **7** Inequalities

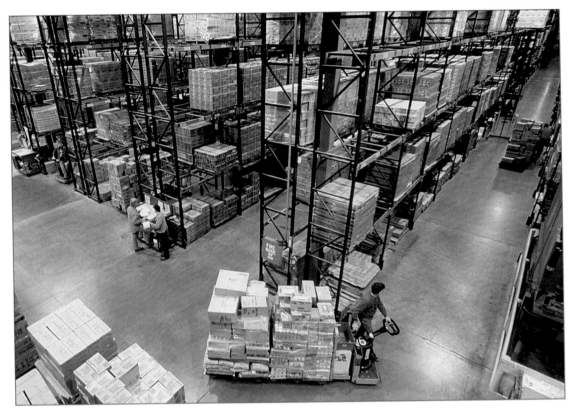

Inequalities can show a business how much stock to keep in its warehouse. The warehouse needs enough stock to fill orders. What happens when a warehouse has too much stock?

Learning Objectives

- Solve and graph the solution of an inequality with one variable.

- Solve an inequality with two variables.

- Graph the solution of an inequality with two variables.

- Use a calculator to check a solution of an inequality.

- Solve a problem by using an inequality.

- Apply concepts and skills to using solutions of inequalities.

Words to Know

graph of a solution	points on the number line or coordinate plane that show the solutions of an equation or inequality
inequality	a statement that shows "greater than," "greater than or equal to," "less than," or "less than or equal to"
$\leq$	the symbol for "is less than or equal to" also means "at most" or "no greater than"
$\geq$	the symbol for "is greater than or equal to" also means "at least" or "no less than"

Height Project

Measure, in inches, the height of each of your classmates. Be sure to have someone measure your own height. Then record the measurements in a table. Identify the greatest number written in the table, and write an inequality to show that no one in the class is taller than that measure. Identify the least number written in the table and write an inequality to show that no one in the class is shorter than that measure. Explain in writing what the inequalities mean.

Student	Height
Joseph	75 in.
Susan	66 in.

Project See the Classroom Resource Binder for a scoring rubric to assess this project.

More practice is provided in Exercises 37 and 39 of the Workbook.

7·1 Solutions on the Number Line

Getting Started

Write the symbols $<$ and $>$ on the chalkboard. Ask for volunteers to choose two numbers to make the inequalities true. For example, $4 > 1$ and $-2 < 3$.

You can **graph a solution** to an equation with one variable on a number line.

$$x = -2$$
The only solution is -2.

The statement $x > -2$ is an **inequality.** It means that x is greater than -2. You can also graph its solution.

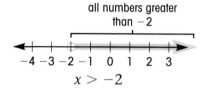

all numbers greater than -2

$$x > -2$$

An open dot means -2 is not a solution of $x > -2$. Any point to the right of -2 is greater than -2. Any point to the right of -2 is a solution.

▶ **EXAMPLE 1**

Graph the solution. $x < 4$

Place an open dot at 4.

Shade the number line to the left of 4.

The inequality $x \le 1$ means x is less than or equal to 1.

1 and all numbers less than 1

$$x \le 1$$

A solid dot means 1 is a solution of the inequality. Any point to the left of 1 is also a solution.

▶ **EXAMPLE 2**

Math Fact
$y \ge 3$ means y is greater than or equal to 3.

Graph the solution. $y \ge 3$

Place a solid dot at 3.

Shade the number line to the right of 3.

Try These

Graph the solution of each inequality.

1. $x \geq 4$ solid
Place a ■ dot at 4.   right
Shade the number line to the ■ of 4.

2. $y < -3$ open
Place an ■ dot at −3.   left
Shade the number line to the ■ of −3.

3. $p > 0$ open
Place an ■ dot at 0.   right
Shade the number line to the ■ of 0.

4. $w \leq 5$ solid
Place a ■ dot at 5.   left
Shade the number line to the ■ of 5.

Practice

Graph the solution of each inequality on a number line.

1. $x > 5$

2. $y \leq -1$

3. $a \geq 2$

4. $t < 7$

5. $k \geq -6$

6. $m \leq 0$

7. $b > -4$

8. $x < 8$

9. $q \geq -5$

10. $y \geq 0$

11. $n \leq -9$

12. $z > 3$

13. $r > -7$

14. $w \geq 1$

15. $s \leq -8$

16. Possible answer: y is greater than or equal to 10. Place a solid dot at 10. Shade the number line to the right of 10.

Cooperative Learning

16. Explain to a partner how to graph the solution of $y \geq 10$. See above.

17. Write an inequality using integers. Ask a partner to graph the solution of the inequality. Check the work. Answers may vary. Check the dot and the direction of the line.

More practice is provided in Exercise 38 of the Workbook.

7·2 Solving Inequalities Using Addition and Subtraction

Getting Started
Use counters to model the inequality $4 > 3$. Then add the same number of counters to both sides of the inequality to show that the inequality is preserved when the same number is added to both sides. Repeat the activity for subtraction.

You have solved equations using addition and subtraction. You can follow the same steps to solve an inequality using addition and subtraction.

$$\text{greater than} \quad \rightarrow \quad 7 > 4$$
$$7 - 2 \; ? \; 4 - 2$$
$$\text{stays greater than} \quad \rightarrow \quad 5 > 2$$

Adding or subtracting the same number from both sides keeps the inequality true.

▶ **EXAMPLE 1**

Solve. Then, graph. Check. $\quad x + 1 > 3$

$$x + 1 > 3$$

Subtract 1 from both sides. $\quad x + 1 - 1 > 3 - 1$

Simplify. Then, graph. $\quad\quad\quad x > 2$

Check: Substitute a number from the shaded part into $x + 1 > 3$. Use 4.
$$x + 1 > 3$$
$$4 + 1 > 3$$
$$5 > 3 \text{ true}$$

▶ **EXAMPLE 2**

Solve. Then, graph. Check. $\quad y - 2 \le -3$

$$y - 2 \le -3$$

Add 2 to both sides. $\quad y - 2 + 2 \le -3 + 2$

Simplify. Then, graph. $\quad\quad\quad y \le -1$

Check: Substitute a number from the shaded part into $y - 2 \le -3$. Use -4.
$$y - 2 \le -3$$
$$-4 - 2 \le -3$$
$$-6 \le -3 \text{ true}$$

▶ **EXAMPLE 3**

Solve. Then, graph. Check. $\quad y + 3 \ge 0$

$$y + 3 \ge 0$$

Subtract 3 from both sides. $\quad y + 3 - 3 \ge 0 - 3$

Simplify. Then, graph. $\quad\quad\quad y \ge -3$

Check: Substitute a number from the shaded part into $y + 3 \ge 0$. Use 0.
$$y + 3 \ge 0$$
$$0 + 3 \ge 0$$
$$3 \ge 0 \text{ true}$$

Try These

Solve each inequality. Then, graph the solution.

1. $x - 4 > -3$

Add 4 to both sides. $x - 4 + \blacksquare^{\,4} > -3 + \blacksquare^{\,4}$

Simplify both sides. $x > \blacksquare 1$

$$\begin{array}{ccccccccc} \text{-1} & 0 & 1 & 2 & 3 & 4 & 5 & 6 \end{array}$$

2. $q + 4 \leq 5$

Subtract $\blacksquare\,4$ from both sides. $q + 4 - \blacksquare^{\,4} \leq 5 - \blacksquare^{\,4}$

Simplify both sides. $q \leq \blacksquare 1$

$$\begin{array}{ccccccccc} \text{-4} & \text{-3} & \text{-2} & \text{-1} & 0 & 1 & 2 & 3 \end{array}$$

Practice

Solve each inequality. Then, graph the solution. Check with a point from the shaded part of the graph. See graphs in Additional Answers, p. 473.

1. $y + 4 > 6$ $y > 2$

2. $x + 3 \leq -4$ $x \leq -7$

3. $b - 2 < 5$ $b < 7$

4. $m - 1 \geq -2$ $m \geq -1$

5. $s + 5 > 3$ $s > -2$

6. $a - 6 \leq 3$ $a \leq 9$

7. $x - 3 < -2$ $x < 1$

8. $p - 2 \geq 8$ $p \geq 10$

9. $w + 7 < -2$ $w < -9$

10. $t + 2 > -7$ $t > -9$

Cooperative Learning

11. Show a partner how to find the solution in number **10** in **Practice.** Subtract 2 from both sides of the inequality. Simplify both sides to get $t > -9$. At -9 place an open dot. Shade to the right of -9.

12. Write an inequality that contains integers. Use addition or subtraction in the inequality. Ask a partner to solve the inequality. Check the work. Answers will vary.

More practice is provided in Exercises 38 and 39 of the Workbook.

7·3 ▶ **Solving Inequalities Using Multiplication and Division**

Getting Started

Write the following on the chalkboard:

$(+2)(+3) =$
$(+2)(-3) =$
$(-2)(+3) =$
$(-2)(-3) =$

Ask for volunteers to write the products. Review the rules for multiplying integers. Repeat for division.

You can use multiplication and division to solve inequalities. Watch what happens to the inequality sign.

Multiply by a positive number.	Multiply by a negative number.
$5 > 3$	$5 > 3$
$5(2) \; ? \; 3(2)$	$5(-2) \; ? \; 3(-2)$
$10 > 6$	$-10 < -6$
The inequality **stays** "is greater than."	The inequality **changes** to "is less than."

Multiplying both sides of an inequality by the same negative number changes the inequality.

▶ **EXAMPLE 1**

Check
Use 8.
$\frac{x}{4} < 3$
$\frac{8}{4} < 3$
$2 < 3$ true

Solve. Then, graph. $\frac{x}{4} < 3$

Multiply both sides by 4. Do not change the inequality.

$$\frac{x}{4} < 3$$
$$\frac{x}{4}(4) < 3 \, (4)$$
$$x < 12$$

Division works the same way.

$10 < 15$	$10 < 15$
$\frac{10}{5} \; ? \; \frac{15}{5}$	$\frac{10}{-5} \; ? \; \frac{15}{-5}$
$2 < 3$	$-2 > -3$
The inequality **stays** "is less than."	The inequality **changes** to "is greater than."

▶ **EXAMPLE 2**

Check
Use −5.
$-5x \geq 20$
$-5(-5) \geq 20$
$25 \geq 20$ true

Solve. Then, graph. $-5x \geq 20$

Divide both sides by −5. Change the inequality.

$$-5x \geq 20$$
$$\frac{-5x}{-5} \leq \frac{20}{-5}$$
$$x \leq -4$$

Try These

Solve each inequality. Then, graph the solution.

1. $\frac{x}{-3} \le 2$

$$\frac{x}{-3} \le 2$$

Multiply both
sides by ■. -3

■ the inequality.
Change

$\frac{x}{-3}$ (■) ■ 2(■)
$-3 \ge -3$

$x \;■\; -6$
$\ge$

$-8\ -7\ -6\ -5\ -4\ -3\ -2\ -1$

2. $-6y > -18$

$$-6y > -18$$

Divide both
sides by ■. -6

■ the inequality.
Change

$\dfrac{-6y}{■} ■ \dfrac{-18}{■}$
${-6}\;<\;{-6}$

$y \;■\; 3$
$<$

$-2\ -1\ \ 0\ \ 1\ \ 2\ \ 3\ \ 4\ \ 5$

Practice

Solve each inequality. Then, graph the solution. See graphs in Additional Answers, p. 474.

1. $\frac{x}{2} > 4$ $x > 8$ **2.** $4b \ge 8$ $b \ge 2$ **3.** $\frac{f}{6} < 6$ $f < 36$ **4.** $8c > 24$ $c > 3$

5. $\frac{m}{-5} \le 6$ $m \ge -30$ **6.** $-3x < 0$ $x > 0$ **7.** $\frac{x}{-4} \ge 5$ $x \le -20$ **8.** $-5d \le 30$ $d \ge -6$

Solve each inequality.

9. $\frac{x}{-2} > 10$
$ x < -20$

10. $3b \ge 21$
$ b \ge 7$

11. $\frac{f}{9} < 0$
$ f < 0$

12. $-7c > 28$
$ c < -4$

13. $\frac{m}{5} \le 7$
$ m \le 35$

14. $-8x < 40$
$ x > -5$

15. $\frac{x}{-6} \ge 5$
$ x \le -30$

16. $11d \le 88$
$ d \le 8$

Cooperative Learning

17. Explain to a partner how to solve the inequality in number **6**
in **Practice.** Possible answer: First, you divide both sides by -3. Since you are dividing by a
negative number, you change the inequality to $>$. Zero divided by any number is 0. The answer is $x > 0$.

18. Write an inequality with $\frac{x}{3}$ on the left side. Write an integer on
the right. Ask a partner to solve your inequality. Check the work.
Answers will vary. The solution should be a multiple of 3.

More practice is provided in Exercise 38 of the Workbook.

Getting Started
Ask a volunteer
to solve the
equation
$4x + 6 = 14$ on the
chalkboard. Have another
volunteer be the
commentator and explain
each step as it is done.

7·4 Solving Inequalities Using More Than One Step

Some inequalities contain more than one operation. You undo the operations the same way you undo them when solving equations. First, undo addition or subtraction. Then, undo multiplication or division.

▶ **EXAMPLE 1**

Solve. Then, graph. $3x - 6 < 9$

Add 6 to both sides. $3x - 6 + 6 < 9 + 6$

Simplify. $3x < 15$

Divide both sides by 3. $\dfrac{3x}{3} < \dfrac{15}{3}$

Simplify. Graph the inequality. $x < 5$

```
←+—+—+—+—+—+○—+—+→
  0  1  2  3  4  5  6  7
```

▶ **EXAMPLE 2**

Solve. Then, graph. $-5a + 2 \geq 22$

Subtract 2 from both sides. $-5a + 2 - 2 \geq 22 - 2$

Simplify. $-5a \geq 20$

Divide both sides by -5.
Change the inequality. $\dfrac{-5a}{-5} \leq \dfrac{20}{-5}$

Simplify. Graph the inequality. $a \leq -4$

Check
Use -5.
$-5a + 2 \geq 22$
$-5(-5) + 2 \geq 22$
$25 + 2 \geq 22$
$27 \geq 22$ true

```
←—+—+—+—+●—+—+—+→
 -9 -8 -7 -6 -5 -4 -3 -2
```

▶ **EXAMPLE 3**

Solve. Then, graph. $\dfrac{m}{-4} + 3 < 0$

Subtract 3 from both sides. $\dfrac{m}{-4} + 3 - 3 < 0 - 3$

Simplify. $\dfrac{m}{-4} < -3$

Multiply both sides by -4.
Change the inequality. $\dfrac{m}{-4}(-4) > -3(-4)$

Simplify. Graph the inequality. $m > 12$

Check
Use 16.
$\dfrac{m}{-4} + 3 < 0$
$\dfrac{16}{-4} + 3 < 0$
$-4 + 3 < 0$
$-1 < 0$ true

```
←+—+—○—+—+—+—+—+→
 10 11 12 13 14 15 16 17
```

Try These

Solve each inequality. Then, graph the solution.

1. $\frac{x}{3} + 6 \geq 12$

$$\frac{x}{3} + 6 \geq 12$$

Subtract ■ from both sides.
$$\frac{x}{3} + 6 - \blacksquare \geq 12 - \blacksquare$$
(with 6 above, 6 and 6 below)

Simplify.
$$\frac{x}{3} \geq \blacksquare \, 6$$

Multiply both sides by ■. Do not change the inequality. (3 at left)
$$\frac{x}{3}(3) \geq 6(3)$$

Simplify.
$$x \geq \blacksquare$$
(18 above)

Graph the inequality.

$$\xleftarrow{\hspace{1cm}} \underset{16\ \ 17\ \ 18\ \ 19\ \ 20\ \ 21\ \ 22\ \ 23}{+\!\!+\!\!+\!\!+\!\!+\!\!+\!\!+\!\!+} \xrightarrow{\hspace{1cm}}$$

2. $-6y - 4 > -22$

$$-6y - 4 > -22$$

Add ■ to both sides. (4 above)
$$-6y - 4 + \blacksquare > -22 + \blacksquare$$
(4 and 4 below)

Simplify.
$$-6y > \blacksquare -18$$

Divide both sides by ■. Change the inequality. (-6 at left)
$$\frac{-6y}{-6} \; \overset{<}{\blacksquare} \; \frac{\blacksquare -18}{-6}$$

Simplify.
$$y \; \overset{<}{\blacksquare} \; 3$$

Graph the inequality.

$$\xleftarrow{\hspace{1cm}} \underset{-2\ -1\ \ 0\ \ 1\ \ 2\ \ 3\ \ 4\ \ 5}{+\!\!+\!\!+\!\!+\!\!+\!\!+\!\!+\!\!+} \xrightarrow{\hspace{1cm}}$$

Practice

Solve each inequality. Then, graph the solution. See graphs in Additional Answers, p. 474.

1. $2x - 8 > 16$ $\quad x > 12$

2. $2y + 6 < 18$ $\quad y < 6$

3. $-9x + 3 \geq 21$ $\quad x \leq -2$

4. $\frac{a}{3} + 2 > 3$ $\quad a > 3$

5. $\frac{m}{2} - 4 \geq -1$ $\quad m \geq 6$

6. $\frac{n}{5} + 4 \leq 7$ $\quad n \leq 15$

Solve each inequality.

7. $-3x + 15 < 0$ $\quad x > 5$

8. $-5g + 3 \geq 28$ $\quad g \leq -5$

9. $\frac{m}{-3} - 6 \leq 1$ $\quad m \geq -21$

10. $\frac{x}{-5} + 8 > 3$ $\quad x < 25$

11. $-8a + 19 > -5$ $\quad a < 3$

12. $\frac{x}{9} + 13 \geq 5$ $\quad x \geq -72$

Cooperative Learning

13. Explain to a partner how to solve the inequality in number **8** in **Practice**. Possible answer: First, subtract 3 from both sides. Then, divide both sides by -5. Change the inequality since you divided by a negative number. $g \leq -5$.

14. Write the inequality $2a \geq 20$. Think of an even number. Subtract it from the left side of $2a \geq 20$. Ask a partner to solve your inequality. Graph the solution. Then, check. Possible answer: $2a - 4 \geq 20$; $2a - 4 + 4 \geq 20 + 4$; $2a \geq 24$; $a \geq 12$.

$$\xleftarrow{\hspace{0.5cm}} \underset{12}{\bullet} \xrightarrow{\hspace{2cm}}$$

More practice is provided in Exercises 39 and 40 of the Workbook.

7·5 ▶ Solutions in the Coordinate Plane

Getting Started
Shade an area on a coordinate plane. Have volunteers identify points in the shaded area. Then write the ordered pair for each point.

You have graphed linear equations on a coordinate plane. The graphs are solutions to the equation. You can also graph inequalities on a coordinate plane.

The shaded areas are graphs of the solutions of the inequalities. Substitute the x- and y-values of any ordered pair in the shaded area. You will have a true statement.

Math Facts
Points on the dotted line are not solutions.
Points on the solid line are solutions.

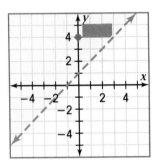

$$y > x + 1$$
Check (0, 4).
$$4 > 0 + 1$$
$$4 > 1 \text{ true}$$

$$y \le -x + 2$$
Check (0, 0).
$$0 \le -0 + 2$$
$$0 \le 2 \text{ true}$$

▶ **EXAMPLE 1**

Tell whether (1, 2) is a solution of $y < 2x + 3$.

$$y < 2x + 3$$

Substitute 1 for x and 2 for y.

$$2 < 2(1) + 3$$

Simplify.

$$2 < 2 + 3$$
$$2 < 5 \text{ true}$$

(1, 2) is a solution of $y < 2x + 3$.

▶ **EXAMPLE 2**

Tell whether (2, −1) is a solution of $y \ge -x + 1$.

$$y \ge -x + 1$$

Substitute 2 for x and −1 for y.

$$-1 \ge -(2) + 1$$

Simplify.

$$-1 \ge -2 + 1$$
$$-1 \ge -1 \text{ true}$$

(2, −1) is a solution of $y \ge -x + 1$.

Try These

Tell whether each point is a solution of the inequality.

1. $(-1, 0)$; $y < 2x + 2$

Substitute ■ for -1
x and ■ for y.

$$■ < 2(■) + 2$$

Simplify.

$$0 ■ < ■ + 2$$

$$0 ■ < ■ \text{ false}$$

is not
$(-1, 0)$ ■ a solution of $y < 2x + 2$.

2. $(2, 3)$; $y \le -x + 4$

Substitute ■ for 2
x and ■ for y.

$$■ \le -(■) + 4$$

Simplify.

$$3 ■ \le ■ \text{ false}$$

is not
$(2, 3)$ ■ a solution of $y \le -x + 4$.

Practice

Tell whether each point is a solution of $y > x + 1$.

1. $(-1, 1)$ yes

2. $(1, 2)$ no

3. $(2, -1)$ no

4. $(0, 0)$ no

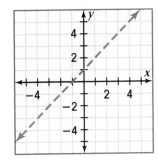

Tell whether each point is a solution of $y \ge -2x$.

5. $(-2, -1)$ no

6. $(-1, 2)$ yes

7. $(0, 4)$ yes

8. $(1, -1)$ yes

9. Possible answer: Use the equation $y > x + 1$. Substitute 1 for x and 2 for y. $2 > 1 + 1$. Simplify. $2 > 2$ is false. The point $(1, 2)$ is not a solution of the inequality.

Cooperative Learning

9. Explain to a partner how to solve number **2** in **Practice**. See above.

10. Pick any three points. Have a partner tell whether they are solutions of $y > 3x$. Check the work. Answers will vary.

7·6 Solving Inequalities with Two Variables

Getting Started
Write the equation
$y = 3x + 1$ on the
chalkboard. Ask students
to identify the slope (3) and
the y-intercept (1).

You can solve inequalities with two variables. First, graph the equation. Then, find the area that contains the solutions to the inequality. To find the area, pick a point on either side of the line. Substitute for x and y to see if it is in the solution.

 EXAMPLE 1

Math Fact
x means $1x$.

Graph the solution. $y < x + 2$

Graph the line $y = x + 2$.

Use y-intercept $= 2$ and slope $= 1$.

Draw a dotted line through the points to show $<$.

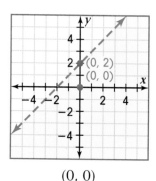

Math Fact
It is easiest to use (0, 0) if the line does not pass through the origin.

Pick a point on one side of the line. $(0, 0)$

Substitute into the inequality. $0 < 0 + 2$

Simplify. $0 < 2$ true

Shade the side of the line that contains $(0, 0)$.

 EXAMPLE 2

Graph the solution. $y \leq -2x$

Graph the line $y = -2x$.

Use y-intercept $= 0$ and slope $= -2$.

Draw a solid line through the points to show $\leq$.

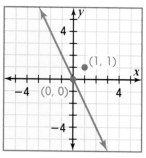

Pick a point on one side of the line. $(1, 1)$

Substitute into the inequality. $1 \leq -2(1)$

Simplify. $1 \leq -2$ false

Shade the side of the line that does not contain $(1, 1)$.

Try These

Graph the solution of each inequality.

1. $y \leq \frac{2}{5}x - 2$

Graph $y = \frac{2}{5}x - 2$.

Use y-intercept = . (0, −2)

Use slope = ▉. $\frac{2}{5}$

Draw a ▉ line through the points. solid

Pick a point. Use (0, 0).

Substitute into the inequality. $0 \leq \frac{2}{5}(0) - 2$

Simplify. $0 \leq 0 - 2$

$0 \leq -2$ false

Shade the side of the line that does not contain (0, 0).

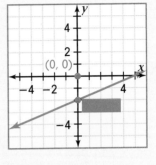

2. $y > x$

Graph $y = x$.

Use y-intercept = ▉. (0, 0)

Use slope = ▉. 1

Draw a ▉ line through the points. dotted

Pick a point. Use (0, 1).

Substitute into the inequality. $1 > 0$ true

Shade the side of the line that contains (0, 1).

7. Possible answer: y-intercept is 3. Draw a point at (0, 3). Then from there, move down 2 and right 3. Draw a point at (3, 1). Draw a solid line through the points. Substitute (0, 0) into the inequality: $0 \leq 0 + 3$; $0 \leq 3$. This is true, so you shade the side of the line that contains (0, 0).

Practice

Graph the solution of each inequality.

See Additional Answers, p. 474.

1. $y > 2x + 1$

2. $y < 3x$

3. $y \leq \frac{-2}{3}x + 3$

4. $y > -3x + 4$

5. $y \geq \frac{1}{2}x - 2$

6. $y < -x$

Cooperative Learning

7. Explain to a partner how to graph the inequality in number **3** in **Practice**. See above.

8. Write an inequality. Write y on one side. Ask a partner to graph the inequality. Check the work. Answers will vary. Check the line and shading of students' work.

Getting Started
Remind students
that $\frac{7}{5}$ means
7 divided by 5.
Have students use their
calculators to divide.
$(7 \div 5 = 1.4)$

7·7 ▶ **Calculator: Checking Solutions**

The graph of an inequality contains all solutions. Some ordered pairs in the solution contain decimals. You can use a calculator to check these ordered pairs.

▶ **EXAMPLE 1**

Is (1.5, 2.5) a solution of $y < 2x + 1$?

$$y < 2x + 1$$

Substitute 1.5 for x and 2.5 for y. $2.5 < 2 \bullet 1.5 + 1$

Use your calculator to simplify the right side.   **Display**

Enter 2 by pressing:	[2]	2
Multiply 1.5 by pressing:	[×][1][.][5][=]	3
Add 1 by pressing:	[+][1][=]	4

$2.5 < 4$ is true. (1.5, 2.5) is a solution of $y < 2x + 1$.

▶ **EXAMPLE 2**

Is (2.4, 1.2) a solution of $y > 3x - 2$?

$$y > 3x - 2$$

Substitute 2.4 for x and 1.2 for y. $1.2 > 3 \bullet 2.4 - 2$

Use your calculator to simplify the right side.   **Display**

Enter 3 by pressing:	[3]	3
Multiply 2.4 by pressing:	[×][2][.][4][=]	7.2
Subtract 2 by pressing:	[−][2][=]	5.2

$1.2 > 5.2$ is false. (2.4, 1.2) is not a solution of $y > 3x - 2$.

▶ **EXAMPLE 3**

Is (3.9, .65) a solution of $y < \frac{x}{6}$?

$$y < \frac{x}{6}$$

Substitute 3.9 for x and .65 for y. $.65 < \frac{3.9}{6}$

Use your calculator to simplify the right side.   **Display**

Enter 3.9 by pressing:	[3][.][9]	3.9
Divide 6 by pressing:	[÷][6][=]	0.65

$.65 < .65$ is false. (3.9, .65) is not a solution of $y < \frac{x}{6}$.

Practice

Tell whether each ordered pair is a solution of the inequality.

1. (1.1, 1.8); $y < 2x + 5$ yes

2. (2.1, 1.6); $y \geq 3x - 1$ no

3. (1.3, 7.2); $y \leq 4x + 2$ yes

4. (2.6, 1.4); $y > \frac{x}{2} - 4$ yes

5. (1.7, 2.8); $y > 2x + 2$ no

6. (3.5, 5.1); $y < 5x - 2$ yes

7. (2.3, 1.9); $y < \frac{x}{5} - 5$ no

8. (3.9, 4.1); $y \leq 3x - 8$ no

On-the-Job Math

RESTAURANT MANAGER

Do you like to cook and serve good food? Can you plan meals and shopping lists? Do you like people? If so, you might enjoy a career as a restaurant manager.

Restaurant managers run a business. They make sure customers get good food and service. There must be enough food, clean napkins, plates, and silverware. The right numbers of servers, cooks, and helpers are needed too.

To keep track, managers need to be good at math. They estimate the number of customers. They plan on how much food to buy. Suppose you worked for a fine restaurant, and the chef has made a new fish recipe. The fish must be very fresh. You need to buy just enough for the customers who will want it. If you buy too much, it may be wasted. You can use an inequality to help decide how much to buy.

A manager keeps a restaurant from losing money. If the service and food are poor, customers will stop coming. If too much food is ordered, it will be wasted. Good food and service mean more customers and more money.

More practice is provided in Exercise 41 of the Workbook.

7·8 ▶ Problem Solving: Using Inequalities

Getting Started

Use manipulatives such as play money and cards to model a problem involving inequality. For example, Dashiell has $22. If soccer cards cost at least $5, what is the greatest number of cards he can buy? (4)

You can use inequalities to solve many problems. It is helpful to know other words for the inequality symbols.

$\geq$	$\leq$
at least	at most
no less than	no greater than

To begin, pick variables for the numbers you do not know. Then, use symbols for the other words.

The **number of students is at least 200.**

don't know	$\geq$	200
n	$\geq$	200

▶ **EXAMPLE**

Coach Roberts needs to buy baseballs for the team. Each baseball costs $5.00. How many baseballs can he buy if he wants to spend at most $45.00?

READ   **What do you need to find out?**
You need to find how many baseballs Coach Roberts can buy for $45.00 or less.

PLAN   **What do you need to do?**
You need to write an inequality for the word problem. Then solve the inequality.

DO   **Follow the plan.**

Write the inequality.   baseballs   each $5   at most $45

Choose a variable.   don't know   •   5 $\leq$ 45

Use b for baseballs. $5b \leq 45$

Solve the inequality. $\dfrac{5b}{5} \leq \dfrac{45}{5}$

$b \leq 9$

CHECK   **Does your answer make sense?**
10 baseballs costs $50. This is too much money. He cannot buy 10. ✓

Coach Roberts can buy no more than 9 baseballs.

1. To go on vacation this summer, the 3 members of the Garner family must save more than $1,500. How much must each member save?

   Choose a variable, and write the inequality. Use d for dollars.

   $d \bullet 3 \blacksquare 1,500 >$

   $3d \blacksquare 1,500 >$

   Solve the inequality.

   $\dfrac{3d}{3} \blacksquare \dfrac{1,500}{3} >$

   $d > \blacksquare$ 500

   Each member must save more than $\blacksquare$. 500

2. A caterer wants to make at least $2,000 at an event with 50 people. How much should the caterer charge per person?

   Choose a variable, and write the inequality. Use m for money.

   $m \bullet 50 \blacksquare 2,000 \geq$

   $50m \blacksquare 2,000 \geq$

   Solve the inequality.

   $\dfrac{50m}{50} \blacksquare \dfrac{2,000}{50} \geq$

   $m \geq \blacksquare$ 40

   The caterer should charge at least $\blacksquare$ per person. 40

Practice

Write an inequality for each problem. Then, solve the inequality.

1. Maria wants to buy tickets to a concert. How many $12 tickets can she buy if she wants to spend less than $48.00? $12t < 48$; $t < 4$ tickets

2. Chris decides to wash cars to earn money for a ski trip. He charges $20.00 per car. How many cars will he have to wash to earn at least $300.00? $20c \geq 300$; $c \geq 15$ cars

3. Jason has to write a report that is at least 15 pages long. He has written 7 pages already. How many more pages will he need to write?

   $7 + p \geq 15$; $p \geq 8$ pages

Cooperative Learning

4. Explain to a partner how you solve the inequality in number 2 in **Practice.** Possible answer: Write the inequality. Choose c for number of cars. $20c \geq 300$. Simplify. $c \geq 15$. Chris must wash 15 or more cars.

5. Write a problem that can be solved with an inequality. Ask a partner to solve. Answers will vary.

More practice is provided in Exercise 42 of the Workbook.

Getting Started
Have groups of
students role play
the problem in
Example 1.

7·9 ▶ **Application: Using Solutions**

The shaded area of a graph shows all the solutions of an inequality. It also contains the answers to problems.

▶ **EXAMPLE 1**

Malik has $10.00 to buy milk and bread for the week. Milk costs $2.00 a gallon. Bread costs $1.00 a loaf. Can he buy 3 gallons of milk and 1 loaf of bread?

The inequality shows how much he can buy. Use *m* for the number of gallons of milk. Use *b* for the number of loaves of bread.

$$2m + 1b \leq 10$$

The shaded area of the graph shows the ordered pairs of (milk, bread) that make the inequality true.

Use the ordered pair (3, 1) to show 3 gallons of milk and 1 loaf of bread.

Locate (3, 1) on the graph. (3, 1) is in the shaded area.

Malik can buy 3 gallons of milk and 1 loaf of bread.

▶ **EXAMPLE 2**

Jaye wants a workout that will burn at least 300 calories. Jogging burns 12 calories a minute. Swimming burns 6 calories a minute. Is 10 minutes of jogging and 20 minutes of swimming enough exercise?

The inequality shows how much of each exercise she needs. Use *j* for jogging and *s* for swimming.

$$12j + 6s \geq 300$$

The shaded area of the graph shows the ordered pairs of (jog, swim) that make the inequality true.

Use (10, 20) to show 10 minutes of jogging and 20 minutes of swimming.

Locate (10, 20) on the graph. It is not in the shaded area.

This is not enough exercise.

Try These

The hockey team needs at least 20 more points to make the playoffs. The team gets 2 points for a win and 1 point for a tie. Use the ordered pair (wins, ties) to show the amount of each.

$$2w + 1t \geq 20$$

Use the graph of the solution of the inequality to answer the questions.

1. Will the team make the playoffs with 6 wins and 6 ties?
   Use (■, ■) to show the wins and ties.
   6 6
   Locate the point on the graph.

   (6, 6) ■ in the shaded area. is not

   The team ■ make the playoffs.
   will not

2. Will the team make the playoffs with 8 wins and 4 ties?
   Use (■, ■) to show the wins and ties.
   8 4
   Locate the point on the graph.

   (8, 4) is in the shaded area.

   The team ■ make the playoffs.
   will

Practice

Liu has less than $3.00 in coins. All of the coins are nickels or dimes. The ordered pair (nickels, dimes) tells the number she has of each. Use the graph of the inequality to answer the questions.
$.05n + .10d < 3.00$

1. Could Liu have 10 nickels and 20 dimes?
   Yes; (10, 20) is in the shaded region.
2. Could Liu have 20 nickels and 25 dimes?
   No; (20, 25) is not in the shaded region.
3. Could Liu have 10 nickels and 25 dimes?
   No; (10, 25) is on the dotted line and not in the shaded region.

4. Possible answer: Use (10, 20) to show nickels and dimes;
   Locate the point on the graph; (10, 20) is in the shaded region.

Cooperative Learning

4. Explain to a partner how you solve number **1** in **Practice**. See above.

5. Choose new numbers of nickels and dimes. Ask a partner if Liu could have that number of coins. Check the work. Answers will vary.

Summary

You can graph the solution of an inequality containing one variable on a number line.
You can solve an inequality with two variables by adding or subtracting the same number from both sides.
You can solve an inequality by multiplying or dividing both sides by the same number.
Multiplying or dividing both sides of an inequality by a negative number changes the inequality.
You can solve inequalities that contain more than one operation by undoing each operation. Undo addition or subtraction. Then, undo multiplication or division.
You can use coordinate planes to graph the solution of inequalities with two variables.
The points on a dotted line are not solutions of an inequality. Points on a solid line are solutions.
You can solve problems by writing and using graphs of inequalities.

More vocabulary review is provided in Exercise 61 of the Classroom Resource Binder.

graph of a solution
inequality
≤
≥

Vocabulary Review

Complete the sentences with words from the box.

  1. Use the symbol ____ to show "greater than or equal to" or "at least." ≥

  2. The ____ is the set of points on a number line or coordinate plane that shows the solutions of an equation or inequality. graph of a solution

  3. A statement that shows "greater than," "greater than or equal to," "less than," or "less than or equal to" is an ____. inequality

  4. Use the symbol ____ to show "less than or equal to" or "no more than." ≤

Chapter Quiz   More **assessment** is provided in the Classroom Resource Binder.

Solve each inequality. Then, graph the solution on a number line.
See Additional Answers p. 474.

1. $x > 4$

2. $b \leq -7$

3. $y \geq 6$

4. $b + 2 \leq 6$
$b \leq 4$

5. $x - 1 > 5$
$x > 6$

6. $\frac{x}{3} < 4$
$x < 12$

7. $-5b \geq 10$
$b \leq -2$

8. $2g - 2 > 6$
$g > 4$

9. $-6m + 2 \leq 14$
$m \geq -2$

Tell whether each point is a solution of $y \leq 3x - 1$.

10. $(2, 3)$ yes

11. $(-1, 2)$ no

12. $(2, 5)$ yes

Graph the solution of each inequality.   See Additional Answers p. 474.

13. $y < -3x + 4$

14. $y > \frac{2}{3}x - 2$

15. $y \geq x - 3$

16. $y \leq 2x + 1$

17. $y < \frac{1}{2}x + 2$

18. $y > -x$

Write the inequality. Then, solve it.

19. Tina has put 15 of her old CDs in a storage crate. How many more CDs can she store in the crate if it can hold no more than 23 CDs?
$15 + c \leq 23$; $c \leq 8$; Tina can store up to 8 more CDs.

Use the graph of the inequality to answer the question.

20. Bob is sending postcards and letters. He has $10.00 to spend on stamps. Stamps for letters cost $.33 each. Stamps for postcards cost $.21 each. The ordered pair (letters, postcards) tells how many of each. The inequality gives the ordered pairs that have a total cost less than or equal to $10.00.

Can he send 15 letters and 20 postcards?
Yes; (15, 20) is in the shaded region.

$.33l + .21p \leq 10.00$

Additional Practice for this chapter is provided on p. 419 of this text.

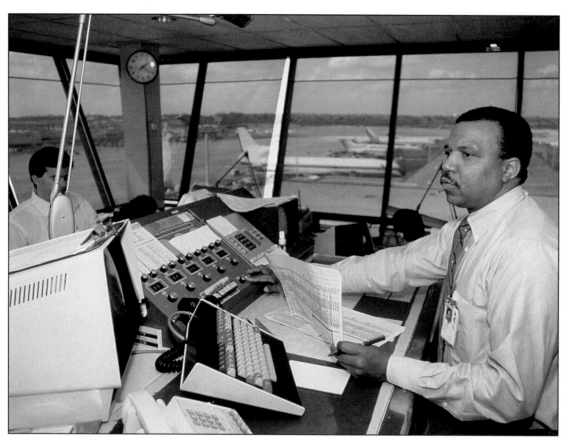

An air traffic controller keeps track of where planes are, at all times as they approach the airport. The controller can use a system of equations to do this. Why is it important to keep track of the planes?

Learning Objectives

- Identify a system of linear equations.

- Solve a system of linear equations.

- Identify a system of linear inequalities.

- Solve a system of linear inequalities.

- Use a calculator to check the solution of a system of linear equations.

- Solve problems using systems of linear equations.

- Apply concepts and skills to find minimum and maximum value.

Words to Know

system of linear equations	two or more linear equations with the same variables
eliminating a variable	removing one variable in a system of equations
system of linear inequalities	two or more linear inequalities with the same variables
maximum	largest number in a group
minimum	smallest number in a group

Timetable Project

Train A leaves the station at noon and travels 30 miles per hour. Use the equation $d = 30t$ to make a timetable that shows how far the train has traveled by 1:00 P.M., 2:00 P.M., 3:00 P.M., 4:00 P.M., and 5:00 P.M.

Train A: $d = 30t$	
Time	Distance
noon	0 miles
1:00 P.M.	30 miles
2:00 P.M.	60 miles

Train B leaves the station at 1:00 P.M. and travels 40 miles per hour. Use the equation $d = 40t$ to make a timetable to show how far the train has traveled by 1:00 P.M., 2:00 P.M., 3:00 P.M., 4:00 P.M., and 5:00 P.M.

Graph both equations on the same grid. At what time do trains A and B meet? How do you know?

The trains meet at 4:00 P.M. That is the time at which each has traveled 120 miles. The lines of the graph cross at (4:00 P.M., 120 miles).

Project See the Classroom Resource Binder for a scoring rubric to assess this project.

More practice is provided in Exercise 43 of the Workbook.

Getting Started
On the chalkboard, write the equation $y = 3x + 1$. Ask students to graph the equation. Elicit that the points on the graph are solutions to the equation.

Two linear equations with the same variables are a **system of linear equations.** The solution to the system is the point where the two lines cross or intersect.

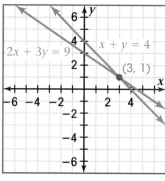

1 solution

no solution

Math Fact
(3, 1) is a point on the graph of $x + y = 4$ and $2x + 3y = 9$.

The solution of the system $x + y = 4$ and $2x + 3y = 9$ is (3, 1). The ordered pair for this point makes both equations true.

Check
Substitute (3, 1) into each equation.

$$x + y = 4$$
$$3 + 1 \ ? \ 4$$
$$4 = 4 \text{ true}$$

$$2x + 3y = 9$$
$$2(3) + 3(1) \ ? \ 9$$
$$9 = 9 \text{ true}$$

▶ **EXAMPLE 1**

Tell whether $(-2, -1)$ is the solution of the system.

$$2y - 3x = 4$$
$$x + 2y = -4$$

Substitute -2 for x and -1 for y.

$$2y - 3x = 4$$
$$2(-1) - 3(-2) \ ? \ 4$$
$$-2 + 6 \ ? \ 4$$
$$4 = 4 \text{ true}$$

$$x + 2y = -4$$
$$-2 + 2(-1) \ ? \ -4$$
$$-2 - 2 \ ? \ -4$$
$$-4 = -4 \text{ true}$$

$(-2, -1)$ is the solution of the system.

▶ **EXAMPLE 2**

Tell whether (2, 3) is the solution of the system.

$$x + y = 5$$
$$x - y = 1$$

Substitute 2 for x and 3 for y.

$$x + y = 5$$
$$2 + 3 \ ? \ 5$$
$$5 = 5 \text{ true}$$

$$x - y = 1$$
$$2 - 3 \ ? \ 1$$
$$-1 \ ? \ 1$$

(2, 3) is not the solution of the system.

Try These

Tell whether the ordered pair is the solution of the system.

1. $(-2, 0)$; $x = -2$
$-x + y = 2$

Substitute $\blacksquare$ for x and $\blacksquare$ for y. (with -2 over first box, 0 over second box)

$x = -2$ $-x + y = 2$
$-2\blacksquare = -2$ $-(\blacksquare) + \blacksquare 0? 2$ (with -2 under box)
true $2\blacksquare = 2$
  true

(is)
$(-2, 0)\ \blacksquare$ the solution of the
system.

2. $(6, 1)$; $\frac{1}{2}x + y = 4$
$-2x + y = -6$

Substitute $\blacksquare$ for x and $\blacksquare$ for y. (with 6 over first box, 1 over second box)

$\frac{1}{2}x + y = 4$ $-2x + y = -6$
$\frac{1}{2}(\blacksquare) + \blacksquare 1? 4$ $-2(\blacksquare) + \blacksquare 1? -6$ (with 6 under first box, 6 under second box)
$4\blacksquare = 4$ $-11\blacksquare \neq -6$
true

(is not)
$(6, 1)\ \blacksquare$ the solution of the
system.

Practice

Tell whether the ordered pair is the solution of the system.

1. $(1, 3)$; $x + y = 4$ yes
$2x + y = 5$

2. $(2, -2)$; $y = 2$ no
$2x + y = 6$

3. $(6, 3)$; $x + y = 9$ no
$-2x + y = 0$

4. $(-1, -3)$; $3x + y = -6$ yes
$2x - y = 1$

5. $(2, -1)$; $3x + 2y = 4$ yes
$-x + 3y = -5$

6. $(4, 6)$; $2x - y = 2$ no
$4x + 3y = 24$

7. $(2, 0)$; $-2x + y = -4$ yes
$\frac{1}{2}x + y = 1$

8. $(3, 1)$; $x + 6y = 15$ no
$-2x + 3y = -3$

9. Possible answer: Substitute 2 for x and 0 for y in both equations.
Equation 1: $-2(2) + 0 = -4$; $-4 = -4$ true.
Equation 2: $\frac{1}{2}(2) + 0 = 1$; $1 = 1$ true. $(2, 0)$ makes both
equations true. So, $(2, 0)$ is the solution of the system.

Cooperative Learning

9. Explain to a partner how to tell if the ordered pair is the solution
of the system in number **7** in **Practice.** See above.

10. Work with a partner to tell if $(3, 6)$ is the solution of the system
in number **3** in **Practice.** You check one equation and have your
partner check the other. $(3, 6)$ is the solution. Check that students substitute for the
correct variables.

More practice is provided in Exercises 43 and 45 of the Workbook.

Getting Started
Review the
concept that the
graph of equations
which have a common
solution will intersect.

8·2 ▶ **Solving Systems by Graphing**

You can find the solution of a system of equations by graphing. Graph each equation on the same set of axes. Then, find the point where the lines intersect.

▶ **EXAMPLE 1**

Solve by graphing. $y = x + 2$
                     $y = 2x + 4$

First, graph $y = x + 2$.

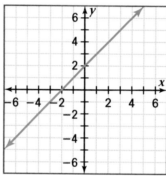

Then, graph $y = 2x + 4$ on the same axes.

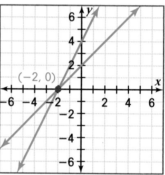

The lines intersect at $(-2, 0)$. $(-2, 0)$ is the solution of the system.

▶ **EXAMPLE 2**

Solve by graphing. $y = 3x + 4$
                     $y = 3x - 5$

First, graph $y = 3x + 4$.

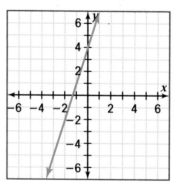

Then, graph $y = 3x - 5$ on the same axes

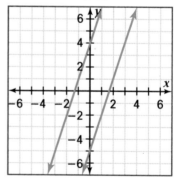

The lines do not intersect. The system does not have a solution.

Try These

Graph each system of linear equations to find the solution. Then, check.

1. $y = -2$
$y = 3x + 1$

Graph $y = -2$.
Then, graph
$y = 3x + 1$ on
the same axes.
Find the
intersection.

$(\blacksquare, \blacksquare)$
$\;\;-1\;\;-2$

Check:
$-2\blacksquare = -2$ true
$-2\blacksquare = 3(\blacksquare) + 1$ true
$\qquad\qquad -1$

2. $y = x - 2$
$y = -\dfrac{1}{2}x + 4$

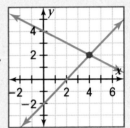

Graph $y = x - 2$.
Then, graph
$y = -\dfrac{1}{2}x + 4$ on
the same axes.
Find the
intersection.

$(\blacksquare, \blacksquare)$
$\;\;4\;\;2$

Check:
$2\blacksquare = \blacksquare - 2$ true
$2\blacksquare = \dfrac{4}{2}\dfrac{1}{4}(\blacksquare) + 4$ true

Practice

Graph each system of linear equations to find the solution. See Additional Answers, p. 475.

1. $y = x + 1$ $(-1, 0)$
$y = 3x + 3$

2. $y = x - 2$ $(-4, -6)$
$y = 2x + 2$

3. $y = -1$ $(1, -1)$
$y = 2x - 3$

4. $y = x - 2$ no solution
$y = x + 4$

5. $y = -2x - 3$ no solution
$y = -2x + 2$

6. $y = 2$ $(6, 2)$
$y = x - 4$

7. $y = x + 5$ $(-6, -1)$
$y = \dfrac{1}{2}x + 2$

8. $y = x - 5$ $(6, 1)$
$y = -\dfrac{1}{2}x + 4$

9. $y = x + 2$ $(-1, 1)$
$y = -x$

10. Possible answer: Graph equation 1: Graph the y-intercept -2; Move up 1 and right 1; Draw a dot at $(1, -1)$. Graph equation 2: Graph the y-intercept; Move up 2 and right 1; Draw a dot at $(1, 4)$.

Cooperative Learning Find the intersection at $(-4, -6)$.

10. Explain to a partner how to graph to solve the system in number **2** in **Practice.** See above.

11. Write the equation $y = x + 2$. Then, write another equation. Have a partner graph the equations to find the solution of the system. Check the work. Answers will vary.

8·3 ▶ Using Substitution

Getting Started
Present students with the
equations $y = 2x$ and $y = 4$.
Ask students to find the
solution to the system. (2,4)
Invite a volunteer to explain
how he or she found the
solution.

You can rewrite a system of equations with two variables as a system with one variable. This is called **eliminating a variable.** Then, you can solve for the other variable. You can do this by substituting an equivalent expression for one of the variables.

$$y = x + 3 \rightarrow y \text{ and } x + 3 \text{ and are equivalent.}$$
$$y = 5 \quad\quad \rightarrow y \text{ and } 5 \text{ are equivalent.}$$

So, substitute 5 for y, or substitute $x + 3$ for y.

$$5 = x + 3 \text{ or } x + 3 = 5 \rightarrow x = 2 \text{ and } y = 5$$

▶ **EXAMPLE 1**

Solve. $y = x + 4$
$\quad\quad\quad y = 3x$

$y = x + 4$ and $y = 3x$

Substitute $3x$ for y. $3x = x + 4$

Solve for x. $2x = 4$

$x = 2$

Use $x = 2$ to find y in either equation. $y = x + 4$

Check $y = 2 + 4$

$y = x + 4$	$y = 3x$	$y = 6$
$6 = 2 + 4$	$6 = 3(2)$	
$6 = 6$ true	$6 = 6$ true	

(2, 6) is the solution of the system.

▶ **EXAMPLE 2**

Solve. $y = -x - 5$
$\quad\quad\quad y = x + 3$

$y = -x - 5$ and $y = x + 3$

Math Fact
You could also substitute
$-x - 5$ for y.

Substitute $x + 3$ for y. $x + 3 = -x - 5$

Solve for x. $2x = -8$

$x = -4$

Use $x = -4$ to find y in either equation. $y = -x - 5$

$y = -(-4)-5$

$y = -1$

(−4, −1) is the solution of the system.

Try These

Solve each system of linear equations.

1. $y = -x - 3$
$x = -2$

$y = -x - 3$
$x = -2$

Substitute ■ for x. $\quad$ $y = -(\blacksquare) - 3$ $\quad\overset{-2}{}$

Solve for y. $\qquad\qquad y = \blacksquare - 1$

Solve for x. $\qquad\qquad x = \blacksquare - 2$

($\blacksquare$, $\blacksquare$) $-2, -1$

Check:

$x = -2$ and $\qquad\qquad y = -x - 3$

$\qquad\qquad\qquad\qquad -1\blacksquare = -(\blacksquare) - 3 -2$

$-2\blacksquare = -2$ true $\quad -1\blacksquare = \blacksquare$ true -1

($\blacksquare$, $\blacksquare$) is the solution of the
system. $-2, -1$

2. $y = -x + 15$
$y = 4x$

$y = -x + 15$
$y = 4x$

$\overset{4x}{}$
Substitute ■ for y. $\quad 4x\blacksquare = -x + 15$

Solve for x. $\qquad\qquad x = \blacksquare\, 3$

Substitute 3 for x $\qquad y = -x + 15$
to find y in either $\qquad y = -(\blacksquare) + 15$
equation. $\qquad\qquad\qquad\qquad\overset{3}{}$

($\blacksquare$, $\blacksquare$) 3, 12 $\qquad\qquad y = \blacksquare\, 12$

Check:

$y = -x + 15$ and $\quad y = 4x$

$12\blacksquare = \frac{1}{12}(\blacksquare) + 15$ $\quad 12\blacksquare = 4(\blacksquare)\, 3$

$12\blacksquare = \blacksquare$ true $\qquad 12\blacksquare = \blacksquare$ true 12

($\blacksquare$, $\blacksquare$) is the solution of the
system. 3, 12

Practice

Solve each system of linear equations.

1. $y = x + 2$ $\;(2, 4)$
$y = 2x$

2. $y = -2x + 6$ $\;(2, 2)$
$y = x$

3. $y = -x - 5$ $\;(-3, -2)$
$x = -3$

4. $y = x - 6$ $\;(2, -4)$
$y = -4$

5. $y = -x - 4$ $\;(-3, -1)$
$y = x + 2$

6. $y = x - 3$ $\;(4, 1)$
$y = -x + 5$

7. Possible answer: Write equation 1: $y = x - 6$. Substitute -4 for y:
$-4 = x - 6$. Solve for x: $x = 2$. You already know the value for y

Cooperative Learning

from equation 2: $y = -4$. Check. $-4 = 2 - 6$ true. $-4 = -4$ true.

7. Explain to a partner how to find the solution in number **4**
in **Practice.** See above.

8. Write a system of equations. Make one equation $x = 3$. Write
another equation that uses both x and y. Have a partner solve the
system by substitution. Check the work. Answers will vary. Check students' substitution.

Getting Started
Remind students that when they add or subtract expressions with variables, the variables must be the same. Give the example 4 apples + 6 apples + 2 oranges = 10 apples and 2 oranges. Ask volunteers for other examples.

8·4 ▶ Using Addition or Subtraction

Substitution is one way to eliminate a variable in a system of equations. You can also use addition or subtraction to eliminate one of the variables and solve the system. Use addition when the coefficients of one of the variables are opposites.

▶ **EXAMPLE 1**

Solve. $-x + 2y = 8$
$3x - 2y = 4$

The coefficients of y are 2 and −2.
Add the equations.

$$-x + 2y = 8$$
$$\underline{+3x - 2y = 4}$$
$$2x + 0 = 12$$

Solve for x.

$$2x = 12$$
$$x = 6$$

Check
$-x + 2y = 8$
$-6 + 2(7) = 8$
$8 = 8$ true
$3x - 2y = 4$
$3(6) - 2(7) = 4$
$4 = 4$ true

Substitute 6 for x in either equation to solve for y.

$$-x + 2y = 8$$
$$-6 + 2y = 8$$
$$2y = 14$$
$$y = 7$$

(6, 7) is the solution of the system.

Use subtraction if one of the variables has the same coefficient in both equations.

▶ **EXAMPLE 2**

Solve. $x - 2y = -6$
$x + y = 3$

Math Fact
$-(x + y = 3)$ means
$-x - y = -3$.

The coefficients of x are the same. Subtract the equations.

$$x - 2y = -6 \rightarrow x - 2y = -6$$
$$-(x + y = 3) \rightarrow \underline{-x - y = -3}$$
$$0 - 3y = -9$$

Solve for y.

$$-3y = -9$$
$$y = 3$$

Check
$x - 2y = -6$
$0 - 2(3) = -6$
$-6 = -6$ true
$x + y = 3$
$0 + 3 = 3$
$3 = 3$ true

Substitute 3 for y in either equation to solve for x.

$$x - 2y = -6$$
$$x - 2(3) = -6$$
$$x = 0$$

(0, 3) is the solution of the system.

Try These

Solve each system of equations.

1. $2x + y = -9$
$-2x - 3y = 3$

The coefficients of $\quad 2x + \quad y = -9$
x are opposites. $\quad + -2x - \quad 3y = 3$
Add ■ the equations. $\quad$ ■$x - $■$y = -6$
Solve for ■. y $\quad$ $\dfrac{0 \quad -2■}{-2} \, y = \dfrac{■-6}{-2}$
$\quad y = ■ 3$

Substitute ■ for y. $\quad 2x + y = -9$
$\quad 2x + 3■ = -9$

Solve for ■. x $\quad 2x = ■-12$
$\quad \dfrac{}{-6} \quad x = ■-6$

Check: $\quad 2(■) + 3■ = -9$
$\dfrac{-6 \ 3}{}$ $\quad -2(■) - 3(■) = 3$
$\dfrac{}{-6} \quad \dfrac{}{3}$
(■, ■) is the solution of
the system.

2. $2x - y = 1$
$x - y = 3$

The coefficients of $\quad 2x - \quad y = \quad 1$
y are the same. $\quad \dfrac{-x + \quad y = -3}{}$
Subtract ■ the equations. $\quad x + 0y = \quad ■-2$
Solve for ■. x $\quad x = \quad ■-2$
Substitute ■ for x. $-2 \quad 2x - y = \quad 1$
Solve for ■. $\quad -2 \, 2(■) - y = \quad 1$
$\quad y$ $\quad -4■ - y = \quad 1$
$\quad -y = \quad 5$
$\quad \dfrac{-2 \quad -5}{} y = \quad ■-5$

Check: $\quad 2(■) - (■) = \quad 1$
$\dfrac{-2 \ -5}{}$ $\quad -2■ - (■) = \quad 3$
$\quad \dfrac{}{-5}$
(■, ■) is the solution of
the system.

Practice

Solve each system of equations.

1. $x + y = 6$ $\quad$ (5, 1)
$\quad x - y = 4$

2. $x - y = -3$ $\quad$ (3, 6)
$\quad x + y = 9$

3. $2x + y = -5$ $\quad$ (−2, −1)
$\quad 2x - y = -3$

4. $2x + y = -6$ $\quad$ (−4, 2)
$\quad 3x + y = -10$

5. $4x - y = 5$ $\quad$ (4, 11)
$\quad x - y = -7$

6. $3x + 6y = 48$ $\quad$ (2, 7)
$\quad -5x + 6y = 32$

7. Possible answer: Add the equations: $4x = -8$; $x = -2$;
Substitute -2 for x: $2(-2) + y = -5$; $y = -1$. Check the solution
$(-2, -1)$: $2(-2) + (-1) = -5$ true; $2(-2) - (-1) = -3$ true.

Cooperative Learning

7. Explain to a partner how to use addition to find the solution of
the system of equations in number **3** in **Practice.** See above.

8. Ask a partner to explain what the solution to number **5** in
Practice means. Possible answer: (4, 11) is the point where the two lines cross. (4, 11) is a
solution to both equations.

8-5 ▶ Using Multiplication

Sometimes, you have to multiply to make the coefficients of one of the variables opposites. Then, you can eliminate a variable by adding.

▶ **EXAMPLE 1**

Solve. $3x + y = 2$
$ x + 2y = 4$

Remember
Make coefficients of
x opposites.

Multiply by -3.

$$
\begin{array}{rcl}
3x + y = 2 & \rightarrow & 3x + y = 2 \\
-3(x + 2y = 4) & \rightarrow & -3x - 6y = -12 \\
\hline
 & & 0 - 5y = -10
\end{array}
$$

Add the equations.

Solve for y.

$$-5y = -10$$
$$y = 2$$

Check
$3x + y = 2$
$3(0) + 2 = 2$
$ 2 = 2$ true

$x + 2y = 4$
$0 + 2(2) = 4$
$ 4 = 4$ true

Substitute 2 for y in
either equation.

Solve for x.

$$x + 2y = 4$$
$$x + 2(2) = 4$$
$$x + 4 = 4$$
$$x = 0$$

$(0, 2)$ is the solution of the system.

▶ **EXAMPLE 2**

Solve. $-x + 2y = -4$
$ -2x + 3y = -2$

Remember
Make coefficients of
x opposites.

Multiply by -2.

$$
\begin{array}{rcl}
-2(-x + 2y = -4) & \rightarrow & 2x - 4y = 8 \\
-2x + 3y = -2 & \rightarrow & -2x + 3y = -2 \\
\hline
 & & 0 - y = 6
\end{array}
$$

Add the equations.

Solve for y.

$$-y = 6$$
$$y = -6$$

Check
$-x + 2y = -4$
$-(-8) + 2(-6) = -4$
$ -4 = -4$ true

$-2x + 3y = -2$
$-2(-8) + 3(-6) = -2$
$ -2 = -2$ true

Substitute -6 for y
in either equation.

$$-x + 2(-6) = -4$$

Solve for x.

$$-x - 12 = -4$$
$$x = -8$$

$(-8, -6)$ is the solution of the system.

Try These

Solve each system of linear equations.

1. $2x - 3y = 5$ and $3x + y = 2$

Make coefficients of y opposites.

Multiply $3x + y = 2$ by 3.

Add the equations.

Solve for 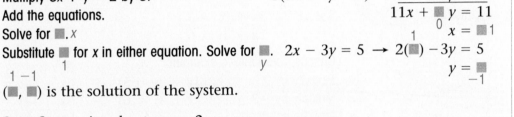. x

Substitute ■ for x in either equation. Solve for ■. y

  1 −1

(■, ■) is the solution of the system.

$$2x - 3y = 5 \rightarrow 2x - {}_3 3y = 5$$
$$3(3x + y = 2) \rightarrow 9x + \blacksquare y = \blacksquare 6$$
$$11x + \blacksquare y = 11$$
$$x = \blacksquare 1$$
$$2x - 3y = 5 \rightarrow 2(\blacksquare) - 3y = 5$$
$$y = \blacksquare$$
       −1

2. $2x + 3y = -4$ and $x + y = -2$

Make coefficients of x ■. opposites

Multiply $x + y = -2$ by ■. −2

Add ■ the equations.

Solve for ■. y

Substitute ■ for y in either equation. Solve for ■. x
  0

  0

(−2, ■) is the solution of the system.

$$2x + 3y = -4 \rightarrow {}_2 2x + 3y = -4$$
$$-2(x + y = -2) \rightarrow \blacksquare x - 2y = 4$$
$$0x + \blacksquare y = \blacksquare 0$$
$$y = \blacksquare 0$$
$$x + y = -2 \rightarrow x + \blacksquare = -2$$
$$x = -2$$

Practice

Solve each system of linear equations.

1. $4x + y = 2$ (0, 2)
    $x + 2y = 4$

2. $-x - 5y = -6$ (1, 1)
    $3x + y = 4$

3. $-3x + 2y = 7$ (−3, −1)
    $x + y = -4$

4. $2x + 3y = 5$ (1, 1)
    $-x + 2y = 1$

5. $-x + 2y = -6$ (−2, −4)
    $4x - 3y = 4$

6. $4x + y = -6$ (−1, −2)
    $3x - 2y = 1$

Cooperative Learning

7. Explain to a partner how to use multiplication to help find the solution in number **6** in **Practice**. Possible answer: Use multiplication to make the y-coefficients opposites. Multiply first equation by 2, and then solve by adding the equations.

8. Take turns with a partner to solve the system of equations on the right. Check each other's work.

    $x + y = 3$
    $2x + y = 4$

The solution is (1, 2).

More practice is provided in Exercise 47 of the Workbook.

8-6 ▷ **Using More Than One Equation**

Sometimes, you have to multiply both equations. Choose a variable to eliminate. Then, multiply both equations so the coefficients of this variable are opposites.

▶ **EXAMPLE 1**

Solve. $3x + 2y = 5$
          $2x + 4y = 6$

Choose a variable to eliminate: x

Multiply by 2. $2(3x + 2y = 5) \rightarrow$ $6x + 4y = 10$
Multiply by −3. $-3(2x + 4y = 6) \rightarrow$ $\underline{-6x - 12y = -18}$
Add the equations. $0x - 8y = -8$

Check
  $3x + 2y = 5$
$3(1) + 2(1) = 5$
   $3 + 2 = 5$
       $5 = 5$ true

  $2x + 4y = 6$
$2(1) + 4(1) = 6$
   $2 + 4 = 6$
       $6 = 6$ true

Solve for y. $-8y = -8$
                                  $y = 1$

Substitute 1 for y. $2x + 4(1) = 6$
Solve for x. $2x + 4 = 6$
                              $x = 1$

$(1, 1)$ is the solution of the system.

▶ **EXAMPLE 2**

Solve. $3x + 6y = 12$
          $x + 4y = 6$

Choose a variable to eliminate: y

Multiply by −2. $-2(3x + 6y = 12) \rightarrow$ $-6x - 12y = -24$
Multiply by 3. $3(x + 4y = 6) \rightarrow$ $\underline{3x + 12y = 18}$
Add the equations. $-3x + 0y = -6$

Check
  $3x + 6y = 12$
$3(2) + 6(1) = 12$
   $6 + 6 = 12$
       $12 = 12$ true

  $x + 4y = 6$
$2 + 4(1) = 6$
   $2 + 4 = 6$
       $6 = 6$ true

Solve for x. $-3x = -6$
                                  $x = 2$

Substitute 2 for x. $3(2) + 6y = 12$
Solve for y. $6 + 6y = 12$
                              $y = 1$

$(2, 1)$ is the solution of the system.

Try These

Solve each system.

1. $3x - 4y = -6$
$-5x + 3y = -1$

Choose a variable to eliminate: y
Multiply by 3. 9 ▪$x - 12y = -18$
Multiply by 4. -20 ▪$x + 12y = -4$
Add. $-11x + 0y = $ ▪-22

Solve for ▪. x $\qquad$ $-11x = -22$
$x = $ ▪ 2
$\qquad\qquad\qquad\qquad\qquad$ 2
Substitute ▪ for x. $3(2) - 4y = -6$
Solve for ▪. y $\qquad -4y = $ ▪-12
$\qquad\qquad\qquad\qquad$ $y = $ ▪ 3
$\qquad$ 2 3
(▪, ▪) is the solution of the system.

2. $2x + 3y = -1$
$-5x + 2y = 12$

Choose a variable to eliminate: x 15
Multiply by 5. $10x + $ ▪$y = -5$
Multiply by 2. $-10x + $ ▪$y = 24$ 4
Add. $0x + 19y = 19$

Solve for ▪. y $\qquad\qquad$ $19y = 19$
$y = $ ▪ 1
$\qquad\qquad\qquad$ 1
Substitute ▪ for y. $2x + 3(1) = -1$
Solve for ▪. x $\qquad\qquad$ $2x = $ ▪-4
$\qquad\qquad\qquad\qquad$ $x = $ ▪-2
$\qquad$ -2 1
(▪, ▪) is the solution of the system.

7. Possible answer: Make the y-coefficients opposites. Multiply equation 1 by -2. Multiply equation 2 by 3.
Add the multiplied equations. $x = -5$. Substitute -5 for x in equation 1. Solve for y. $y = 9$. Check the solution.

Practice

Solve each system.

1. $3x + 2y = 10$ $(6, -4)$
$4x + 3y = 12$

2. $4x + 3y = 3$ $(0, 1)$
$3x - 5y = -5$

3. $5x + 3y = 2$ $(-5, 9)$
$3x + 2y = 3$

4. $5x - 3y = 7$ $(2, 1)$
$2x + 4y = 8$

5. $2x + 3y = -1$ $(-2, 1)$
$5x - 2y = -12$

6. $3x + 2y = -6$ $(-2, 0)$
$4x - 7y = -8$

Cooperative Learning

7. Explain to a partner the steps to find the solution in number **3**
in **Practice.** See above.

8. Write $2x - y = 2$ and $3x + 3y = -6$ on your paper. Solve by
eliminating one of the variables. Have a partner solve by
eliminating the other variable. The solution is $(0, -2)$.

Getting Started
Have students
graph the system
$y = -x + 2$ and
$y = x$. Remind students that
the solution is where the
lines intersect.

8·7 Systems of Inequalities

You have learned that the solution of a linear inequality is an area of ordered pairs. The solution of a **system of linear inequalities** is the area of ordered pairs that make both inequalities true.

$y \geq -x + 1$

$y < 2x - 1$

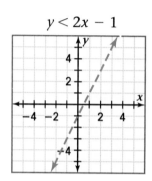

$y \geq -x + 1$
$y < 2x - 1$

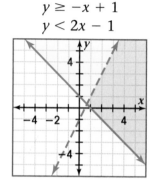

All points in the overlapping shaded area in the last graph are solutions of the system. The ordered pairs in this darker shaded area make both inequalities true.

EXAMPLE 1

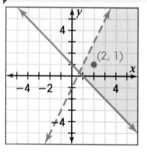

Tell whether (2, 1) is a solution of the system.

$y \geq -x + 1$
$y < 2x - 1$

Substitute 2 for x and 1 for y in each inequality.

$y \geq -x + 1$
$1 \geq -(2) + 1$
$1 \geq -2 + 1$
$1 \geq -1$ true

$y < 2x - 1$
$1 < 2(2) - 1$
$1 < 4 - 1$
$1 < 3$ true

(2, 1) is a solution.

EXAMPLE 2

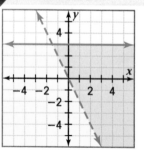

Tell whether (−1, 2) is a solution of the system.

$y \leq 3$
$y > -2x$

Substitute −1 for x and 2 for y in each inequality.

$y \leq 3$
$2 \leq 3$ true

$y > -2x$
$2 > -2(-1)$
$2 > 2$ false

(−1, 2) is not a solution.

Tell whether each ordered pair is a solution of the system.

1. (3, 4); $y > 3$
$\quad\quad\quad\ y \leq x + 1$

Substitute $\blacksquare$ for x and $\blacksquare$ for y in each inequality.
<small>3 for x, 4 for y</small>

$\quad\quad y > 3$
$\quad\quad 4\ \blacksquare > 3$ true

$\quad\quad y \leq x + 1$
$\quad\quad 4\ \blacksquare \leq \blacksquare 3 + 1$
$\quad\quad 4\ \blacksquare \leq \blacksquare 4$ true

<small>is</small>
(3, 4) $\blacksquare$ a solution.

2. (3, −1); $y < 2x + 4$
$\quad\quad\quad\quad\ y > 2x - 3$

Substitute $\blacksquare$ for x and $\blacksquare$ for y in each inequality.
<small>3 for x, −1 for y</small>

$\quad\quad y < 2x + 4$
$\quad\quad -1\ \blacksquare\ ?\ 2(\blacksquare)3 + 4$
$\quad\quad -1\ \blacksquare < \blacksquare$ true
$\quad\quad\quad\quad\quad 10$

$\quad\quad y > 2x - 3$
$\quad\quad -1\ \blacksquare\ ?\ 2(\blacksquare)3 - 3$
$\quad\quad -1\ \blacksquare > \blacksquare 3$ false

<small>is not</small>
(3, −1) $\blacksquare$ a solution.

Practice

Tell whether each ordered pair is a solution of the system.

1. (2, 0); $y < x + 5$ <small>yes</small>
$\quad\quad\quad\quad\ y \leq x - 2$

2. (−2, 3); $y > x + 4$ <small>no</small>
$\quad\quad\quad\quad\quad\ y < 2x + 5$

3. (1, 3); $y > 2$ <small>yes</small>
$\quad\quad\quad\quad\ y \leq x + 3$

4. (−2, −2); $y < -2x + 3$ <small>yes</small>
$\quad\quad\quad\quad\quad\ y \leq 2x + 3$

5. (−1, 4); $y > 2x - 6$ <small>no</small>
$\quad\quad\quad\quad\ y < 2x + 5$

6. (−1, −5); $y < -4$ <small>yes</small>
$\quad\quad\quad\quad\quad\ y > x - 5$

7. Possible answer: Substitute −2 for x and 3 for y in both inequalities. $3 > -2 + 4$; $3 > 2$ true. $3 < 2(-2) + 5$; $3 < 1$ false. (−2, 3) does not make both inequalities true. So, (−2, 3) is not a solution of the system.

Cooperative Learning

7. Explain to a partner how to tell whether the ordered pair is a solution in number **2** in **Practice**. <small>See above.</small>

8. Work with a partner. Find a point that is a solution to number **5** in **Practice**. Check the work. <small>Possible answers: (1, 2), (4, 5), (0, 3).</small>

8-8

Finding a Solution by Graphing

You can graph a system of inequalities. Graph each inequality on the same set of axes. The solution of the system is the area where the solutions overlap.

▶ **EXAMPLE 1**

Solve by graphing. $y < x + 2$
$y > -2x - 1$

Graph $y < x + 2$.

Then, graph $y > -2x - 1$ on the same axes.

Remember
Use a dotted line for $<$ or $>$.

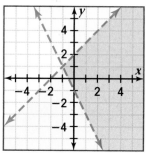

Check: Pick a point in the solution: (2, 2).

$y < x + 2$
$2 < 2 + 2$
$2 < 4$ true

$y > -2x - 1$
$2 > -2(2) - 1$
$2 > -5$ true

▶ **EXAMPLE 2**

Solve by graphing. $y < 3$
$y \geq x + 1$

Remember
Use a solid line for $\geq$.

Graph $y < 3$.

Then, graph $y \geq x + 1$ on the same axes.

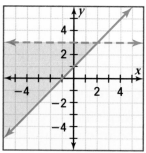

Check: Pick a point in the solution: (−4, 0).

$y < 3$
$0 < 3$ true

$y \geq x + 1$
$0 \geq (-4) + 1$
$0 \geq -3$ true

Try These

Solve by graphing.

1. $y > 1$
$y \leq x + 2$

Graph $y > 1$.
Then, graph
$y \leq x + 2$.

Check: Pick a point in the ■ area. dark shaded
Use (2, 2).

$y > 1$	$y \leq x + 2$
$\underset{2}{■} > 1$ true	$2■ \leq ■2 + 2$
	$2 \leq \underset{4}{■}$ true

2. $y \geq 2x - 2$
$y > -2x + 1$

Graph
$y \geq 2x - 2$.
Then, graph
$y > -2x + 1$.

Check: Pick a point in the ■ area. dark shaded
Use (1, 2).

$y \geq 2x - 2$	$y > -2x + 1$
$2■ \geq 2(■)1 - 2$	$2■ > -2(■) + 1\,1$
$2■ \geq ■2 - 2$	$2■ > ■ + 1\,{-2}$
$2■ \geq \underset{0}{■}$ true	$2■ > \underset{-1}{■}$ true

Practice   See Additional Answers, p. 476.

Solve by graphing.

1. $y < x + 1$
$y \leq -x - 3$

2. $y > x + 2$
$y < 2x + 1$

3. $y > 2$
$y \leq x + 2$

4. $y \leq 2x + 2$
$y < -\frac{2}{3}x + 4$

5. $y < 2x + 1$
$y > \frac{1}{2}x - 3$

6. $y < -2$
$y > x - 4$

7. $y \geq 1$
$y > -2x + 3$

8. $y \geq -2x - 1$
$y \leq 2x - 4$

9. $y < x$
$y \leq 0$

10. Possible answer: Graph $y \leq 2x + 2$. Check (2, 2); yes, it is a solution. Shade below the line.
Graph $y < -\frac{2}{3}x + 4$. Check (2, 2); yes, it a solution. Shade below the line. The solution is the part of the graph that is shaded for both lines.

Cooperative Learning

10. Explain to a partner how to find all the solutions of the system by graphing in number **4** in **Practice.** See above.

11. Write two inequalities in slope-intercept form. Have a partner find all the solutions of the system by graphing. Check the work.
Answers will vary. Check direction of shading and type of lines.

Getting Started
On the
chalkboard, write
$3x + 2y = 9$.
Have students use their
calculators to verify that $(1, 3)$
is a solution. See Lesson 6.6.

Calculator: Checking Possible Solutions

You can use a calculator to check solutions of linear systems.

▶ **EXAMPLE**

Tell if $(1.3, .6)$ is the solution of the system.

$x + 5y = 4.3$
$2x - y = 2$

Check $x + 5y = 4.3$ first.

$x + 5y = 4.3$

Substitute 1.3 for x and .6 for y.

$1.3 + 5(.6) = 4.3$

Use your calculator to simplify.

Remember
Multiply before adding or subtracting.

		Display
Enter 5 by pressing:		5
Multiply by .6 by pressing:	⊠ . 6 =	3
Add 1.3 by pressing:	+ 1 . 3 =	4.3

$4.3 = 4.3$ true

Check $2x - y = 2$ next.

$2x - y = 2$

Substitute 1.3 for x and .6 for y.

$2(1.3) - .6 = 2$

Use your calculator to simplify.

		Display
Enter 2 by pressing:	2	2
Multiply by 1.3 by pressing:	⊠ 1 . 3 =	2.6
Subtract .6 by pressing:	− . 6 =	2

$2 = 2$ true

$(1.3, .6)$ is the solution of the system.

Practice

Tell whether each ordered pair is the solution of the system.

1. (14, 21); $x + y = 35$ yes
$22x + y = 329$

2. (2, −4); $2x - 1.5y = 10$ yes
$.3x - .05y = .8$

3. (−2, 2); $6.2x + 4.65y = -3.1$ no
$1.5x + 6.2y = 9.3$

4. (12, 18); $x + y = 30$ no
$6.9x + 4.5y = 14$

5. (22, 28); $x + y = 50$ yes
$.15x + .24y = 10.02$

6. (15, 7.4); $2x - 3y = 9.4$ no
$5x - 9y = 12.4$

On-the-Job Math

AIR TRAFFIC CONTROLLER

Air traffic controllers direct airplanes as they land and take off. These people work in a tall tower at an airport. From this tower, controllers make sure landings and takeoffs are safe. They also direct the airplanes on the runways.

Air traffic controllers use systems of equations to make flight plans. They keep track of the speed, altitude, and location of many airplanes. They do this to make sure that two airplanes do not get in each other's way.

Air traffic controllers decide which runway each airplane should use. They plan exactly when each airplane should land or take off. They also decide how much time an airplane needs to land and move off the runway. To do this, they must know the weather and wind speed. Then they can direct another airplane to land or take off. This work is important if air traffic is to run smoothly.

Getting Started
Use play money and drawings to model the example.

8-10 Problem Solving: Using Systems

▶ **EXAMPLE**

You can write a system of equations to describe a problem. Then, solve the system to solve the problem.

Five baseballs and two gloves cost $65.00. One baseball and one glove cost $25.00. How much does each cost?

READ **What do you need to find out?**
You need to find the price of each baseball and glove.

PLAN **What do you need to do?**
You need to pick variables for the numbers you do not know. Write a system of equations to describe the problem. Then solve.

DO **Follow the plan.**
Pick variables. Use b for the price of a baseball. Use g for the price of a glove.

Remember
$5b$ is the cost of 5 baseballs.
$2g$ is the cost of 2 gloves.

Write equations.
$$5b + 2g = 65$$
$$b + g = 25$$

Solve the system.

$$5b + 2g = 65 \rightarrow 5b + 2g = 65$$
$$-2(b + g = 25) \rightarrow \underline{-2b - 2g = -50}$$
$$3b + 0g = 15$$

Solve for b.
$$3b = 15$$
$$b = 5$$

Substitute 5 for b.
$$5 + g = 25$$
Solve for g.
$$g = 20$$

CHECK **Does your answer make sense?**
Five baseballs and two gloves cost $65.00.
$5(\$5) + 2(\$20) = \$65.00$ ✓
One baseball and one glove cost $25.00.
$1(\$5) + 1(\$20) = \$25.00$ ✓

A baseball costs $5.00. A glove costs $20.00.

Try These

Four gardeners and their 4 assistants earn $60.00 total in an hour. When 5 gardeners and 2 assistants work, they also earn $60.00 total in an hour.

1. Write a system of equations to describe how much the gardeners and assistants earn.

Use g for the amount a gardener makes in an hour.
Use a for the amount an assistant makes in an hour.
Write how much they make total.
Write the equations as a system.

$$4g \boxed{+} 4a \boxed{=} 60$$
$$5g \boxed{+} 2a \boxed{=} 60$$

2. Use the system to find the amount a gardener makes in an hour.

Write the system.

$$4g + 4a = 60$$
$$5g + 2a = 60$$

Make the coefficients of a opposites.

Multiply $5g + 2a = 60$ by -2.
Add the equations.
Solve for g.

$$-2(5g + 2a = 60) \xrightarrow{} \begin{array}{r} 4g + 4a = 60 \\ \underline{-10\boxed{}g - 4\boxed{}a = -120} \\ -6\boxed{}g + 0a = -60 \end{array}$$

$$-6g = -60$$
$$g = \boxed{} 10$$

A gardener makes $\$\boxed{}$ an hour.
10.00

Practice

Write a system to describe each problem. Then, solve the system.

1. The sum of two numbers is 4. Their difference is 2. Find the numbers. $x + y = 4, x - y = 2$; $(3, 1)$

2. Twice a number plus another number is 4. Their sum is 2. Find the numbers. $2x + y = 4, x + y = 2$; $(2, 0)$

3. Three pounds of tomatoes and 2 pounds of broccoli cost $9.00. One pound of tomatoes and 2 pounds of broccoli cost $7.00. How much does each cost?
$3x + 2y = 9, x + 2y = 7$; tomatoes cost $1.00 a pound; broccoli costs $3.00 a pound.

Cooperative Learning

4. Explain to a partner how to write the equations in number **2** in **Practice.** Possible answer: Translate the words into math: Twice a number plus another number is 4 means $2x + y = 4$. Their sum is 2 means $x + y = 2$. Use the equations to solve for x and y.

5. Work with a partner. Use your answer to number **2** in **Try These** to find the amount an assistant makes in an hour. Check each other's work.
The assistants make $5.00 an hour.

More practice is provided in Exercise 48 of the Workbook.

 8·11 ▶ **Application: Maximum and Minimum**

Getting Started

Write the words *at most* and *at least* on the chalkboard. Ask a volunteer to write the inequality for each phrase. ($\leq$ and $\geq$)

You can write equations and inequalities to describe problems. Then, graph the equations and inequalities to find a **maximum** or a **minimum** value.

A company makes books and disks. It wants to make at least 800 books and disks total. It costs $8.00 to make a book and $2.00 to make a disk. The company needs at most 700 books and 400 disks. How many of each should the company make to minimize the cost?

Remember

Use *b* for the number of books.
Use *d* for the number of disks.

$$\text{Total Cost} = \text{Cost of Books} + \text{Cost of Disks}$$
$$\text{Total Cost} = \$8b + \$2d$$

▶ **EXAMPLE 1**

Write the inequalities to describe the problem.

At most 700 books	$b \leq 700$
At most 400 disks	$d \leq 400$
Total must be at least 800	$b + d \geq 800$

The graphs of these inequalities form a triangle. The maximum and minimum costs will each be at one of the corners of this triangle. The pairs are (books, disks).

▶ **EXAMPLE 2**

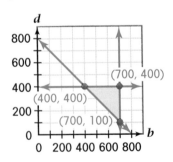

Use the graph of the inequalities to find the number of books and disks that will give the minimum cost.

Find the ordered pairs at the triangle corner points.
(400, 400)
(700, 100)
(700, 400)

Write the cost equation.   Total cost = $8b + $2d

Substitute the ordered pairs into the cost equation.
$4,000 = $8(400) + $2(400)
$5,800 = $8(700) + $2(100)

Find the ordered pair that gives the smallest cost.
$6,400 = $8(700) + $2(400)
(400, 400)

Making 400 books and 400 disks would give the minimum cost.

Try These

A food center has at most $36.00 to spend on cereal each week. The center needs at least 9 pounds of corn and at least 4 pounds of wheat. Corn costs $2.00 per pound, and wheat costs $3.00 per pound.

1. Write the inequalities.

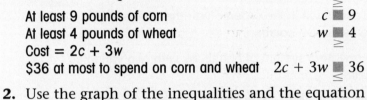

At least 9 pounds of corn $c \geq 9$
At least 4 pounds of wheat $w \geq 4$
Cost $= 2c + 3w$
$36 at most to spend on corn and wheat $2c + 3w \leq 36$

2. Use the graph of the inequalities and the equation Total $= c + w$ to find the maximum number of pounds of each cereal the center can buy.

Find the pairs (corn, wheat) at the corner points. $(9, \underset{4}{\blacksquare})$ $(\underset{12}{\blacksquare}, 4)$ $(9, \underset{6}{\blacksquare})$
Substitute the ordered pairs into the $9 + \blacksquare$ $12\blacksquare + 4$ $9 + \blacksquare 6$
equation Total $= c + w$. $13\underset{4}{\blacksquare}$ $\blacksquare 16$ $15\blacksquare$

The center can buy $\underset{12}{\blacksquare}$ pounds of corn cereal and $\underset{4}{\blacksquare}$ pounds of wheat.

Practice

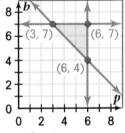

A deli owner orders at least 10 pounds of meat. She needs no more than 7 pounds of beef and 6 pounds of pork. The cost is $8.00 per pound of beef and $6.00 per pound of pork.

1. Write the inequalities for the pounds of beef, pounds of pork, and total number of pounds. Use b for beef and p for pork.
$b \leq 7; p \leq 6; b + p \leq 10$

2. Find the minimum cost of ordering meat using the equation Cost $= 8b + 6p$. Use the ordered pairs (pork, beef).
6 lb of pork and 4 lb of beef minimizes the cost; $68.00

Cooperative Learning

3. Explain to a partner how to find the minimum in number **2** in **Practice.** Possible answer: Substitute the ordered pairs of the vertices into the equation to see which gives the smallest number.

4. Use the equation from number **2** in **Practice.** Write new inequalities for the amount of beef and pork to order. Have a partner solve the new system. Answers will vary. Check students' work. Some inequalities will not give a solution.

Summary

You can graph a system of linear equations to find the solution. The solution of the system is the intersection of the two lines.
The solution of a system of equations is the ordered pair that makes both equations true. Not all systems have a solution.
You can use substitution to rewrite a system of equations with two variables as a system with one variable.
You can solve a system of equations by adding the equations when the coefficients of one of the variables are opposites.
You can multiply an equation by a number to make the coefficients of one of the variables opposites.
Sometimes, you multiply both equations to make the coefficients of a variable opposites.
The solution of a system of linear inequalities is an area of ordered pairs that make both inequalities true.
You can find the solution of a system of inequalities by graphing.
You can apply what you know about graphing inequalities to find the minimum and maximum value for a solution.

More vocabulary review is provided in Exercise 71 of the Classroom Resource Binder.

system of linear
equations

eliminating a variable

system of linear
inequalities

maximum

minimum

Vocabulary Review

Complete the sentences with words from the box.

1. The ____ is the smallest number of a group. minimum

2. The largest number of a group is the ____. maximum

3. A ____ is two or more linear equations with the same variables. system of linear equations

4. When you remove one of the variables in a system, you are ____. eliminating a variable

5. Two or more linear inequalities is a ____.
system of linear inequalities

Chapter Quiz More **assessment** is provided in the Classroom Resource Binder.

Tell whether the ordered pair is the solution of the system.

1. $(2, 0)$; $x + y = 2$
   yes $2x + y = 4$

2. $(-3, -1)$; $x + y = -4$
   yes $-2x + y = 5$

3. $(2, -2)$; $y = 2$
   no $2x + y = 2$

4. $(3, 0)$; $y > -x$
   yes $y \le x - 1$

5. $(-2, 6)$; $y \le x + 8$
   yes $y > 2x + 4$

6. $(0, 5)$; $y < x + 7$
   yes $y \le x + 5$

Graph each system to find its solution. See Additional Answers, p. 476.

7. $y = x + 2$
   $y = 2x + 3$
   $(-1, 1)$

8. $y = x - 2$
   $y = 2x - 1$
   $(-1, -3)$

9. $y < x + 4$
   $y \le x - 6$

10. $y \ge x + 1$
   $y < 2x + 3$

Use substitution to find the solution of each system.

11. $y = x + 2$
   $y = 3x$
   $(1, 3)$

12. $y = x$
   $y = -3x + 8$
   $(2, 2)$

13. $y = x + 4$
   $y = -x - 6$
   $(-5, -1)$

Find the solution of each system with addition, subtraction, or multiplication.

14. $x + y = 8$
   $x - y = 4$
   $(6, 2)$

15. $-x + y = -3$
   $x + y = 11$
   $(7, 4)$

16. $x + 2y = -6$
   $x - 2y = 10$
   $(2, -4)$

17. $3x + 2y = 6$
   $2x + y = 6$
   $(6, -6)$

18. $x - 4y = -2$
   $3x + 2y = 8$
   $(2, 1)$

19. $2x - 3y = 4$
   $4x + 2y = -8$
   $(-1, -2)$

20. The difference of two numbers is 3. Their sum is -5. Find the numbers.

   The numbers are -1 and -4.

The book and disk company sells its books for a \$3.00 profit and its disks for a \$4.00 profit. The company needs at least 1,000 books and disks total and at most 700 books and 400 disks. Its profit is shown by the equation Profit $= 3b + 4d$.

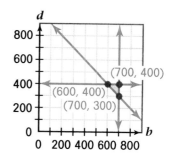

21. Use the graph and the equation Profit $= 3b + 4d$ to find how many books and disks give the maximum income.

   700 books and 400 disks would give the maximum profit.

Additional Practice for this chapter is provided on p. 420 of this text.

Chapter 8 • Systems of Equations and Inequalities   **213**

More About Data and Data Analysis

Marketing departments of companies gather data about people's interests, tastes, and hobbies. They use data analysis to design the products. What new products have come on the market?

Learning Objectives

- Find the mean, mode, and median.
- Make a frequency table.
- Make a stem-and-leaf plot.
- Make a scatter plot.
- Use a calculator to find the mean of large numbers.
- Solve problems by deciding whether to use the mean, mode, or median.
- Apply concepts and skills to finding quartiles.

Words to Know

data	information gathered from surveys or experiments
statistics	the study of collecting and organizing data
mean	sum of the data divided by the number of data; also called average
mode	number or numbers that appear most often in a set of data
median	middle number when data are ordered from least to greatest
range	difference between maximum and minimum values in a set of data
frequency table	chart that shows the number of times an item appears in a set of data
stem-and-leaf plot	tool that uses place value to arrange and display data
scatter plot	graph that shows two sets of related data as ordered pairs
positive correlation	the data in two sets increase together
negative correlation	the data in one set increase while the data in the second set decrease
quartiles	numbers that divide the set of data into four parts

Student Age Project

Project See the Classroom Resource Binder for a scoring rubric to assess this project.

Record the age, in months, of each student in your class. Find the mean, mode, and median of the data you collect. Which best describes the data? Why? Make a stem-and-leaf plot to display the information.

Name	Age
Sue	156 months
Gervase	168 months

More practice is provided in Exercises 49 and 50 of the Workbook.

Getting Started
Ask students to bring in examples of statistics from newspapers and magazines. For example, have them bring in sports stats. Display and discuss the examples.

9-1 Mean

People take surveys and do experiments to gather information. This information is called **data.** Often, data is shown as collections or sets of numbers. The study of data is called **statistics.**

Math Fact
The mean is sometimes called the average.

Finding the **mean** is one way to describe data. You find the mean of a set of data by adding the numbers in the set. Then, divide the sum by the number of items in that set.

▶ **EXAMPLE 1**

Find the mean of the set of data.   1, 2, 1, 4, 3, 1

Add the numbers. $1 + 2 + 1 + 4 + 3 + 1 = 12$

Count the number of items.   6 items

Divide the sum by 6. $12 \div 6 = 2$

The mean of the set of data is 2.

▶ **EXAMPLE 2**

Kristin counted 24, 26, 19, 28, and 13 students in five college history classes. Find the mean number of students.

Add the number of students. $24 + 26 + 19 + 28 + 13 = 110$

Divide by the number of classes. $110 \div 5 = 22$

The mean number of students is 22.

▶ **EXAMPLE 3**

A bank gives the daily balance of an account. For three days, the balance is $12.00, $9.00, and $6.00. Find the average daily balance, or mean, for these days.

Add the 3 balances. $12 + 9 + 6 = 27$

Divide by the number of days. $27 \div 3 = 9$

The average daily balance for the three days is $9.00.

Try These

1. Find the mean temperature for four days in Alaska. The temperatures were 2°, −5°, −10°, and −7°.

Add the degrees.

Divide by the number of days.

$$2 + (-5) + (-10) + (-7) = -20$$

$$-20 \div \underset{4}{\blacksquare} = -5$$

The mean temperature was ■°. −5

2. Juan made $2.00, $4.00, $4.00, $2.00, and $3.00 baby-sitting for five days. What was the mean amount he made?

Add the amounts.

$$\underset{2}{\blacksquare} + \underset{4}{\blacksquare} + \underset{4}{\blacksquare} + \underset{2}{\blacksquare} + \underset{3}{\blacksquare} = \underset{15}{\blacksquare}$$

Divide by the number of days.

$$\underset{15}{\blacksquare} \div 5 = \underset{3}{\blacksquare}$$

The mean amount is $■. 3

Practice

Find the mean.

1. 25, 30, 35 30

2. 112, 114, 116, 118 115

3. 423, 523, 412, 446 451

4. 2, −4, −3, 10, 21, 4 5

5. −20, 30, −40 −10

6. 32, 42, 12, 8, 46 28

7. −4, −8, −6, −2 −5

8. $2, $4, $3, $7, $2, $6 $4

9. A scout troop records the amount of cookies its members sold each day for a week: 12, 15, 19, 18, 30, 54, and 62 boxes. What was the mean number of boxes they sold per day for the week? 30 boxes

Cooperative Learning

10. Explain to a partner how to find the mean in number **4** in **Practice.** Add the numbers. 2 + −4 + −3 +10 + −1 + 8 = 12. Divide the total by 6. 12 ÷ 6 = 2.

11. Write four dollar amounts. Ask a partner to find the mean.
Possible answer: Suppose the student writes $5, $8, $3, and $8. The partner adds the amounts and divides by 4 to get a mean of $6.

9-2 ▶ Mode and Median

Getting Started
Review numerical order. Have students place the following numbers in order, from least to greatest: 2, 6, 5, 7, 4, 4, 3.

You have learned about the mean, which is one way to describe data. There are other ways to describe a set of data. The **mode** is the number or numbers that appear most often in a set of data.

▶ **EXAMPLE 1**

Remember
Count the items to be sure you did not forget any.

Find the mode of the set of data.   5, 4, 6, 5, 4, 6, 6

Order the numbers from least to greatest.   4, 4, 5, 5, 6, 6, 6

Find the number that appears most often.   4, 4, 5, 5, 6, 6, 6

The mode is 6.
A set of data can have more than one mode.

▶ **EXAMPLE 2**

Find the mode of the set of data.   9, 5, −6, 9, −6, 10

Order the numbers from least to greatest.   −6, −6, 5, 9, 9, 10

Find the numbers that appear most often.   −6, −6, 5, 9, 9, 10

The modes are −6 and 9.
When you order a set of data from least to greatest, the middle number is the called the **median.**

▶ **EXAMPLE 3**

Find the median of the set of data.   5, 4, 6, 5, 4, 6, 6

Order the numbers from least to greatest.   4, 4, 5, 5, 6, 6, 6

Find the middle number.   4, 4, 5, 5, 6, 6, 6

The median is 5.
When the number of items in a set of data is even, the median is the average of the two middle numbers.

▶ **EXAMPLE 4**

Remember
To find the average of two numbers, add them, and then divide by 2.

Find the median of the set of data.   9, 5, −6, 9, −6, 10

Order the numbers from least to greatest.   −6, −6, 5, 9, 9, 10

There are 6 items in the set of data.   −6, −6, 5, 9, 9, 10

Find the average of the two middle numbers. $\frac{5 + 9}{2} = \frac{14}{2} = 7$

The median is 7.

Try These

1. Find the mode of the set of data. 1, −2, 1, 4, 4, 3, 1

Order the numbers from least to greatest. −2, 1, 1, 1, 3, 4, 4

Find the number that appears most often. 1 ■ appears most often.

The mode is ■. 1

2. Find the median of the set of data. 4, 12, 1, 4, 1, 8, 10, 8

Order the numbers from least to greatest.

There are ■ items in the set of data. 8

Find the average of the two middle numbers.

The median is ■. 6

$$\frac{■, ■, ■, ■, ■, ■, ■, ■}{1 \quad 1 \quad 4 \quad 4 \quad 8 \quad 8 \quad 10 \quad 12}$$

$$\frac{4 + ■}{2} = \frac{■}{2} = ■$$

Practice

Find the mode.

1. −3, 4, 9, −3, 8, 4, −3 −3

2. 24, 25, 26, 24, 22, 28, 30 24

3. 16, 20, 32, 34, 16, 24, 34, 16 16

4. 4, 6, 3, 4, 4, 9, 6, 6 4 and 6

5. −1, 6, 4, 0, 12, −1, 0 −1 and 0

6. −100, −500, 300, 200, 0 no mode

Find the median.

7. −3, 4, 9, −3, 8, 4, −3 4

8. 24, 25, 26, 24, 22, 28, 30 25

9. 16, 20, 32, 34, 16, 24, 34, 16 22

10. 4, 6, 3, 4, 4, 9, 6, 6 5

11. 0, 0, 52, 3, 12 3

12. −450, 100, 500, −600, −500 −450

Cooperative Learning

13. Explain to a partner how to find the mode in number **3** in **Practice.** Order the numbers: 16, 16, 16, 20, 24, 32, 34, 34. 16 appears the most often.

14. Write a set of data that has seven numbers. Make some of the numbers the same. Have a partner find the median and mode.
Answers will vary. Check that students order the numbers and that they do not confuse mode and median.

Getting Started
Have students
find the smallest
value in this set
of data: 3, 9, −1, 6, −3.

9-3 ▶ Minimum, Maximum, and Range

Another way to describe data is to find the smallest value, called the minimum, and the largest value, called the maximum.

▶ **EXAMPLE 1**

Find the minimum and maximum of the set of data.   15, 4, −1, 6, −5, 10

Order the numbers from least to greatest.	−5, −1, 4, 6, 10, 15
Find the smallest value or minimum.	−5, −1, 4, 6, 10, 15
Find the largest value or maximum.	−5, −1, 4, 6, 10, 15

The minimum is −5. The maximum is 15.

The **range** is the difference between the minimum and maximum values. To find the range, subtract.

▶ **EXAMPLE 2**

Find the range of the set of data.   −8, −12, −2, −20, −3, −7

Order the numbers from least to greatest.	−20, −12, −8, −7, −3, −2
Find the minimum.	−20, −12, −8, −7, −3, −2
Find the maximum.	−20, −12, −8, −7, −3, −2
Subtract the minimum from the maximum.	$-2 - (-20) = -2 + 20 = 18$

The range is 18.

▶ **EXAMPLE 3**

Find the range of the set of data.   −5, 8, −1, 3, 2, 2, 4, 5, 7

Order the numbers from least to greatest.	−5, −1, 2, 2, 3, 4, 5, 7, 8
Find the minimum.	−5, −1, 2, 2, 3, 4, 5, 7, 8
Find the maximum.	−5, −1, 2, 2, 3, 4, 5, 7, 8
Subtract the minimum from the maximum.	$8 - (-5) = 8 + 5 = 13$

The range is 13.

Try These

1. Find the minimum and maximum of the set of data. 1, 9, 2, 3, 8

Order the numbers from least to greatest. 1, 2, 3, 8, 9

Find the smallest value or ■. minimum ■ 1

Find the largest value or ■. maximum ■ 9

The minimum is ■. The maximum is ■.
1   9

2. Find the range of the set of data. 3, −5, 9, −2, 12

Order the numbers from least to greatest.
−5 −2 3 9 12
■, ■, ■, ■, ■

Find the ■. minimum ■ −5

Find the ■. maximum ■ 12

Subtract the ■ from the ■. maximum
minimum
■ − ■ = ■
12 −5   17

The range is ■. 17

Practice

Find the minimum, maximum, and range.

1. 2, 9, 0, 4, 12, 6, 4, 8, 3, 5
0; 12; 12

2. 23, 88, 36, 96, 41, 75, 21, 20, 68
20; 96; 76

3. −8, −2, −6, −7, −9, −5, −7
−9; −2; 7

4. −10, −4, −20, −18, −5, −22, −35
−35; −4; 31

5. 0, 2, −2, 1, −4, 3, −6
−6; 3; 9

6. −54, 65, −21, 33, 48, −12, 85, 61
−54; 85; 139

7. 59, 752, 411, 688, 325, 102
59; 752; 693

8. 1,005; 965; 1,548; 845; 1,656
845; 1,656; 811

Cooperative Learning

9. Explain to a partner how to find the range in number **2** in **Practice.** Order the numbers from smallest to largest: 20, 21, 23, 36, 41, 68, 75, 88, 96. The minimum is 20; the maximum is 96. Subtract the minimum from the maximum: 96 − 20 = 76; The range is 76.

10. Write a set of data that contains six numbers. Ask a partner to find the minimum, maximum, and range. Check the work. Answers will vary. Check that minimum and maximum are not reversed.

9·4 ▶ Frequency Tables

Getting Started
Show students how to use
tally marks to count objects.

A **frequency table** makes it easy to see how many times each item appears. You make a tally mark for each time an item in the set of data appears. Then, you count the tallies.

▶ **EXAMPLE 1**

There are 22 students in a class. On their final exam, they received the following grades: B, A, C, A, B, B, C, A, B, A, A, C, C, B, A, A, B, C, B, C, A, B. Make a frequency table.

For each grade, make a tally mark in the Tally column.

Math Fact
The sum of the frequencies should equal the number of items in the set of data.

Write the total for each row in the Frequency column.

Add the frequencies.

Mark	Tally	Frequency
A's	⫴⫴⫴ III	8
B's	⫴⫴⫴ III	8
C's	⫴⫴⫴ I	6
	Total	22

Sometimes, you group data to show items in a group.

▶ **EXAMPLE 2**

The ages of people at a restaurant are 21, 2, 18, 44, 6, 12, 10, 32, 15, 11, 16, 42, 19, and 50. Use the frequency table to show how many people of each age group are at the restaurant.

There are five age groups of 10 years each from ages 1 to 50.

For each age listed, make a tally mark in the Tally column next to the correct age group.

Write the total for each row.

Add the frequencies.

Age group	Tally	Frequency
1–10	III	3
11–20	⫴⫴⫴ I	6
21–30	I	1
31–40	I	1
41–50	III	3
	Total	14

Try These

1. Students in a survey said they spent the following amount of time studying each day: 1 h, 3 h, 2 h, 5 h, 7 h, 4 h, 3 h, 4 h, 1 h, and 6 h. Complete the frequency table.

Time	Tally	Frequency
0–2 h	▪ |||	▪ 3
3–5 h	▪ ЖᴕГ	▪ 5
6–8 h	▪ ||	▪ 2
	Total	▪ 10

2. Look at the table. Which time range is the least common?

The lowest frequency is ▪. 2

The least common time range is ▪. 6–8 h

3. Look at the table. How many students study less than 6 hours?

Identify the groups that study less than 6 hours.

Add the frequencies. $\overset{5}{▪} + \overset{3}{▪} = \overset{8}{▪}$

8 ▪ students study less than 6 hours.

Practice

1. Complete the frequency table for the following ages: 5, 2, 12, 23, 1, 13, 29, 8, 13, 5, 7, 22.

	Time	Tally	Frequency
ЖᴕГ		1–10	?	? 6
|||	11–20	?	? 3
|||	21–30	?	? 3
		Total	? 12

2. How many people were over 10 years of age?
6 people

3. What was the most common age range?
1–10 years

4. The baseball team is ordering shirts. Make a frequency table for the sizes: S, L, M, S, S, M, S, L, L, M, L, S, M, L, S. Describe the results. The team ordered 15 shirts: 6 small shirts, 4 medium shirts, and 5 large shirts. See table in Additional Answers, p. 477.

Cooperative Learning

5. Explain to a partner how you complete the table in number **1** in **Practice.** Possible answer: For each value, make a tally in the correct row in the Tally column. Write the total for each row in the Frequency column. Add the frequency totals for the overall total.

6. Write a question that can be answered with the table in number **4** in **Practice.** Have a partner answer the question. Check the work. Answers will vary.

9.5 Stem-and-Leaf Plots

Like a frequency table, a **stem-and-leaf plot** is a way to display data. It uses place value. The leaves can represent the ones place. The stem can represent the tens place. With a stem-and-leaf plot, you can easily see the number of items in groups of data.

▶ **EXAMPLE 1**

The ages of people at a restaurant are 21, 18, 44, 12, 10, 57, 11, 42, 19, and 50. Make a stem-and-leaf plot.

Order the data from least to greatest.

10, 11, 12, 18, 19, 21, 42, 44, 50, 57

Write the tens-place digits from least to greatest under Stem.

For each age, write the ones-place digit under Leaves next to the correct stem. There are no people in the 30s age group.

Stem	Leaves
1	0 1 2 8 9
2	1
3	
4	2 4
5	0 7

The stem can be more than one digit. It may show both the tens and hundreds place.

▶ **EXAMPLE 2**

The number of pennies in 10 piggy banks was 128, 104, 124, 113, 104, 108, 117, 121, 132, and 125. Make a stem-and-leaf plot. Describe the results.

Order the data from least to greatest.

104, 104, 108, 113, 117, 121, 124, 125, 128, 132

Write the hundreds- and tens-place digits from least to greatest under Stem.

Write the ones-place digits under Leaves next to the correct stems.

Stem	Leaves
10	4 4 8
11	3 7
12	1 4 5 8
13	2

The greatest number of piggy banks had between 120 and 129 pennies. The smallest number of piggy banks had between 130 and 139 pennies.

Try These

1. Make a stem-and-leaf plot for the set of data.   235, 241, 254, 236, 238, 247, 248

235; 236; 238; 241; 247; 248; 254

Order the data from least to greatest.

Write the hundreds- and tens-place digits from least to greatest under stem.

Write the ones-place digit for each number next to the correct stem.

■, ■, ■, ■, ■, ■, ■

Stem	Leaves
23	■ ■ ■ 5 6 8
24	■ ■ ■ 1 7 8
25 ■	■ 4

2. Look at the stem-and-leaf plot. Describe the results.

The ■ group has five items.   560 to 569

The ■ group has one item.   550 to 559

Stem	Leaves
55	1
56	2 4 4 5 8
57	3 5
58	6 7 9

The smallest number of items appears in the ■ group. 550 to 559
The greatest number of items appears in the ■ group. 560 to 569

Practice

Make a stem-and-leaf plot for each set of data.

1. 23, 21, 31, 15, 28, 36, 14, 42, 21, 35, 48, 33

2. 147, 158, 167, 131, 141, 142, 168, 157, 130, 128

3. 748, 724, 735, 748, 758, 761, 749, 764, 720, 748

1.
Stem	Leaves
1	4 5
2	1 1 3 8
3	1 3 5 6
4	2 8

2.
Stem	Leaves
12	8
13	0 1
14	1 2 7
15	7 8
16	7 8

3.
Stem	Leaves
72	0 4
73	5
74	8 8 8 9
75	8
76	1 4

Cooperative Learning

4. Explain to a partner how you choose the stems in number 3 in **Practice.** Order the data from least to greatest. Write the hundreds and tens places in order in a column: 72, 73, 74, 75, 76.

5. Write eight numbers between 10 and 40. Ask a partner to make a stem-and-leaf plot to display the numbers. Have your partner describe the data. Answers will vary. Check that the stems and leaves are appropriate.

Getting Started
Have students
write the number
of nickels and their
value as ordered pairs.
(1, 5), (2, 10), (3, 15)

9-6 ▶ Scatter Plots

Some data are in pairs. You can plot them as ordered pairs to make a graph called a **scatter plot**.

▶ **EXAMPLE 1**

A zookeeper measures the length and weight of eight pythons. Use the data from the chart. Make a scatter plot.

Length (feet)	Weight (pounds)
2	2
5	6
3	4
4	5
3	5
4	6
5	8
2	3

Read each pair of data.

Plot each ordered pair on the scatter plot.

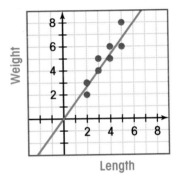

Math Fact
A line that goes up from the lower left has a positive slope.

Notice that the weight increases as the length increases. This is called **positive correlation**. A line drawn through the data has a positive slope.

A scatter plot can also show **negative correlation**. A line drawn through the data will have a negative slope.

▶ **EXAMPLE 2**

Copy costs vary based on the number of copies you make. Use the table to make a scatter plot. Is the correlation positive or negative?

Number of Copies	Cost per Copy
1	15
5	10
10	8
20	6
30	5
40	4

Read each pair of data.

Plot each ordered pair on the scatter plot.

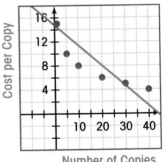

Math Fact
A line that goes down from the upper left has a negative slope.

The cost per copy decreases as the number of copies increases. This is a negative correlation.

Try These

1. Use the data from the chart.
   Make a scatter plot.

Hours (h)	Miles (mi)
1	60
3	175
2	130
3	150
1	30
4	200

Read each ■ of data. pair

Plot each ordered pair on the ■.
scatter plot

2. Look at the scatter plot. Tell whether there is a positive or negative correlation.

   The miles increase as the hours ■. increase

   There is a ■ correlation. positive

Practice

Make a scatter plot for each set of data. Then, tell if the correlation is positive or negative. See Additional Answers, p. 477.

1.

Number of Guests	Cost ($) per guest
1	$34
2	$22
3	$18
4	$16

2.

Height of Tree (ft)	Cost ($)
4	$10
6	$15
8	$30
10	$50
12	$100

Cooperative Learning

3. Explain to a partner how to find the correlation in number 2 in **Practice**. Possible answer: The cost increases as the height of the tree increases, so it is positive.

4. Draw a scatter plot. Ask a partner to identify whether the scatter plot shows a positive or negative correlation. Answers will vary. Check for graphs that do not show any correlation.

Calculator: Finding the Mean

Some sets of data have large numbers. You can use a
calculator to find the mean of sets of large numbers.

▶ **EXAMPLE 1**

Find the mean.   896; 943; 823; 992; 1,322

Display

Remember
To find the mean, add the data.
Then, divide the sum by the
number of data items.

Enter 896 by pressing:	8 9 6	896
Add 943 by pressing:	+ 9 4 3	943
Add 823 by pressing:	+ 8 2 3	823
Add 992 by pressing:	+ 9 9 2	992
Add 1,322 by pressing:	+ 1 3 2 2	1322
Find the total by pressing:	=	4976

There are 5 items in the set of data.

Divide by 5 by pressing: ÷ 5 =   995.2

The mean is 995.2.

You can also use a calculator to find the mean of sets
containing decimals.

▶ **EXAMPLE 2**

Find the mean.   1.202, 1.049, 1.726, 1.903

Display

Enter 1.202 by pressing:	1 . 2 0 2	1.202
Add 1.049 by pressing:	+ 1 . 0 4 9	1.049
Add 1.726 by pressing:	+ 1 . 7 2 6	1.726
Add 1.903 by pressing:	+ 1 . 9 0 3	1.903
Find the total by pressing:	=	5.88

There are 4 items in the set of data.

Divide by 4 by pressing: ÷ 4 =   1.47

Practice

Find the mean. Round to three decimal places.

1. 327, 928, 778, 824 714.25

2. 3.246, 4.003, 3.192, 4.325 3.692

3. 901, 854, 972, 995 930.5

4. .075, .105, 1.244, .662 .522

5. 654, 687, 610, 701, 722 674.8

6. 7.044, 7.035, 7.108, 7.184 7.093

7. 104, 118, 25, 103, 161 102.2

8. 1.004, .302, .651, .117, .018 .418

On-the-Job Math

PHYSICIAN'S ASSISTANT

You may have been to a doctor's office or hospital at some time. If so, you might have been helped by a physician's assistant. Physician's assistants are somewhat like nurses. They both work closely with a doctor.

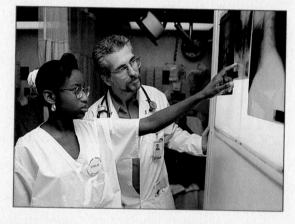

Assistants help doctors by doing basic tasks. This way, the doctors can spend more time on complex cases. Assistants give exams and checkups. They can order special tests, such as blood work and X-rays. They can also order medicines, with the doctor's permission.

Doctors and physician's assistants use many statistics in their jobs. They read medical charts. They use terms like *average cure rate* and *median age*. This helps them learn about an illness.

Assistants must speak clearly. They talk with patients about how the patients are feeling. They also pass on information to doctors about their patients. Assistants keep the patients' files in order and up-to-date, too.

If you like helping sick people, you might like to be a physician's assistant.

More practice is provided in Exercise 53 of the Workbook.

Getting Started
Ask students to
find the mean,
mode, and median
of the following set of data:
2, 3, 4, 4, 5, 6. (mean 4,
mode 4, median 4)

9-8 Problem Solving: The Best Description

You can use the mean, mode, or median to represent data. Sometimes, one or two of these better describe the data.

▶ **EXAMPLE**

A company president has four employees. The president earns $80.00 an hour. The employees each earn $10.00 an hour. Which is a good description of the typical wage: mean, mode, or median?

READ **What do you need to find out?**
You need to determine if mean, mode or median best describes the typical wage.

PLAN **What do you need to do?**
You need to calculate the mean, mode, and median. Then, decide which describes a typical wage.

DO **Follow the plan.**

List the wages. 10, 10, 10, 10,   80

                four employees   president

Find the mean. The sum is 120.
120 ÷ 5 = 24

Find the mode. 10 appears most often.

Find the median. 10, 10, 10, 10, 80

The mean is $24.00. The median is $10.00. The mode is $10.00. A typical wage is $10.00.

CHECK **Does your answer make sense?**
Four of the five people earn $10.00 an hour. ✓

The mode and median are better descriptions of the typical wage earned at the company.

Try These

Find the mean, mode, and median of each set of data. Then, tell which best describes the data.

1. 2, 3, 3, 5, 6, 35

    Find the mean.   sum = 54

                         54 ÷ 6 = 9

    Find the mode.   ■ 3

    Find the median.   (3 + 5) ÷ 2 = ■ 4
    mean
The ■ is higher than most of the numbers. The ■ and ■ are better descriptions of the data. median; mode

2. 12, 12, 45, 46, 59, 70, 71

    Find the mean.   sum = ■ 315

                     315 ■ ÷ 7 = 45

    Find the mode.   ■ 12

    Find the median.   ■ 46
    mode
The ■ is lower than most of the numbers. The ■ and ■ are better descriptions of the data. mean; median

Practice

Find the mean, median, and mode. Then, tell which is the best description for each set of data.

1. 60, 74, 3, 4, 3, 60
mean 34, median 32, modes 3 and 60; mean, median

2. 38, 1, 34, 33, 34
mean 28, median 34, mode 34; median, mode

3. A store was surveyed for the cost of tennis shoes. The prices of six different brands of shoes were $84.00, $15.00, $16.00, $80.00, $15.00, and $90.00. mean 50, median 48, mode 15; mean, median

4. You poured five bowls of cereal to find out the number of fruit flavored pieces you get in a bowl. The fruit flavored pieces numbered 3, 23, 20, 23, and 21. mean 18, median 21, mode 23; median

Cooperative Learning

5. Explain to a partner how you choose the best descriptions of the data in number **2** in **Practice.** Possible answer: The mean of 28 is lower than most of the numbers. The median and mode are both 34 and are closer in value to most of the data.

6. Write five numbers. Work with a partner to find the mean, mode, and median. Decide which you think are good descriptions of the data. Answers will vary. Either the mean or the median could be good descriptors for numbers with values close together. If the values vary widely, one descriptor is usually better than the others.

9-9 ▸ Application: Quartiles

Getting Started
Ask students to describe the term *median* in their own words. Then have them describe how to find the median.

Sometimes, **quartiles** are used to describe test results. To find a quartile, first find the median. Then, look at the data above and below the median.

10, 10, 12, 13, 13, 14, 15, 16, 16, 17, 17

        ↑   ↑   ↑

    1st   median   3rd
  quartile   quartile

Math Fact
The quartiles divide a set of data into four parts.

The first quartile is the middle number in the group less than the median. The third quartile is the middle number in the group greater than the median. The median is sometimes called the 2nd quartile.

▸ **EXAMPLE 1**

Find the quartiles in the set of data.
52, 50, 57, 64, 66, 68, 65

Order the data from least to greatest.	50, 52, 57, 64, 65, 66, 68.
Find the median.	50, 52, 57, 64, 65, 66, 68
Find the first quartile.	50, 52, 57
Find the third quartile.	65, 66, 68

The quartiles are 52, 64, and 66.

▸ **EXAMPLE 2**

Find the quartiles in the set of test scores.
80, 50, 52, 74, 75, 85, 70, 66, 63, 90, 99

Order the data from least to greatest.	50, 52, 63, 66, 70, 74, 75, 80, 85, 90, 99
Find the median.	50, 52, 63, 66, 70, 74, 75, 80, 85, 90, 99
Find the first quartile.	50, 52, 63, 66, 70
Find the third quartile.	75, 80, 85, 90, 99

The quartiles are 63, 74, and 85.

Try These

Find the quartiles in each set of data.

1. Number of family members: 9, 2, 3, 7, 3, 4, 6

Order the data from least to greatest.	2, 3, 3, 4, 6, 7, 9
Find the median.	2, 3, 3, ■, 6, 7, 9 4
Find the first quartile.	2, ■, 3 3
Find the third quartile.	6, ■, 9 7

The quartiles are ■, ■, and ■.
                       3   4   7

2. Daily bank balance: $35.00, $33.00, $25.00, $28.00, $29.00, $41.00, $27.00, $52.00, $23.00, $44.00, $53.00

Order the data from least to greatest.	23, 25, 27, 28, 29, 33, 35, 41, 44, 52, 53
Find the median.	23, 25, 27, 28, 29, ■, 35, 41, 44, 52, 53 33
Find the first quartile.	23, 25, ■, 28, 29 27
Find the third quartile.	35, 41, ■, 52, 53 44

The quartiles are ■, ■, and ■. $44
                  $27
                  $33

Practice

Find the quartiles in each set of data.

1. 97, 82, 94, 84, 87, 88, 91   84, 88, 94   **2.** 5, 7, 11, 8, 1, 9, 1, 6, 11, 2, 10   2, 7, 10

3. Miles driven each day: 4, 6, 8, 4, 5, 7, 9, 2, 3, 2, 9   3, 5, 8

4. Daily temperatures for the week: 62°, 52°, 42°, 31°, 53°, 48°, 37°   37°, 48°, 53°

Cooperative Learning

5. Explain to a partner how you find the quartiles in number **1** in **Practice.** Order the data. Find the median. Look at the first half of the data set. Find the first quartile. Look at the second half of the data set. Find the third quartile.

6. Write a set of data containing seven numbers. Ask a partner to find the quartiles. Answers will vary.

Summary

Sets of data can be described using mean, mode, median, maximum, minimum, and range.
Sets of data can be organized using frequency tables and stem-and-leaf plots.
Paired sets of data can be graphed using a scatter plot. The data may show a positive or negative correlation.
You can decide which of mean, mode, or median are the better descriptions of a set of data.
You can find quartiles in a set of data.

More vocabulary review is provided in Exercise 81 of the Classroom Resource Binder.

data

statistics

mean

mode

median

frequency table

stem-and-leaf plot

scatter plot

positive correlation

quartiles

Vocabulary Review

Complete the sentences with words from the box.

1. The number that appears most often in a set of data is the _____. mode

2. A chart that shows how many times an item appears in a set of data is called a _____. frequency table

3. To arrange data by place value, use a _____. stem-and-leaf plot

4. Information that is gathered from surveys and experiments is called _____. data

5. The numbers that divide the set of data into four parts are _____. quartiles

6. The study of collecting and organizing data is _____. statistics

7. When two sets of data increase together, there is a _____. positive correlation

8. The middle number in a set of data is the _____. median

9. A graph that shows two sets of data as ordered pairs is called a _____. scatter plot

10. If you divide the sum of the data by the number of items, you get the average or _____. mean

Chapter Quiz <small>More assessment is provided in the Classroom Resource Binder.</small>

Find the mean, mode, and median.

1. 6, 5, 5, 3, 6, 5, 12
mean 6; mode 5; median 5

2. 15, 8, 20, 10, 10, 10, 14, 12, 18
mean 13; mode 10; median 12

Find the minimum, maximum, and range.

3. 4, 64, 2, 32, 5, 14, 6, 7, 3, 22
min. 2; max. 64; range 62

4. 100, 88, 22, 43, 10, 75, 54, 23, 18
min. 10; max. 100; range 90

5. Make a frequency table for the set of data of shirt sizes: S, L, M, M, S, M, S, S, L, M, L, M, M, L, S. Describe the results.
There are 15 shirts: 5 small, 6 medium, and 4 large. See table in Additional Answers, p. 477.

6. Use the frequency table from number **5** to tell how many more medium shirts were ordered than large. 2 shirts

Make a stem-and-leaf plot for each set of data. See below.

7. 10, 12, 15, 21, 24, 31, 32, 33

8. 72, 92, 74, 83, 73, 87, 95, 74, 99

For each scatter plot, tell whether the correlation is positive or negative.

9.

positive

10.

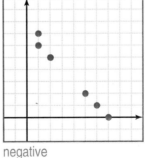

negative

7.

Stem	Leaves
1	0 2 5
2	1 4
3	1 2 3

8.

Stem	Leaves
7	2 3 4 4
8	3 7
9	2 5 9

Find the mean, mode, and median of each set of data. Then, tell which of the mean, mode, and median best describes the data.

11. 2, 2, 2, 32, 37, 39 mean 19; mode 2; median 17; mean and median

12. 94, 97, 1, 97, 99, 5, 97 mean 70; mode 97; median 97; median and mode

Find the quartiles in each set of data.

13. 12, 14, 16, 19, 32, 35, 37
14; 19; 35

14. 58, 49, 43, 47, 43, 53, 55
43; 49; 55

Additional Practice for this chapter is provided on p. 421 of this text.

Unit 3 Review

Choose the letter for the correct answer.

Use the graph to answer Questions 1 and 2.

A club needs to raise at least $200. It has a bake sale. They earn $5 for each cake. They earn $2 for each bread.

1. Which ordered pair is a solution? A

   A. (80, 30)
   B. (40, 20)
   C. (60, 10)
   D. not given

2. Which phrase means the same as the ordered pair (30, 60)? C

   A. 60 bread and 30 cakes
   B. $30 and $60
   C. 30 bread and 60 cakes
   D. $60 and $30

3. Aaron earns $8 an hour. He wants to save at least $120. What is the inequality for this problem? C

   A. $8x \leq 120$
   B. $8 + x \geq 120$
   C. $8x \geq 120$
   D. $x - 8 \leq 120$

4. Cindy is making gifts for her friends. The materials for each cost $6. She cannot spend more than $75. Find the greatest number of gifts Cindy can make. B

   A. 10
   B. 12
   C. 15
   D. 24

5. Which is the mean of this set of data? 20, 7, 8, 14, 9, 20, 20 C

   A. 20
   B. 13
   C. 14
   D. 15

6. Which are the quartiles in this set of data? $11, $21, $15, $9, $15, $12, $10 D

   A. 11, 12, 15
   B. 10, 12, 21
   C. 10, 11, 15
   D. not given

Critical Thinking

When 2 parents and 3 children visit a theme park, the admission cost is $57. The cost is $33 for 1 parent and 2 children. Find the cost for 1 adult and the cost for 1 child. $a = \$15, c = \$9$

CHALLENGE A group of adults and children can spend at most $90 for admission. Write an inequality.
$9c + 15a \leq \$90$

Critical Thinking See the Classroom Resource Binder for a scoring rubic to access this Critical Thinking Question.

Unit Four

Exponents and Functions

Some functions increase very quickly. Bacteria cells grow as a function of time. One cell could become millions in just a few hours. How many zeros does 20 million have?

Learning Objectives

- Multiply and divide with exponents.
- Use zero and negative exponents.
- Find numbers named by scientific notation.
- Make a table of values to graph an exponential function.
- Find the value of powers using a calculator.
- Solve problems by drawing a tree diagram to count choices.
- Apply concepts and skills to finding compound interest.

Words to Know

exponent	the number that tells how many times the base is used as a factor
power	the product when the factors are the same; in $3^2 = 9$, 9 is the power
base	a factor; In 3^2, 3 is the base used as a factor two times
scientific notation	a number written as the product of two factors; the first is a number greater than 1 and less than 10 and the second is a power of 10
exponential functions	functions of the form $y = a \bullet b^x$, where b is a positive number not equal to 1
tree diagram	a way of showing choices so you can count them
compound interest	interest earned on your previous interest

Scientific Notation Project

Look for very large numbers in newspapers and almanacs. These could be population figures, the federal budget, or space facts. Look for very small numbers such as the size of insects, bacteria, or dust. Record your findings in a table. In one column, write the number in standard form. In another column, write the number in scientific notation.

What Is It?	Standard Form	Scientific Notation
Speed of light	300,000,000 m/sec	3×10^8 m/sec
Mass of a dust particle	.000000000753 kg	7.53×10^{-10} kg

Project See the Classroom Resource Binder for a scoring rubric to assess this project.

More practice is provided in Exercise 55 of the Workbook.

10·1 ▶ Finding Powers

Getting Started
Review exponents. Write 3^2 on the chalkboard. Invite a volunteer to identify the exponent and explain the meaning of 3^2. (3 is used as a factor 2 times; $3^2 = 3 \times 3$)

You have already used exponents to write numbers.

exponent
$$\downarrow$$
base $\rightarrow$ $4^2 = 4 \bullet 4 = 16$ $\leftarrow$ power

You have also written variables with exponents.

$$a^3 = aaa \rightarrow a \text{ is used as a factor } 3 \text{ times.}$$
$$a^2b^4 = aabbbb \rightarrow a \text{ is used as a factor } 2 \text{ times.}$$
$$b \text{ is used as a factor } 4 \text{ times.}$$

▶ **EXAMPLE 1**

Use an exponent to rewrite $xxxx$.

$$x \bullet x \bullet x \bullet x$$

x is used as a factor 4 times. $\quad x^4$

$$xxxx = x^4$$

▶ **EXAMPLE 2**

Rewrite a^5y without an exponent.

$$a^5y$$

Math Fact
y is the same as y^1.

a is used as a factor 5 times. $\quad aaaaay$
y is used as a factor 1 time.

$$a^5y = aaaaay$$

▶ **EXAMPLE 3**

Rewrite $-y^4$ without an exponent.

$$-y^4$$

Math Fact
$-y^4$ means $-(y^4)$.

y is used as a factor 4 times. $\quad -yyyy$

$$-y^4 = -yyyy$$

You can also find the value of a power.

▶ **EXAMPLE 4**

Find the value of b^3 when b is -4.

b is used as a factor 3 times. $\quad b^3$

Math Fact
The product of three negative numbers is negative.

Substitute -4 for b. $\quad bbb$

Multiply. $\quad (-4)(-4)(-4) = -64$

$$b^3 = -64 \text{ when } b \text{ is } -4.$$

Try These

Use exponents to rewrite each product.

1. *nnn*

    n is used as a factor $\qquad$ $n \cdot n \cdot n$

    3 ■ times.

    Write with an exponent. $n^{■}$ 3

Find the value of each power.

3. c^2 when *c* is -2

    c is used as a factor $\qquad$ c^2

    2 ■ times.

    Substitute -2 for *c*. $\qquad$ *cc*

    Multiply. $\qquad\qquad$ $(-2)(■)^{-2}$

    $\qquad\qquad\qquad\qquad$ ■ 4

2. *xyy*

    x is used as a factor $\qquad$ $x \cdot ■ \cdot ■^{y\ \ y}$

    1 ■ time.

    y is used as a factor

    2 ■ times.

    Write with an exponent. $xy^{■}$ 2

4. a^4 when *a* is 3

    a is used as a factor $\quad$ a^4

    4 ■ times.

    Substitute 3 for *a*. $\qquad$ *aaaa*

    Multiply. $\qquad\qquad$ $■ \cdot ■ \cdot ■ \cdot ■^{3\ \ \ 3\ \ \ 3\ \ \ 3}$

    $\qquad\qquad\qquad\qquad$ ■
    $\qquad\qquad\qquad\qquad$ 81

Practice

Use exponents to rewrite each product.

1. *ggg* $\ g^3$ **2.** *ppq* $\ p^2q$ **3.** *aabbbb* $\ a^2b^4$ **4.** *hhhh* $\ h^4$

5. *rr* $\ r^2$ **6.** *bccc* $\ bc^3$ **7.** *yyyyy* $\ y^5$ **8.** *mmnn* $\ m^2n^2$

Find the value of each power.

9. a^3 when *a* is 4 64   **10.** x^3 when *x* is -1 -1 **11.** $-y^5$ when *y* is 2 -32

12. b^2 when *b* is -3 9   **13.** w^4 when *w* is 1 1   **14.** c^2 when *c* is 7 49

Cooperative Learning

15. Explain to a partner how to rewrite the expression in number **6**
in **Practice.** Possible answer: *b* is used as a factor 1 time. *c* is used as a factor 3 times.
$bccc = bc^3$.

16. Pick a number between 1 and 5. Have a partner find x^3 when *x* is
your number. Check the work. Possible answers: $1^3 = 1$; $2^3 = 8$; $3^3 = 27$; $4^3 = 64$; $5^3 = 125$

More practice is provided in Exercise 56 of the Workbook.

10·2 Multiplying with Exponents

You can multiply powers when the bases are the same. First, rewrite each power as the product of factors. Then, see how many times each base is used as a factor.

EXAMPLE 1

Multiply. $a^2 \cdot a^3$

$$a^2 \cdot a^3$$

Write as factors. $aa \cdot aaa$

$aaaaa$

Rewrite with an exponent. a^5

$a^2 \cdot a^3 = a^5$

EXAMPLE 2

Multiply. $b^2 \cdot ab$

$$b^2 \cdot ab$$

Remember
The Commutative Property of Multiplication lets you rearrange the factors.

Write as factors. $bb \cdot ab$

Rearrange the factors. $abbb$

Rewrite with an exponent. ab^3

$b^2 \cdot ab = ab^3$

EXAMPLE 3

Multiply. $ab^2 \cdot a^2b^3$

$$ab^2 \cdot a^2b^3$$

Write as factors. $abb \cdot aabbb$

Rearrange the factors. $aaabbbbb$

Rewrite with exponents. a^3b^5

$ab^2 \cdot a^2b^3 = a^3b^5$

Multiply any coefficients first.

EXAMPLE 4

Multiply. $3x^2y \cdot 2x$

Multiply the coefficients. $3x^2y \cdot 2x$

Write as factors. $6xxy \cdot x$

Rearrange the factors. $6xxxy$

Rewrite the variables with an exponent. $6x^3y$

$3x^2y \cdot 2x = 6x^3y$

Multiply.

1. $b^4 \cdot 3b^2$

Write as factors. $b^4 \cdot 3b^2$
$bbbb \cdot 3\blacksquare\, bb$

Rearrange the factors. $3bbbbbb$

Rewrite with an exponent. $3b^{\blacksquare\,6}$

$b^4 \cdot 3b^2 = \blacksquare\, 3b^6$

2. $-2c^2d \cdot 5cd$

Multiply the coefficients. $-2c^2d \cdot 5cd$
$-10\,\blacksquare\, c^2dcd$

Write as factors. $-10\,\blacksquare\, ccdcd$

Rearrange the factors. $-10\,\blacksquare\, cccdd$

Rewrite the variables with exponents. $-10\,\blacksquare\, c^{\blacksquare\,3}d^{\blacksquare\,2}$

$-2c^2d \cdot 5cd = \blacksquare\, -10c^3d^2$

Practice

Multiply.

1. $c^3 \cdot c$
c^4

2. $d^2 \cdot d^5$
d^7

3. $x^3 \cdot x^3$
x^6

4. $5a^3 \cdot 2ab^2$
$10a^4b^2$

5. $xy \cdot x$
x^2y

6. $4c^2d \cdot 5c^2d$
$20c^4d^2$

7. $-3a \cdot -2b$
$6ab$

8. $5 \cdot 3t^2$
$15t^2$

9. $x \cdot 2x$
$2x^2$

10. $x^2y^2 \cdot x^2y$
x^4y^3

11. $-3a^3d \cdot ad^2$
$-3a^4d^3$

12. $2bc^4 \cdot 3b^2c^2$
$6b^3c^6$

13. $6b^4 \cdot 2ab^2$
$12ab^6$

14. $x^6y \cdot 3x^5y$
$3x^{11}y^2$

15. $-2h^3g^4 \cdot -4h^2g^2$
$8h^5g^6$

16. $7np^3 \cdot 3np$
$21n^2p^4$

17. $3y^2 \cdot -y$
$-3y^3$

18. $-4ab \cdot -6ab$
$24a^2b^2$

Cooperative Learning

19. Explain to a partner how to find the product in number 6
in **Practice.** Possible answer: Rewrite without exponents: $4ccd \cdot 5ccd$. Combine common factors:
$4 \cdot 5ccccdd$. Multiply 4 times 5, and rewrite with exponents: $20c^4d^2$.

20. Write a power. Use n as the base and choose an exponent. Ask a
partner to find the product of that power and n^3. Possible answer: Picks 9. Writes
$n^9 \cdot n^3$. The partner writes n^{12}.

10-3 Rules for Multiplication

Getting Started
Invite students to find the pattern and identify the exponent for the expression,
b. $bbbb = b^4$; $bbb = b^3$; $bb = b^2$; $b = ?$ (b^1)

You have multiplied powers with the same base by rewriting as a product of factors.
$$a^3 \bullet a^2 = aaa \bullet aa = aaaaa = a^5$$

You can also multiply by adding the exponents.
$$a^3 \bullet a^2 = a^{3+2} = a^5$$

To multiply powers with the same base, add the exponents and keep the base.

▶ **EXAMPLE 1**

Multiply. $x^5 \bullet x^7$

$$x^5 \bullet x^7$$

Add the exponents of x. $5 + 7 = 12$

Write the base with the sum of the exponents. x^{12}

$$x^5 \bullet x^7 = x^{12}$$

▶ **EXAMPLE 2**

Multiply. $4b^2c^4 \bullet 3bc^2$

$$4b^2c^4 \bullet 3bc^2$$

Multiply the coefficients. $12b^2c^4 \bullet bc^2$

Math Fact
b is the same as b^1.

Add the exponents of b. $2 + 1 = 3$

Add the exponents of c. $4 + 2 = 6$

Write the bases with the sums of the exponents. $12b^3c^6$

$$4b^2c^4 \bullet 3bc^2 = 12b^3c^6$$

Sometimes, the base of a power is another power. Rewrite the product as factors.

▶ **EXAMPLE 3**

Multiply. $(a^3)^2$

$$(a^3)^2$$

Use a^3 as a factor 2 times. $a^3 \bullet a^3$

Add the exponents. $3 + 3 = 6$

Write the base with the sum of the exponents. a^6

$$(a^3)^2 = a^6$$

Try These

Multiply.

1. $2\,x^2y \cdot 5xy$

$$2x^2y \cdot 5xy$$

Multiply the coefficients. $10 \;\blacksquare\; x^2y \cdot xy$

Add the exponents of x. $2 + 1 = \blacksquare^{3}$

Add the exponents of y. $1 + \blacksquare^{1} = \blacksquare^{2}$

Write the bases with the sums of the exponents. $10x^{\blacksquare 3}\, y^{\blacksquare 2}$

2. $(c^4)^3$

$$(c^4)^3$$

c^4 is used as a factor $c^4 \cdot c^4 \cdot c^4$
$3\;\blacksquare$ times.

Add the exponents. $\blacksquare^{4} + \blacksquare^{4} + \blacksquare^{4} = 12$

Write the base with the sum of the exponents. $(c^4)^3 = c^{\blacksquare 12}$

Practice

Multiply.

1. $x^4 \cdot x^6$
x^{10}

2. $a^2b \cdot a^3$
a^5b

3. $w^2x^3 \cdot w^3x^3$
w^5x^6

4. $x^7 \cdot x^3$
x^{10}

5. $b^6c^6 \cdot b^2c^6$
b^8c^{12}

6. $5w^4x^5 \cdot x^2$
$5w^4x^7$

7. $a^2 \cdot 3a^2$
$3a^4$

8. $2b^3 \cdot 4wb^4$
$8wb^7$

9. $5c^5q^3 \cdot 6cq$
$30c^6q^4$

10. $-6a^4b \cdot 2a^5b^6$
$-12a^9b^7$

11. $(a^3)^3$
a^9

12. $(4c^2)^3$
$64c^6$

13. $(d^5)^2$
d^{10}

14. $(x^6)^2$
x^{12}

15. $(y^4)^5$
y^{20}

16. $x^4y^5 \cdot -4$
$-4x^4y^5$

17. $-8n^5 \cdot 4n^2p$
$-32n^7p$

18. $-6x^5y \cdot 6xy^5$
$-36x^6y^6$

Cooperative Learning

19. Explain to a partner how to find the product in number **4**
in **Practice**. Possible answer: Add the exponents: $7 + 3$. Write the expression using the sum: x^{10}.

20. Write a power using a and b as bases. Have a partner write
another power using a and b as bases. Multiply the powers.
Possible answer: Write a^2b^3. Partner writes a^4b^5. Multiply: $a^2b^3 \cdot a^4b^5 = a^6b^8$.

More practice is provided in Exercise 57 of the Workbook.

Getting Started
Present division problems. Have students write each as a fraction. For example,

$5 \div 3 \quad x \div y \quad ab \div ac$

$\left(\frac{5}{3}, \frac{x}{y}, \frac{ab}{ac}\right)$

10-4 ▶ Division with Exponents

To divide two powers with the same base, write the division as a fraction. Then, remove common factors.

$$a^4 \div a^2 = \frac{\cancel{a}\cancel{a}aa}{\cancel{a}\cancel{a}} = \frac{1aa}{1} = a^2$$

▶ **EXAMPLE 1**

Math Fact
A number divided by itself equals 1.

Divide. $\qquad a^5 \div a^2$

Write as a fraction. $\qquad \dfrac{a^5}{a^2}$

Rewrite as factors. Remove common factors. $\qquad \dfrac{aaaaa}{aa} = \dfrac{\cancel{a}\cancel{a}aaa}{\cancel{a}\cancel{a}}$

Simplify. $\qquad aaa$

Rewrite with an exponent. $\qquad a^3$

$a^5 \div a^2 = a^3$

▶ **EXAMPLE 2**

Divide. $\qquad b^4c^3 \div b^2c^2$

Write as a fraction. $\qquad \dfrac{b^4c^3}{b^2c^2}$

Rewrite as factors. Remove common factors. $\qquad \dfrac{bbbbccc}{bbcc} = \dfrac{\cancel{b}\cancel{b}bbb\cancel{c}\cancel{c}c}{\cancel{b}\cancel{b}\cancel{c}\cancel{c}}$

Simplify. $\qquad bbc$

Rewrite with an exponent. $\qquad b^2c$

$b^4c^3 \div b^2c^2 = b^2c$

Be sure to divide the coefficients.

▶ **EXAMPLE 3**

Divide. $\qquad 10x^2y \div 5x$

Write as a fraction. $\qquad \dfrac{10x^2y}{5x}$

Divide the coefficients. $\qquad \dfrac{2x^2y}{x}$
$10 \div 5 = 2$

Rewrite as factors. Remove common factors. $\qquad \dfrac{2xxy}{x} = \dfrac{2\cancel{x}xy}{\cancel{x}}$

Simplify. $\qquad 2xy$

$10x^2y \div 5x = 2xy$

Try These

Divide.

1. $12w^3 \div 6w^2$

Write as a fraction. $\dfrac{12w^3}{6w^2}$

Divide the coefficients. $\dfrac{2\,\blacksquare w^3}{w^2}$

Rewrite as factors.
Remove common factors. $\dfrac{2\,\blacksquare www}{ww}$

Simplify. $\blacksquare\, 2w$

$12w^3 \div 6w^2 = \blacksquare\, 2w$

2. $a^2b^4 \div ab^2$

Write as a fraction. $\dfrac{a^2b^4}{ab^2}$

Rewrite as factors. $\dfrac{aabbbb}{abb}$

Remove common factors.

Simplify. $\blacksquare\, abb$

Rewrite with exponents. $ab^{\blacksquare\,2}$

$a^2b^4 \div ab^2 = \blacksquare\, ab^2$

Practice

19. Possible answer: Write as a fraction: $\dfrac{15w^4}{3w}$. Rewrite as factors: $\dfrac{(5)(3)wwww}{3w}$. Remove common factors. Simplify to $5www$ and rewrite with exponents: $5w^3$.

Divide.

1. $b^4 \div b^3$
b

2. $x^2y \div x$
xy

3. $5c^2d^3 \div cd^2$
$5cd$

4. $15w^4 \div 3w$
$5w^3$

5. $s^2t^8 \div st^3$
st^5

6. $14x^3y^4 \div 7x^2y$
$2xy^3$

7. $6n^2p \div np$
$6n$

8. $12x^4y^5 \div -4x^3y^4$
$-3xy$

9. $9x^2y \div y$
$9x^2$

10. $8m^4n^2 \div 2mn^2$
$4m^3$

11. $pq^4 \div pq^2$
q^2

12. $x^3y^4 \div x^2y$
xy^3

13. $r^4k^3 \div r^3k^3$
r

14. $24xy^5 \div 4xy$
$6y^4$

15. $ab^2c \div bc$
ab

16. $-21x^4y^2 \div 3x^2$
$-7x^2y^2$

17. $18x^6y^3 \div 3x^2y$
$6x^4y^2$

18. $4a^3b \div 4b$
a^3

Cooperative Learning

19. Explain to a partner how to find the quotient in number **4** in **Practice**. See above.

20. Work with a partner to find the quotient of $15a^3b^5 \div 3a^2b^3$. The quotient is $5ab^2$.

More practice is provided in Exercise 57 of the Workbook.

Getting Started
Ask students to simplify the following:

$x^2 + x^2 = ?$ $(2x^2)$
$7x^2 - 2x^2 = ?$ $(5x^2)$
$x^3 \cdot x^2 = ?$ (x^5)
$x^5 \div x^3 = ?$ (x^2)

Elicit that you can add or subtract exponents only when bases are the same and terms are multiplied or divided.

You have divided two powers with the same base using properties of division and multiplication.

$$\frac{x^5}{x^3} = \frac{xxxxx}{xxx} = \frac{1 \cdot xx}{1} = x^2$$

You can also divide by subtracting the exponents.

$$x^5 \div x^3 = x^{5-3} = x^2$$

To divide powers with the same base, keep the base and subtract the exponent in the denominator from the exponent in the numerator.

▶ **EXAMPLE 1**

Divide. $\quad \dfrac{x^7}{x^2}$

$$\frac{x^7}{x^2}$$

Subtract the exponents of x. $\qquad 7 - 2 = 5$

Write the base with the difference of exponents. $\quad x^5$

$$\frac{x^7}{x^2} = x^5$$

▶ **EXAMPLE 2**

Divide. $\quad \dfrac{a^6 b^3}{a^2}$

$$\frac{a^6 b^3}{a^2}$$

Subtract the exponents of a. $\qquad 6 - 2 = 4$

The exponent of b stays 3.

Write the bases with the difference of exponents. $\quad a^4 b^3$

$$\frac{a^6 b^3}{a^2} = a^4 b^3$$

▶ **EXAMPLE 3**

Divide. $\quad \dfrac{12c^5}{3c^2}$

Divide the coefficients.

$$\frac{4c^5}{c^2}$$

Subtract the exponents of the factors of c. $\qquad 5 - 2 = 3$

Write the base with the difference of exponents. $\quad 4c^3$

$$\frac{12c^5}{3c^2} = 4c^3$$

Try These

Divide.

1. $\dfrac{8x^6}{2x^3}$

Divide the coefficients. $\dfrac{8x^6}{2x^3} = \dfrac{4x^6}{x^3}$

Subtract the exponents of x. $\underset{6}{\blacksquare} - \underset{3}{\blacksquare} = 3$

Write the base with the difference of the exponents. $4x^{\blacksquare}\,3$

$\dfrac{8x^6}{2x^3} = \blacksquare\ 4x^3$

2. $\dfrac{g^6h^5}{g^2h^3}$

$\dfrac{g^6h^5}{g^2h^3}$

Subtract the exponents of g. $\underset{5}{6} - \underset{3}{\blacksquare} = \underset{2}{\blacksquare}$

Subtract the exponents of h. $\blacksquare - \blacksquare = \blacksquare$

Write the bases with the differences of the exponents. $g^{\blacksquare\,4}h^{\blacksquare\,2}$

$\dfrac{g^6h^5}{g^2h^3} = \blacksquare\ g^4h^2$

Practice

Divide.

1. $\dfrac{b^8}{b^6}$ b^2

2. $\dfrac{a^5}{a^4}$ a

3. $\dfrac{6r^7}{2r^3}$ $3r^4$

4. $\dfrac{x^4y}{x^2}$ x^2y

5. $\dfrac{c^5d^3}{cd}$ c^4d^2

6. $\dfrac{w^5g}{w^2}$ w^3g

7. $\dfrac{10m^4n^5}{2mn^2}$ $5m^3n^3$

8. $\dfrac{7b^6c^5}{b^2c}$ $7b^4c^4$

9. $\dfrac{x^7y^4}{x^2y}$ x^5y^3

10. $\dfrac{b^2c^4}{bc^3}$ bc

11. $\dfrac{18x^4y^3}{3x^2y}$ $6x^2y^2$

12. $\dfrac{a^2b^2c^6}{abc^3}$ abc^3

13. Possible answer: Divide 10 by 2. Subtract exponents of m: $4 - 1 = 3$. Subtract exponents of n: $5 - 2 = 3$. Rewrite bases with the differences of the exponents and the coefficient: $5m^3n^3$.

Cooperative Learning

13. Explain to a partner how to find the quotient in number **7** in **Practice.** See above.

14. Write a variable expression with a positive exponent. Write another expression with the same variable and a smaller positive exponent. Ask a partner to find the quotient. Check the work.
Possible answer: Write a^8b^6 and a^3b^3. Partner writes a^5b^3.

More practice is provided in Exercise 56 of the Workbook.

10-6 ▶ Zero As an Exponent

Getting Started

On the chalkboard, write $\frac{2x}{2x} = 1$.

Ask students to write other fractions that equal 1. Encourage them to use variables with exponents.

Zero can be an exponent. Use the rules for dividing to find the value of a power with an exponent of 0.

$$1 = \frac{a^3}{a^3} = a^3 \div a^3 = a^{3-3} = a^0$$

Any power with a zero exponent = 1.

▶ **EXAMPLE 1**

Multiply. $a^2 \bullet a^0$

$$a^2 \bullet a^0$$

Write 1 for the power with a 0 exponent. $a^2 \bullet 1$

Simplify. a^2

$a^2 \bullet a^0 = a^2$

▶ **EXAMPLE 2**

Divide. $\frac{c^3 d^5}{c^3 d^2}$

$$\frac{c^3 d^5}{c^3 d^2}$$

Subtract the exponents of c. $3 - 3 = 0$

Subtract the exponents of d. $5 - 2 = 3$

Write the bases with the exponents. $c^0 d^3$

Write 1 for the power with a 0 exponent. Simplify. $1 \bullet d^3 = d^3$

$\frac{c^3 d^5}{c^3 d^2} = d^3$

▶ **EXAMPLE 3**

Divide. $\frac{15x^4 y^6}{x^4 y^6}$

$$\frac{15x^4 y^6}{x^4 y^6}$$

Subtract the exponents of x. $4 - 4 = 0$

Subtract the exponents of y. $6 - 6 = 0$

Write the bases with the exponents. $15x^0 y^0$

Write 1 for the powers with 0 exponents. Simplify. $15 \bullet 1 \bullet 1 = 15$

$\frac{15x^4 y^6}{x^4 y^6} = 15$

Try These

Divide.

1. $\dfrac{a^3b^5}{a^3b^3}$

$$\dfrac{a^3b^5}{a^3b^3}$$

Subtract the exponents of a. $3 - 3 = \blacksquare\ 0$

Subtract the exponents of b. $5 - 3 = \blacksquare\ 2$

Write the bases with the exponents. $a_{\blacksquare 0} b_{\blacksquare 2}$

Write 1 for the power with a 0 exponent. $1 \cdot b^{\blacksquare 2}$

Simplify. $b^{\blacksquare 2}$

$$\dfrac{a^3b^5}{a^3b^3} = b^{\blacksquare 2}$$

2. $\dfrac{xy^4}{y^4}$

$$\dfrac{xy^4}{y^4}$$

Subtract the exponents of y. $4 - 4 = \blacksquare\ 0$

Write the bases with the exponents. $x_{1}^{\blacksquare} y_{0}^{\blacksquare}$

Write 1 for the power with a 0 exponent. $\blacksquare \cdot \blacksquare$ x 1

Simplify. $\blacksquare\ x$

$$\dfrac{xy^4}{y^4} = \blacksquare\ x$$

Practice

Multiply.

1. $b^0 \cdot b^6$ b^6

2. $x^4y \cdot x^2y^0$ x^6y

3. $c^3de^0 \cdot c^0d^5e^0$ c^3d^6

Divide.

4. $\dfrac{m^4}{m^4}$ 1

5. $\dfrac{s^2t^5}{s^2t}$ t^4

6. $\dfrac{h^8g^3}{hg^3}$ h^7

7. $\dfrac{y^4z^5}{z^5}$ y^4

8. $\dfrac{b^2c^5}{b^2c^3}$ c^2

9. $\dfrac{x^2y^4z^6}{xy^4}$ xz^6

10. $\dfrac{q^2r^8}{q^2r^8}$ 1

11. $\dfrac{h^2j^5k^7}{h^2j^5k^7}$ 1

12. $\dfrac{t^7u}{t^6u}$ t

13. Possible answer: Add the exponents of c: $3 + 0 = 3$. Add the exponents of d: $1 + 5 = 6$. Add the exponents of e: $0 + 0 = 0$. Write bases with the sums of the exponents: $c^3d^6e^0$. Simplify: c^3d^6.

Cooperative Learning

13. Explain to a partner how you find the product in number **3** in **Practice.** See above.

14. Write a division or multiplication problem that uses a zero exponent. Have a partner solve your problem. Check the work.

Possible answer: Divide: $\dfrac{c^5b^2}{c^3b^2}$. Subtract the exponents of b: $2 - 2 = 0$. Subtract the exponents of c: $5 - 3 = 2$. Write bases with the exponents: b^0c^2. Simplify: c^2.

Getting Started
Have students
follow a pattern
to determine the
value of 2^{-1}. Present
$2^3 = 8$
$2^2 = 4$
$2^1 = 2$
$2^0 = 1$
$2^{-1} = ?$
Ask students to guess what
2^{-1} might be. ($\frac{1}{2}$; you divide
by 2 from line to line.)

10·7 Negative Exponents

An exponent can be negative. You can find the meaning of a negative exponent by using what you know about division and exponents.

$$\frac{a^2}{a^3} = \frac{aa}{aaa} = \frac{1}{a} \text{ and } \frac{a^2}{a^3} = a^{2-3} = a^{-1}$$

A number with a negative exponent is the same as 1 divided by the number with a positive exponent.

▶ **EXAMPLE 1**

Write with a positive exponent. a^{-6}

Write as a fraction with a positive exponent. $\frac{1}{a^6}$

$a^{-6} = \frac{1}{a^6}$

▶ **EXAMPLE 2**

Divide. $\frac{b^4}{b^8}$ Then, write with a positive exponent.

$\frac{b^4}{b^8}$

Subtract the exponents of b. $4 - 8 = -4$

Write the base with the exponent. b^{-4}

Write as a fraction with a positive exponent. $\frac{1}{b^4}$

$\frac{b^4}{b^8} = \frac{1}{b^4}$

▶ **EXAMPLE 3**

Divide. $\frac{x^2y^6}{x^4y^2}$ Then, write with positive exponents.

$\frac{x^2y^6}{x^4y^2}$

Subtract the exponents of x. $2 - 4 = -2$

Subtract the exponents of y. $6 - 2 = 4$

Write the bases with the exponents. $x^{-2}y^4$

Write with positive exponents. $\frac{1}{x^2}y^4$

Simplify. $\frac{y^4}{x^2}$

$\frac{x^2y^6}{x^4y^2} = \frac{y^4}{x^2}$

Try These

Multiply or divide.

1. $x^{-6}y^9 \cdot x^2y^{-6}$

$$x^{-6}y^9 \cdot x^2y^{-6}$$

Add the exponents of x. $-6 + 2 = \blacksquare\ -4$

Add the exponents of y. $9 + (-6) = \blacksquare\ 3$

Write the bases with the exponents. $x^{\blacksquare -4}y^{\blacksquare 3}$

Write using positive exponents. $\dfrac{1}{x^4}\blacksquare \cdot \blacksquare\ y^3$

Simplify. $\dfrac{y^{\blacksquare 3}}{x^{\blacksquare 4}}$

$$x^{-6}y^9 \cdot x^2y^{-6} = \dfrac{y^{\blacksquare 3}}{x^{\blacksquare 4}}$$

2. $\dfrac{a^4b^5}{a^2b^8}$

$$\dfrac{a^4b^5}{a^2b^8}$$

Subtract the exponents of a. $4 - 2 = \blacksquare\ 2$

Subtract the exponents of b. $5 - 8 = \blacksquare\ -3$

Write the bases with the exponents. $a^{\blacksquare 2}b^{\blacksquare -3}$

Write using positive exponents. $a^2 \cdot \blacksquare\ \dfrac{1}{b^3}$

Simplify. $\blacksquare\ \dfrac{a^2}{b^3}$

$$\dfrac{a^4b^5}{a^2b^8} = \blacksquare\ \dfrac{a^2}{b^3}$$

Practice

Multiply. Then, write with a positive exponent.

1. $b^{-6} \cdot b^8$ b^2

2. $n^2 \cdot n^{-5}$ $\dfrac{1}{n^3}$

3. $c^5d^{-4} \cdot c^{-6}d^7$ $\dfrac{d^3}{c}$

4. $x^{-2}y \cdot x^2y^{-3}$ $\dfrac{1}{y^2}$

5. $q^{-1}r^5 \cdot q^{-2}r$ $\dfrac{r^6}{q^3}$

6. $w^{-7}z^2 \cdot w^3z^{-4}$ $\dfrac{1}{w^4z^2}$

Divide. Then, write with a positive exponent.

7. $\dfrac{m^4}{m^9}$ $\dfrac{1}{m^5}$

8. $\dfrac{p^3}{p^8}$ $\dfrac{1}{p^5}$

9. $\dfrac{bc^5}{b^{-9}c}$ $b^{10}c^4$

10. $\dfrac{y^{-2}z^4}{y^5z^4}$ $\dfrac{1}{y^7}$

11. $\dfrac{j^6k}{jk^3}$ $\dfrac{j^5}{k^2}$

12. $\dfrac{d^5e}{de^4}$ $\dfrac{d^4}{e^3}$

Cooperative Learning

13. Explain to a partner how you find the product in number **2** in **Practice.** Possible answer: Add the exponents of n: $2 + (-5) = -3$. Write the base with the exponent: n^{-3}. Write the expression as a fraction with positive exponents: $\dfrac{1}{n^3}$.

14. Write a division problem. Use a and b as bases. Have a partner find the answer. Check the work. Possible answer: $\dfrac{a^3b^2}{a^6b^2} = \dfrac{1}{a^3}$.

10-8 ▶ Scientific Notation

Getting Started
Have students explain how to find the product of 5.23 × 1000. Encourage students to count the number of zeros in 1000. (3) Then, move the decimal point in 5.23 three places to the right. (5,230)

Scientific notation is used to name large numbers such as 324,000. A number in scientific notation has two factors.

3.24   × 10^5

first factor   second factor

a number between 1 and 10   a power of 10

You can find the large number by multiplying.
$3.24 \times 10^5 = 3.24 \times 100,000 = 324000. = 324,000$

Move the decimal point one place for each zero in the power of ten. This is the same as the exponent in the second factor. Move to the right when the exponent is positive.

▶ **EXAMPLE 1**

3 is the exponent in 10^3.

Find the number named by 9.2×10^3.

10^3 is equal to 1,000. $9.2 \times 1,000$

Move the decimal point 3 places to the right. $9200. = 9,200$

$9.2 \times 10^3 = 9,200$

▶ **EXAMPLE 2**

Find the number named by 4.32×10^5.

10^5 is equal to 100,000. $4.32 \times 100,000$

Move the decimal point 5 places to the right. $432000. = 432,000$

$4.32 \times 10^5 = 432,000$

You can use a negative exponent to name a very small number. Move the decimal point one place to the left for each decimal place in the power of 10.

▶ **EXAMPLE 3**

Find the number named by 3.8×10^{-4}.

10^{-4} is equal to .0001. $3.8 \times .0001$

Move the decimal point 4 places to the left. $.00038 = .00038$

$3.8 \times 10^{-4} = .00038$

Practice

Find each number named in scientific notation.

1. 1.61×10^2 161

2. 8.4×10^3 $\quad$ 8,400

3. 9.24×10^5 924,000

4. 5.29×10^4 52,900

5. 2.742×10^5 274,200

6. 3.9×10^2 $\quad$ 390

7. 2.6×10^{-2} .026

8. 1.04×10^{-3} .00104

9. 4.1×10^{-5} .000041

10. 6.08×10^4 60,800

11. 4.7×10^{-6} .0000047

12. 1.9×10^5 $\quad$ 190,000

Find the number written in scientific notation in each sentence.

13. The distance from the earth to the sun is about 9.3×10^7 miles.
93,000,000

14. One atom of oxygen has a mass of 2.66×10^{-23} grams.
.0000000000000000000000266

Cooperative Learning

15. Write a number in scientific notation. Ask a partner to find the number you named. Answers will vary.

16. Pick a decimal number between 1 and 10. Ask a partner to find the product of your number and 10^4. Possible answer: $1.54 \times 10^4 = 15,400$.

10-9 ▶ Exponential Functions

Getting Started
To review ordered pairs, write the equation $y = x^2 + 5$ on the chalkboard. Have a volunteer show that $(2, 9)$ is a solution to the equation. Ask for other solutions.

In some functions, the exponent is a variable. These are called **exponential functions**.

$$y = 2^x \leftarrow \text{exponent is a variable}$$

You can find ordered pairs for these functions by substituting values for the variable. Then, you can make a table of values.

▶ **EXAMPLE 1**

Find four ordered pairs for $y = 2^x$.
Make a table of values.

Math Fact
$2^0 = 1$.

Substitute 0 for x. Simplify 2^0.

Substitute 1 for x. Simplify 2^1.

Substitute 2 for x. Simplify 2^2.

Substitute 3 for x. Simplify 2^3.

x	2^x	y
0	2^0	1
1	2^1	2
2	2^2	4
3	2^3	8

$(0, 1)$, $(1, 2)$, $(2, 4)$, and $(3, 8)$ are four ordered pairs.

▶ **EXAMPLE 2**

Find four ordered pairs for $y = 2 \cdot 3^x$.
Make a table of values.

Substitute 0 for x. Simplify $2 \cdot 3^0$.

Substitute 1 for x. Simplify $2 \cdot 3^1$.

Substitute 2 for x. Simplify $2 \cdot 3^2$.

Substitute 3 for x. Simplify $2 \cdot 3^3$.

x	$2 \cdot 3^x$	y
0	$2 \cdot 3^0$	2
1	$2 \cdot 3^1$	6
2	$2 \cdot 3^2$	18
3	$2 \cdot 3^3$	54

$(0, 2)$, $(1, 6)$, $(2, 18)$, and $(3, 54)$ are four ordered pairs.

▶ **EXAMPLE 3**

Find four ordered pairs for $y = -4^x$.
Make a table of values.

Math Fact
-4^x means $-1 \cdot 4^x$.

Substitute 0 for x. Simplify $-1 \cdot 4^0$.

Substitute 1 for x. Simplify $-1 \cdot 4^1$.

Substitute 2 for x. Simplify $-1 \cdot 4^2$.

Substitute 3 for x. Simplify $-1 \cdot 4^3$.

x	$-1 \cdot 4^x$	y
0	$-1 \cdot 4^0$	-1
1	$-1 \cdot 4^1$	-4
2	$-1 \cdot 4^2$	-16
3	$-1 \cdot 4^3$	-64

$(0, -1)$, $(1, -4)$, $(2, -16)$, and $(3, -64)$ are four ordered pairs.

Try These

Find five ordered pairs for each function. Make a table of values.

1. $y = 5^x$

Substitute:

0 for x

1 for x

2 for x

3 for x

4 for x

x	5^x	y
0	$5^{\blacksquare\,0}$ ▦	1
1	$5^{\blacksquare\,1}$ ▦	5
2	$5^{\blacksquare\,2}$ ▦	25
3	$5^{\blacksquare\,3}$ ▦	125
▦4	$5^{\blacksquare\,4}$ ▦	625

$$\underset{1}{}\quad\underset{5}{}\quad\underset{25}{}\quad\underset{125}{}$$

(0, ▦), (1, ▦), (2, ▦), (3, ▦), and 4; 625 (▦, ▦) are five ordered pairs for $y = 5^x$.

2. $y = 4 \bullet 2^x$

Substitute:

0 for x

1 for x

2 for x

3 for x

4 for x

x	$4 \bullet 2^x$	y
0	$4 \bullet 2^0$ ▦	4
1	$4 \bullet 2^{\blacksquare\,1}$ ▦	8
2	$4 \bullet 2^{\blacksquare\,2}$ ▦	16
3	$4 \bullet 2^{\blacksquare\,3}$ ▦	32
▦4	$4 \bullet 2^{\blacksquare\,4}$ ▦	64

$$\underset{4}{}\quad\underset{8}{}\quad\underset{16}{}\quad\underset{32}{}$$

(0, ▦), (1, ▦), (2, ▦), (3, ▦), and 4; 64 (▦, ▦) are five ordered pairs for $y = 4 \bullet 2^x$.

Practice

Find five ordered pairs for each function. Make a table of values. Begin with $x = 0$. See Additional Answers, p. 477.

1. $y = 4^x$

2. $y = 3^x$

3. $y = -2 \bullet 5^x$

Find four ordered pairs for each function. Make a table of values. Begin with $x = 0$. See Additional Answers, p. 477.

4. $y = 10^x$

5. $y = 8^x$

6. $y = 20^x$

Cooperative Learning

7. Explain to a partner how you find the ordered pairs in number **2** in **Practice**. Substitute 0, 1, 2, 3, and 4 for x. Find the value of y for each value of x. Write the ordered pairs from the table.

8. Write x^4 and 4^x. Ask a partner to find the base in each. Then, ask your partner to find the exponent in each. Finally, have your partner find the value of x^4 and 4^x when x is 3. Why are the values different? Possible answer: The bases for x^4 and 4^x are x and 4, respectively; The exponents are 4 and x; $3^4 = 3 \bullet 3 \bullet 3 \bullet 3 = 81$ and $4^3 = 4 \bullet 4 \bullet 4 = 64$. Different bases with different exponents are different powers.

More practice is provided in Exercise 58 of the Workbook.

10·10 Graphing Exponential Functions

Getting Started
To review graphing, have students create a table of values for $y = 2x + 3$. Ask for volunteers to write and then graph the ordered pairs.

You have written tables of ordered pairs from exponential functions. You can use these tables to graph the ordered pairs.

When you look at the tables, you can see that the value of y increases much faster than the value of x. You cannot connect the points with a straight line. You connect them with a curved line.

▶ **EXAMPLE 1**

Graph $y = 3^x$ using the five ordered pairs from the table.

x	3^x	y
0	3^0	1
1	3^1	3
2	3^2	9
3	3^3	27
4	3^4	81

Write each row as an ordered pair.
(0, 1), (1, 3), (2, 9), (3, 27), (4, 81)

Graph the points on a coordinate plane.

Connect the points with a curve.

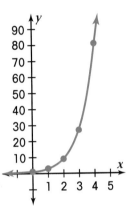

▶ **EXAMPLE 2**

Graph $y = 10^x$ using the five ordered pairs from the table.

x	10^x	y
0	10^0	1
1	10^1	10
2	10^2	100
3	10^3	1,000
4	10^4	10,000

Write each row as an ordered pair.
(0, 1), (1, 10), (2, 100), (3, 1,000), (4, 10,000)

Graph the points on a coordinate plane.

Connect the points with a curve.

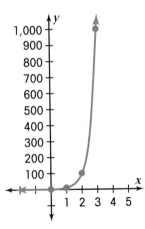

Try These

1. Find five ordered pairs for $y = 4^x$.

x	4^x
0	1
1	4
2	16
3	64
4	256

Write each row as an ordered pair.

(0, 1)
(1, ■) 4
(2, ■) 16
(3, ■) 64
(4, ■) 256

2. Write five ordered pairs from the graph.

(0, 3)
1 (■, 6)
2 (■, 12)
3 (■, 24)
4 (■, 48)

Practice

Graph each function using the five ordered pairs from the table. See Additional Answers, p. 478.

1.

x	2^x
0	1
1	2
2	4
3	8
4	16

2.

x	$5 \cdot 2^x$
0	5
1	10
2	20
3	40
4	80

3.

x	6^x
0	1
1	6
2	36
3	216
4	1,296

Cooperative Learning

4. Explain to a partner how you graph the ordered pairs in number 2 in **Practice.** Plot each row of the table as an ordered pair on a coordinate plane. Label each point. Connect the points with a smooth curve.

5. Write an exponential function. Pick a positive number for the base. Use x for the exponent. Have a partner find three ordered pairs for your function. Answers will vary. Make sure the students use a positive integer for the base and a variable for the exponent.

Getting Started
Have students
use their
calculators to
evaluate 2^3, 3^4, 4^3, and 5^4.
(8; 81; 64; 625)

10·11 ▶ Calculator: Finding Values of Powers

Sometimes, the base of a power is a decimal. You can use a calculator to evaluate a power with a decimal base.

▶ **EXAMPLE 1**

Find the value. 1.5^3

	Display
Enter 1.5 by pressing: `1` `.` `5`	1.5
Find the second power by pressing: `×` `1` `.` `5` `=`	2.25
Find the third power by pressing: `×` `1` `.` `5` `=`	3.375

$1.5^3 = 3.375$

Math Fact
$1.5^3 = 1.5 \bullet 1.5 \bullet 1.5$

When you find a power of a decimal, the number of decimal places gets larger each time you multiply. You can round your answer to two or three decimal places.

▶ **EXAMPLE 2**

Find the value. 1.2^5

	Display
Enter 1.2 by pressing: `1` `.` `2`	1.2
Find the second power by pressing: `×` `1` `.` `2` `=`	1.44
Find the third power by pressing: `×` `1` `.` `2` `=`	1.728
Find the fourth power by pressing: `×` `1` `.` `2` `=`	2.0736
Find the fifth power by pressing: `×` `1` `.` `2` `=`	2.48832

1.2^5 is about 2.49

Math Fact
$1.2^5 =$
$1.2 \bullet 1.2 \bullet 1.2 \bullet 1.2 \bullet 1.2$

▶ **EXAMPLE 3**

Find the value. $.25^3$

	Display
Enter .25 by pressing: `.` `2` `5`	0.25
Find the second power by pressing: `×` `.` `2` `5` `=`	0.0625
Find the third power by pressing: `×` `.` `2` `5` `=`	0.015625

$.25^3$ is about .016

Practice

Find the value of each power. Round your answer to two decimal places.

1. 7^4 2,401

2. $2 \cdot 4^3$ 128

3. $9 \cdot 5^2$ 225

4. $.1^5$ .00001

5. 9^4 6,561

6. 4^3 64

7. 1.8^2 3.24

8. $.6^5$ .078

9. 3.8^5 792.35

10. 1.2^4 2.07

11. 2.9^3 24.39

12. 1.31^2 1.72

People in Math

CHIEN-SHIUNG WU

Chien-Shiung Wu was born in China in 1912. Her name in Chinese means "strong hero." As a young girl, she loved solving puzzles. Her interest in puzzles and math led her to study physics.

Madame Wu, as she was called, moved to the United States in 1936. Here she received her Ph.D. in physics in 1940.

Madame Wu worked in physics. She planned one project that changed science. Her work helped scientists better understand how nuclear particles react.

Chien-Shiung Wu (1912–1997)

Madame Wu won many awards for her work, including the National Medal of Science. In the United States, this is the highest award in science a person can receive. An asteroid was named in her honor in 1990.

Other work she did helped scientists find the cause of sickle-cell anemia. This blood disease causes people to become very weak. Much of her work has helped the whole world. Madame Wu died in 1997.

More practice is provided in Exercise 59 of the Workbook.

10·12 ▶ Problem Solving: Counting Choices

▶ **EXAMPLE**

You can use a **tree diagram** to show choices.

In a class election, there are 3 candidates for president, (Tia, Nelson, and Michael). There are 2 candidates for vice president (Darryl and Joanne). How many ways are there to choose a president and vice president?

READ **What do you need to find out?**
You need to find how many ways the class can choose a president and vice president.

PLAN **What do you need to do?**
You need to make a tree diagram by listing the choices for president and the choices for vice president. Then count the pairs.

DO **Follow the plan.**

CHECK **Does your answer make sense?**
3 choices • 2 choices = 6 choices. ✓

There are 6 ways to choose a president and vice president.

Try These

1. Draw a tree diagram to show all the choices for 1 hat and 1 pair of gloves if you have two hats (blue and tan) and three pairs of gloves (black, brown, and red).

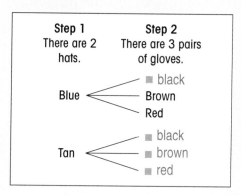

Step 1
There are 2 hats.

Step 2
There are 3 pairs of gloves.

Blue
— ■ black
— Brown
— Red

Tan
— ■ black
— ■ brown
— ■ red

2. Now do **Step 3.** List all the possible choices.

blue ■ hat and Black gloves

blue ■ hat and Brown gloves

blue ■ hat and Red gloves

tan ■ hat and ■ gloves   black

tan ■ hat and ■ gloves   brown

tan ■ hat and ■ gloves   red

You have ■ different choices.
6

Practice

Find the number of choices using a tree diagram.

1. You have three pairs of socks (red, blue, and white) and two pairs of sneakers (black and green). How many different combinations of socks and sneakers can you wear? 6 choices. See diagram in Additional Answers, p. 478.

2. You have two hats (blue and green) and four jackets (black, grey, brown, and red). How many different combinations of hat and jacket can you wear? 8 choices. See diagram in Additional Answers, p. 478.

Cooperative Learning

3. Explain to a partner how you draw the tree diagram in number 2 in **Practice.** Draw the two choices for the hats. For each hat, draw the four choices for the jackets. Count the total choices: eight.

4. Choose two different numbers that go together. Write a problem about choices. Do not use the numbers 2 or 3 for the number choices. Have a partner solve the problem. Answers will vary.

More practice is provided in Exercise 60 of the Workbook.

10-13 ▶ Application: Compound Interest

When you save money in a bank, your money earns interest every month, or year, or other time period. After the first time period, the interest is added to your money for a new total. Then, interest is earned on this new total. So, you earn interest on the interest.

First Period $100.00 at 10% interest   earn $10.00
Second Period $110.00 at 10% interest   earn $11.00
Third Period $121.00 at 10% interest   earn $12.10

This is called **compound interest.** You can use a formula to find your new total.

initial deposit   rate of interest
↓   ↓
$$\text{Total} = a(1 + r)^x \leftarrow \text{number of periods}$$

▶ **EXAMPLE 1**

Find the total after 2 years. The initial deposit is $100. The rate of interest is 5% a year. Use the formula $T = 100(1.05)^x$.

Math Facts
$5\% = .05 = .05$
$1 + .05 = 1.05$

$(1.05)^2 =$
$1.05 \cdot 1.05 = 1.1025$

Substitute 2 for x.

Simplify. Use a calculator to help you find the power.

$T = 100(1.05)^x$
$T = 100(1.05)^2$
$T = 100(1.1025)$
$T = 110.25$

The total is $110.25 after 2 years.

▶ **EXAMPLE 2**

Find the total after 3 years. The initial deposit is $20. The rate of interest is 10%. Use the formula $T = 20(1.1)^x$.

Math Facts
$(1.1)^3 = 1.1 \cdot 1.1 \cdot 1.1$
$(1.1)^3 = 1.331$

Substitute 3 for x.

Simplify.

$T = 20(1.1)^x$
$T = 20(1.1)^3$
$T = 20(1.331)$
$T = 26.62$

The total is $26.62 after 3 years.

Try These

Find the total after 2 years. Use the formula.

1. $T = 1,000(1.08)^x$

	$T = 1,000(1.08)^x$
Substitute 2 for x.	$T = 1,000(1.08)^{\blacksquare\, 2}$
Simplify.	$T = 1,000(\blacksquare)\, 1.1664$
	$T = \blacksquare\, 1166.4$

After 2 years, the total is ■. $1,160.40

2. $T = 500(1.15)^x$

	$T = 500(1.15)^x$
Substitute 2 for x.	$T = 500(1.15)^{\blacksquare\, 2}$
Simplify.	$T = 500(\blacksquare)\, 1.3225$
	$T = \blacksquare\, 661.25$

After 2 years, the total is ■. $661.25

Practice

In each equation find the initial balance and the interest rate.

1. $T = 1,000(1 + .05)^x$
$a = \$1,000;\ r = 5\%$

2. $T = 200(1 + .10)^x$
$a = \$200;\ r = 10\%$

3. $T = 150(1 + .08)^x$
$a = \$150;\ r = 8\%$

4. $T = 2,500(1 + .15)^x$
$a = \$2,500;\ r = 15\%$

5. $T = 10(1 + .05)^x$
$a = \$10;\ r = 5\%$

6. $T = 10,000(1 + .02)^x$
$a = \$10,000;\ r = 2\%$

Find each total after the given number of periods.

7. 1 year $385.00
$T = 350(1.1)^x$

8. 3 years $463.05
$T = 400(1.05)^x$

9. 0 years $50,000.00
$T = 50,000(1.18)^x$

10. 3 years $15,608.96
$T = 10,000(1.16)^x$

11. 2 years $605.00
$T = 500(1.1)^x$

12. 1 year $2,728.50
$T = 2,550(1.07)^x$

Cooperative Learning

13. Explain to a partner how you find the total in number **8** in **Practice**. Possible answer: Substitute 3 for x. Multiply 400 • 1.05 • 1.05 • 1.05 = $463.05.

14. Pick an initial deposit and an interest rate. Have a partner find the total after 3 years. Check the work. Answers will vary.

Summary

To write a power, use a base and an exponent.
When the bases are the same, multiply powers by adding exponents.
When the bases are the same, divide powers by subtracting exponents.
A power with a zero exponent is equal to 1.
Use negative exponents to indicate that a power is a fraction.
You can use scientific notation to write very small or very large numbers.
You can write ordered pairs for a function with an exponent and graph the ordered pairs on a coordinate plane.
Use a tree diagram to count choices.
Use an exponential function to find compound interest.

More vocabulary review is provided in Exercise 91 of the Classroom Resource Binder.

exponent

power

base

scientific notation

exponential functions

tree diagram

compound interest

Vocabulary Review

Complete the sentences with the words from the box.

1. Interest that a bank pays on your previous year's interest is called _____. compound interest

2. The product of multiplying when the factors are the same is called a _____. power

3. You use a _____ to see all the choices so you can count them. tree diagram

4. In 5^3, the 5 is called the _____. base

5. Functions of the form $y = a \bullet b^x$ are called _____. exponential functions

6. In 5^3, the 3 is called an _____. exponent

7. In _____, numbers are written as the product of two factors. The first factor is between 1 and 10. The second factor is a power of 10. scientific notation

Chapter Quiz

Chapter Quiz More assessment is provided in the Classroom Resource Binder.

Use exponents to rewrite each product.

1. $www\ w^3$

2. $stt\ st^2$

3. $pppqqqq\ p^3q^4$

Find the value of each power.

4. b^5 when b is $-1\ -1$

5. a^3 when a is 3 27

6. n^2 when n is 6 36

Multiply. Write using positive exponents.

7. $-3x^6 \cdot 2x^5\ -6x^{11}$

8. $6b^4c^5 \cdot b^6c^8\ 6b^{10}c^{13}$

9. $(w^2)^3\ w^6$

10. $pn^4 \cdot 4n^3\ 4pn^7$

11. $x^{-3}y \cdot x^3y^{-5}\ \frac{1}{y^4}$

12. $(a^0)^4\ 1$

Divide. Write using positive exponents.

13. $\frac{b^9}{b^7}\ b^2$

14. $\frac{3x^6y^4}{x^4}\ 3x^2y^4$

15. $\frac{6c^8d^9}{2cd}\ 3c^7d^8$

16. $\frac{3b^8}{b^4}\ 3b^4$

17. $\frac{c}{c^2}\ \frac{1}{c}$

18. $\frac{y^{-3}z^5}{y^2z^6}\ \frac{1}{y^5z}$

Find each number named in scientific notation.

19. $1.3 \times 10^2\ 130$

20. $2.7 \times 10^5\ 270{,}000$

21. $1.03 \times 10^{-4}\ .000103$

22. $2.32 \times 10^6\ 2{,}320{,}000$

23. $9.8 \times 10^{-3}\ .0098$

24. $3.4 \times 10^4\ 34{,}000$

25. (0, 3), (1, 6), (2, 12), (3, 24), (4, 48). See graph in Additional Answers, p. 478.

25. Find five ordered pairs for the function $y = 3 \cdot 2^x$. Make a table. Graph the function on a coordinate plane. See above.

26. Use a tree diagram to find how many different combinations of coat and boots you can wear if you have two coats (black and brown) and four pairs of boots (red, yellow, blue, and green). 8 combinations. See diagram in Additional Answers, p. 478.

27. Find the total savings after 2 years. Use the formula $T = 100(1.07)^x$. $114.49

Additional Practice for this chapter is provided on p. 422 of this text.

Chapter 10 • Exponents and Functions   267

Quadratic Functions and Equations

The path of a bouncing ball can be described using a quadratic function. The same curved path forms when you throw a ball. In what sports can this be seen?

Learning Objectives

- Graph quadratic functions.
- Find minimum, maximum, or zeros of functions from their graphs.
- Find square roots.
- Find zeros of quadratic functions.
- Solve quadratic equations.
- Use a calculator to find square roots.
- Solve problems by writing quadratic equations.
- Apply concepts and skills to using the vertical motion formula.

Try These

Find the zeros of each quadratic function from its graph.

1. $y = -x^2 + 4$

Find the points
where the graph
crosses the x-axis.
-2 0   2 0
(■, ■) and (■, ■)

Find the x-values of
the ordered pairs.

The zeros are ■ and ■.
              -2 2

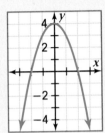

2. $y = x^2 + x + 2$

The line does not
cross the x-axis.

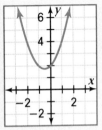

The function has ■ zeros.
               no

Practice

Find the zeros of each quadratic function from its graph.

1. $y = x^2 + 2x + 1$ -1 **2.** $y = x^2 - 1$ -1 and 1   **3.** $y = x^2 - 6x + 9$ 3

Cooperative Learning

    4. Explain to a partner how to find the zeros in number **2**
in **Practice.** Possible answer: Look at where the graph crosses the x-axis. Write the
x-coordinates of the two points.

    5. Draw the graph of a quadratic function that has two zeros.
Ask a partner to find the zeros. Answers will vary. Functions can have 2, 1, or no zeros.

More practice is provided in Exercise 63 of the Workbook.

11·5 ▶ Square Roots

Getting Started

Have students work in pairs to find the following squares:

6^2 $(-6)^2$
7^2 $(-7)^2$
8^2 $(-8)^2$
9^2 $(-9)^2$
10^2 $(-10)^2$

(36, 36; 49, 49; 64, 64; 81, 81; 100, 100)

To **square** a number is to multiply it by itself.

$$5^2 = 5 \bullet 5 = 25 \quad \text{and} \quad (-5)^2 = -5 \bullet -5 = 25$$

To find a **square root** of a number, you find one of two equal factors of a number.

All positive numbers have two square roots. One is positive, and one is negative. The symbol $\pm$ means "positive or negative." For example, ± 2 means $+2$ or -2.

$\pm\sqrt{25} \longrightarrow$ the positive or negative square root of $25 = \pm 5$

$\sqrt{25} \longrightarrow$ the positive square root of $25 = 5$

$-\sqrt{25} \longrightarrow$ the negative square root of $25 = -5$

▶ **EXAMPLE 1**

Find the square roots of 16.
Write 16 as a product of two equal factors. $4 \bullet 4$ or $-4 \bullet -4$
The square roots of 16 are 4 and -4.

▶ **EXAMPLE 2**

Find the value of $\sqrt{144}$.
Write 144 as a product of two
equal positive factors. $12 \bullet 12$
$\sqrt{144} = 12$

▶ **EXAMPLE 3**

Find the value of $-\sqrt{100}$.
Write 100 as a product of two
equal negative factors. $-10 \bullet -10$
$-\sqrt{100} = -10$

▶ **EXAMPLE 4**

Find $\pm\sqrt{400}$.
Write 400 as a product of two equal factors. $20 \bullet 20$ or
                                   $-20 \bullet -20$
$\pm\sqrt{400} = \pm 20$

Try These

1. Find the square roots of 9.

Write 9 as a product of two equal factors. $3 \bullet \blacksquare^{3}$ or $-3 \blacksquare \bullet \blacksquare -3$

The square roots of 9 are $\blacksquare 3$ and $\blacksquare.-3$

2. Find $\pm\sqrt{36}$.

Write 36 as a product of two equal factors. $6 \blacksquare \bullet 6$ or $-6 \blacksquare \bullet \blacksquare -6$

$\pm\sqrt{36} = \blacksquare^{6}$ or $\blacksquare^{-6}$

3. Find $-\sqrt{49}$.
Write 49 as a product of two equal negative factors.

$\blacksquare^{-7} \bullet \blacksquare^{-7}$

$-\sqrt{49} = \blacksquare -7$

4. Find $\sqrt{0}$.
Write 0 as a product of two equal factors.

$\blacksquare^{0} \bullet \blacksquare^{0}$

$\sqrt{0} = \blacksquare 0$

Practice

Find the square roots of each number.

1. 64 8 and -8

2. 81 9 and -9

3. 100 10 and -10

4. 36 6 and -6

5. 1 1 and -1

6. 169 13 and -13

Find the value of each square root.

7. $\sqrt{121}$ 11

8. $\pm\sqrt{16}$ ±4

9. $-\sqrt{9}$ -3

10. $\sqrt{4}$ 2

11. $\pm\sqrt{81}$ ±9

12. $-\sqrt{144}$ -12

13. $-\sqrt{169}$ -13

14. $\sqrt{196}$ 14

15. $\pm\sqrt{225}$ ±15

16. $\pm\sqrt{256}$ ±16

17. $\sqrt{625}$ 25

18. $\sqrt{400}$ 20

Cooperative Learning

19. Explain to a partner how to find the square roots in number 6 in **Practice**. Possible answer: Write 169 as a product of two equal factors: 13 • 13 or -13 • -13. The square roots of 169 are 13 and -13.

20. Think of a number from 1 to 10. Write the square of the number. Have a partner find the square roots of your square. Answers will vary from -10 to 10. Make sure students name both square roots.

More practice is provided in Exercise 63 of the Workbook.

11·6 ▶ Solving Quadratic Equations

Getting Started

To find the zeros of a quadratic function, look for values of x that make $y = 0$. To do this, substitute 0 for y in the function. The result is called a **quadratic equation**.

Quadratic function		**Quadratic equation**
$y = ax^2 + bx + c$	→	$0 = ax^2 + bx + c$
$y = x^2 - 36$	→	$0 = x^2 - 36$

Sometimes you can write a quadratic equation so the x^2 term is on one side and a constant is on the other side. You solve the equation by finding the square roots of the constant.

$$0 = x^2 - 36$$
$$36 = x^2$$
$$\pm\sqrt{36} = x$$
$$\pm 6 = x \rightarrow \text{The solutions are 6 and } -6.$$

Check

Use 6 and −6.

$0 = (6)^2 - 36$

$0 = 36 - 36$

$0 = 0$ $\quad$ true

$0 = (-6)^2 - 36$

$0 = 36 - 36$

$0 = 0$ $\quad$ true

▶ EXAMPLE 1

Check

Use 7 and −7.

$(7)^2 - 9 = 40$

$49 - 9 = 40$

$\qquad 40 = 40$ $\quad$ true

$(-7)^2 - 9 = 40$

$49 - 9 = 40$

$\qquad 40 = 40$ $\quad$ true

Solve. $\quad x^2 - 9 = 40$

Get the x^2 term alone. $\qquad\qquad x^2 - 9 = 40$

Add 9 to both sides. $\qquad x^2 - 9 + 9 = 40 + 9$

Simplify. $\qquad\qquad\qquad\qquad x^2 = 49$

Find the square root of both sides. $\qquad x = \pm\sqrt{49}$

$$x = 7 \text{ or } x = -7$$

The solutions are 7 and −7.

▶ EXAMPLE 2

Check

Use 3 and −3.

$2(3)^2 = 18$

$2(9) = 18$

$\quad 18 = 18$ $\quad$ true

$2(-3)^2 = 18$

$2(9) = 18$

$\quad 18 = 18$ $\quad$ true

Solve. $\quad 2x^2 = 18$

Get the x^2 term alone. $\qquad\qquad\qquad 2x^2 = 18$

Divide both sides by 2. $\qquad\qquad \dfrac{2x^2}{2} = \dfrac{18}{2}$

Simplify. $\qquad\qquad\qquad\qquad\qquad x^2 = 9$

Find the square root of both sides. $\qquad x = \pm\sqrt{9}$

$$x = 3 \text{ or } x = -3$$

The solutions are 3 and −3.

Try These

Solve each equation.

1. $x^2 + 20 = 84$

$$x^2 + 20 = 84$$

Subtract $\blacksquare$ ²⁰ from both sides. $\quad x^2 + 20 - \blacksquare$ ²⁰ $= 84 - \blacksquare$ ²⁰

Simplify. $\qquad\qquad x^2 = \blacksquare 64$

Find the square root of both sides. $\quad x = \pm\sqrt{64}$
$\quad x = 8$ or $x = \blacksquare -8$

The solutions are $\blacksquare$ ⁸ and $\blacksquare.$ −8

Check:
$8^2 + 20 = \blacksquare$ ⁶⁴ $+ 20 = 84 \quad$ true
$(\blacksquare)^2$ ₋₈ $+ 20 = \blacksquare$ ₆₄ $+ 20 = 84 \quad$ true

2. $3x^2 = 48$

$$3x^2 = 48$$

Divide both sides by $\blacksquare.3$ $\qquad \dfrac{3x^2}{\blacksquare 3} = \dfrac{48}{\blacksquare 3}$

Simplify. $\qquad\qquad x^2 = \blacksquare 16$

Find the square root of both sides. $\quad x = \pm\sqrt{\blacksquare} 16$
$\quad x = \blacksquare$ ⁴ or $x = \blacksquare$ ₋₄

The solutions are $\blacksquare$ ⁴ and $\blacksquare.$ ⁻⁴

Check:
$3 \bullet \blacksquare^2$ ⁴ $= 3 \bullet \blacksquare$ ¹⁶ $= 48 \quad$ true
$3 \bullet (\blacksquare)^2$ ₋₄ $= 3 \bullet \blacksquare$ ₁₆ $= 48 \quad$ true

Practice

Solve each equation.

1. $x^2 = 100$ 10 and −10

2. $x^2 = 169$ 13 and −13

3. $x^2 = 121$ 11 and −11

4. $x^2 + 10 = 35$ 5 and −5

5. $x^2 - 60 = 4$ 8 and −8

6. $x^2 - 11 = 70$ 9 and −9

7. $3x^2 = 12$ 2 and −2

8. $5x^2 = 45$ 3 and −3

9. $10x^2 = 10$ 1 and −1

Cooperative Learning

10. Explain to a partner how to solve the equation in number **4** in **Practice.** Possible answer: Subtract 10 from both sides. Then, find the square roots of both sides.

11. Find the square of a number. Write a quadratic equation with the square equal to x^2. Ask a partner to solve the equation. Check the work. Answers will vary. Make sure students give both the positive and negative solution.

More practice is provided in Exercise 64 of the Workbook.

11·7 ▶ Zeros and the Quadratic Formula

Getting Started
Have students identify a, b,
and c in each function.
$y = 4x^2 + 3x - 12$
$(4; 3; -12)$
$y = -4x^2 + 3x + 12$
$(-4; 3; 12)$

Sometimes you cannot find the zeros of a quadratic function easily. To find the zeros of $y = ax^2 + bx + c$, substitute 0 for y and solve for x. When a quadratic equation is in standard form, you can use the **quadratic formula** to solve this equation.

The solutions of $0 = ax^2 + bx + c$ are $x = \dfrac{-b \pm \sqrt{b^2 - 4ac}}{2a}$

So, $x = \dfrac{-b + \sqrt{b^2 - 4ac}}{2a}$ or $x = \dfrac{-b - \sqrt{b^2 - 4ac}}{2a}$.

A quadratic equation has one, two, or no solutions.

▶ **EXAMPLE 1**

Math Fact
$a = 1$, $b = -7$, $c = 12$

Find the zeros of the function. $y = x^2 - 7x + 12$

Substitute 0 for y. Use the quadratic formula.

$$0 = 1x^2 - 7x + 12$$

Substitute 1 for a, -7 for b, and 12 for c.

$$x = \frac{-(-7) \pm \sqrt{(-7)^2 - 4(1)(12)}}{2(1)}$$

Simplify. Square and multiply first. Then, subtract.

$$x = \frac{7 \pm \sqrt{49 - 48}}{2} \qquad x = \frac{7 \pm \sqrt{1}}{2}$$

Find the square root. Add or subtract.
Simplify.

$$x = \frac{7 \pm 1}{2} \ \longrightarrow \ x = \frac{8}{2} \text{ or } \frac{6}{2}$$

$$x = 4 \text{ or } x = 3$$

The zeros of $y = x^2 - 7x + 12$ are 4 and 3.

▶ **EXAMPLE 2**

Math Fact
$a = 1$, $b = -5$, $c = 9$

Find the zeros of the function. $y = x^2 - 5x + 9$

Substitute 0 for y. Use the quadratic formula.

$$0 = 1x^2 - 5x + 9$$

Substitute 1 for a, -5 for b, and 9 for c.

$$x = \frac{-(-5) \pm \sqrt{(-5)^2 - 4(1)(9)}}{2(1)}$$

Simplify. Square and multiply first. Then, subtract.

$$x = \frac{5 \pm \sqrt{25 - 36}}{2}$$

You cannot find the square root of -11.

$$x = \frac{5 \pm \sqrt{-11}}{2}$$

The function $y = x^2 - 5x + 9$ has no zeros.

Try These

1. Write the quadratic formula.

$$x\,\blacksquare = \frac{-\,\blacksquare \pm \sqrt{\blacksquare^2 - 4\,\blacksquare\,\blacksquare}}{2\,\blacksquare\,a} \qquad b;\, b;\, a;\, c$$

2. Use the quadratic formula to find $y = x^2 + 4x + 4$.

Substitute 0 for y.

Find a, b, and c.

$$0 = x^2 + 4x\underset{4}{+} 4\overset{4}{}$$

$$a = 1\blacksquare,\ b = \overset{4}{\blacksquare},\ c = \overset{4}{\blacksquare}$$

Substitute 1 for a, 4 for b, and 4 for c.

$$x = \frac{-\overset{4}{\blacksquare} \pm \sqrt{\blacksquare^2 - 4\,(\overset{1}{\blacksquare})(\overset{4}{\blacksquare})}}{2(1)}$$

Square and multiply. Then, subtract.

$$x = \frac{-4 \pm \sqrt{16 - \blacksquare\,16}}{2}$$

Simplify.

$$x = \frac{-4 - \blacksquare\,0}{2}$$

$$x = \blacksquare\,-2$$

The zero of $y = x^2 + 4x + 4$ is $\blacksquare.\ -2$

Practice

Find the zeros of each function using the quadratic formula.

1. $y = x^2 - 2x + 1$
1

2. $y = x^2 - 3x + 2$
1 and 2

3. $y = x^2 - 5x + 6$
2 and 3

4. $y = x^2 - x - 6$
−2 and 3

5. $y = x^2 + 2x + 1$
−1

6. $y = x^2 - 3x - 4$
−1 and 4

7. $y = x^2 + 6x + 8$
−2 and −4

8. $y = x^2 + 8x + 15$
−3 and −5

9. $y = x^2 - 2x + 15$
no zeros

10. $y = x^2 - 6x + 5$
5 and 1

11. $y = x^2 + 7x + 12$
−3 and −4

12. $y = x^2 + 9x + 20$
−5 and −4

Cooperative Learning

13. Work with a partner to compare your answers to number **8** and number **9** in **Practice**. What is different about the answers? What is the same? See below.

14. Work with a partner to find the zeros of the function $y = x^2 - x - 30$. The zeros are 6 and −5.

13. Possible answer: The a and c values are the same, but since the b value is different, the zeros will be different. In number 8 the zeros are −3 or −5, and in number 9, since you cannot find the square root of −56, there are no zeros.

Getting Started
Alert students
that some
calculators have
a shift key like the shift key
on a keyboard. On these
calculators, students will
have to press the shift key as
well as the $\sqrt{}$ key to find
square root. Have students
practice using these keys.

11·8 ▶ **Calculator: Finding Square Roots**

Most numbers do not have square roots that are easy
to find. Some calculators have a square root key. If your
calculator has a key that looks like $\boxed{\sqrt{}}$, then you can
use it to find the square roots of numbers you do not
know. Your calculator will only show you the positive
square root. You have to remember to find the negative
square root.

▶ **EXAMPLE 1**

Find the square roots of .0081.   **Display**

Enter .0081 by pressing: $\boxed{.}\ \boxed{0}\ \boxed{0}\ \boxed{8}\ \boxed{1}$ $\boxed{.008\ 1}$

Find the square root by pressing: $\boxed{\sqrt{}}$ $\boxed{.09}$

Find the other square root. $-.09$

The square roots of .0081 are .09 and $-.09$.

▶ **EXAMPLE 2**

Find the square roots of 2,025.   **Display**

Enter 2,025 by pressing: $\boxed{2}\ \boxed{0}\ \boxed{2}\ \boxed{5}$ $\boxed{2025}$

Find the square root by pressing: $\boxed{\sqrt{}}$ $\boxed{45}$

Find the other square root. -45

The square roots of 2,025 are 45 and -45.

You cannot find the exact square root of most
numbers. Their square roots have decimals that go on
forever. You can round the square roots to two decimal
places.

▶ **EXAMPLE 3**

Find the square roots of 48.   **Display**

Enter 48 by pressing: $\boxed{4}\ \boxed{8}$ $\boxed{48}$

Find the square root by pressing: $\boxed{\sqrt{}}$ $\boxed{6.9282032}$

Round to two decimal places.   6.93

Find the other square root. -6.93

The square roots of 48 are about 6.93 and -6.93.

Practice

Find the square roots of each number.

1. .0009 .03 and −.03

2. 2 1.41 and −1.41

3. 72 8.49 and −8.49

4. 150 12.25 and −12.25

5. .004 .063 and −.063

6. .16 .4 and −.4

7. 3,600 60 and −60

8. 9,000 94.87 and −94.87

9. 9,801 99 and −99

10. .025 .16 and −.16

11. 1.21 1.1 and −1.1

12. 160 12.65 and −12.65

Math Connection

COMETS

A comet is a frozen ball of dust, water, and gases. A comet flies through space in an orbit. As it nears our sun, the frozen gases melt. This forms the tail. The tail can be up to 10 million kilometers long.

Edmund Halley was a famous astronomer. He studied things in space like moons, planets, and comets. In 1705, he saw a comet and studied it. Back then, no one knew how comets moved. Halley said that they traveled around the sun. He predicted that his comet would return again in 75 years. He was right. This is the famous Halley's Comet. The last time it was seen was in 1985. It will not be seen again until 2061.

The orbit of some comets is in the shape of a quadratic function. Most comets can only be seen with a telescope. Some comets, like Halley's, can be seen without a telescope.

Many people look at the stars as a hobby. They have discovered some of our comets. You can tell it is a comet by its long white tail. If you live in a place with few street lights, you might discover the next comet yourself.

More practice is provided in Exercise 65 of the Workbook.

Getting Started
Encourage
students to draw
and label a
rectangle to represent the
field in the example.

11·9 Problem Solving: Writing and Using Quadratic Equations

You can write quadratic equations to describe some geometry problems.

▶ **EXAMPLE**

A coach is planning a field with an area of 75 square feet. She wants the field to be a rectangle. She also wants the length to be 3 times the width. Find the width.

READ **What do you need to find out?**
You need to find the width of the field.

PLAN **What do you need to do?**
You need to use the formula for the area of a rectangle to find the width.

DO **Follow the plan.**

Write an equation for length.	length is 3 times width $l = 3w$
Write the area formula.	$A = lw$
Substitute 75 for A and $3w$ for l.	$75 = 3ww$
Solve for w^2. Divide by 3.	$75 = 3w^2$
Solve for w.	$25 = w^2$
	$\pm\sqrt{25} = w$
Width cannot be negative.	$5 = w \ or \ {-5} = w$
Use the positive square root	$5 = w$

CHECK **Does your answer make sense?**
The width is 5 feet, so the length is $3 \times 5 = 15$.
Area: $5 \times 15 = 75$ ✓

The width is 5 feet.

Try These

Solve each problem by using a quadratic equation.

1. An architect wants to design a room so that the length is twice the width. She needs the area to be 800 square feet. How long should each side be?

Write an equation for the length.   length is twice the width

$$l = \boxed{2} \, 2w$$

Write the formula for the area of a rectangle. $A = lw$

Substitute $\boxed{800}$ for A and $2w$ for l. $800 \, \boxed{} = 2w^2$

Solve for $\boxed{w}$. Divide by $\boxed{2}$. $\dfrac{800 \, \boxed{}}{2} = \dfrac{2w^2}{2} \rightarrow \boxed{400} = w^2$

Solve for w. Use the $\boxed{\text{positive}}$ square root. $20 \, \boxed{} = w$

Find l. Use $l = 2w$. $l = 2(\boxed{20}) \rightarrow l = \boxed{40}$

The width of the room is $\boxed{20}$ feet and the length is $\boxed{40}$ feet.

2. A decorator has 121 square tiles to cover a square area. How many tiles should he put along each side?

Write the formula for the area of a square. $A = s^2$

The decorator has 121 squares to cover the area. Use $\boxed{121}$ for area. $121 = s^2$

Solve for s. Use the $\boxed{\text{positive}}$ square root. $11 \, \boxed{} = s$

There should be $\boxed{11}$ tiles along each side.

Practice

Solve each problem by using a quadratic equation.

1. The area of a square is 144 square yards. Find the length of a side. 12 yards

2. The area of a rectangle is 144 square yards. The length is 4 times the width. Find the length and width of the rectangle. width = 6 yards and length = 24 yards

Cooperative Learning

3. Work with a partner to find the width of a rectangle. The length the rectangle is twice its width. The area is 72 square meters. The width is 6 meters.

4. Pick a number and square it. Multiply the squared number by 3. Use that number for A in the equation $A = 3w^2$. Ask a partner to solve for w. Answers will vary. If students do not get a whole number as their solution, check their multiplication. Students should include both positive and negative solutions.

More practice is provided in Exercise 66 of the Workbook.

11·10 Application: Vertical Motion Formula

Getting Started
Discuss Galileo's experiments with falling objects. He proved that all objects fall at the same rate, regardless of weight or mass.

When an object is dropped, the height of the object is a quadratic function of time. The vertical motion formula describes the height of the object at any time.

$$h = -16t^2 + vt + s$$

h is the height in feet. v is the starting speed.
t is the time in seconds. s is the starting height.

▶ **EXAMPLE 1**

A rock falls off a cliff 1,600 feet high. At what time is the height of the pebble 1,200 feet?

1,600 ft

cliff

1,200 ft

0 ft

The height is 1,200. Starting speed is 0. Starting height is 1,600.

$$h = -16t^2 + vt + s$$

$$h = 1{,}200,\ v = 0,\ s = 1{,}600$$

Substitute the values you know into the formula. Simplify.

$$1{,}200 = -16t^2 + 0t + 1{,}600$$

Solve for t. Subtract 1,600 from both sides.

$$1{,}200 = -16\,t^2 + 1{,}600$$

Divide both sides by -16. $-400 = -16t^2$

Take the positive square root. $25 = t^2$

$$5 = t$$

The rock is at 1,200 feet after 5 seconds.

▶ **EXAMPLE 2**

At what time does the rock hit the ground?

The height is 0 on the ground. Starting speed is 0. Starting height is 1,600.

$$h = -16t^2 + vt + s$$

$$h = 0,\ v = 0,\ s = 1{,}600$$

Substitute the values you know into the formula. Simplify.

$$0 = -16t^2 + 0t + 1{,}600$$

Solve for t. Subtract 1,600 from both sides.

$$0 = -16t^2 + 1{,}600$$

Divide both sides by -16. $-1{,}600 = -16t^2$

Take the positive square root. $100 = t^2$

$$10 = t$$

The rock hits the ground after 10 seconds.

Try These

Solve each problem using the vertical motion formula.

1. A skydiver jumps out of a plane at a height of 11,400 feet. Her parachute opens at 5,000 feet above ground. At what time does her parachute open?

$$h\blacksquare = -16t^2 + vt + s$$

Find h, v, and s. $h = 5{,}000$, $v = 0$, $s = 11{,}400$

Substitute $5{,}000\,\blacksquare = -16t^2 + 11{,}400$

Subtract 11,400 **from both sides.** $-6{,}400\,\blacksquare = -16t^2$

Divide both sides by $\blacksquare$. -16 $400\,\blacksquare = t^2$ $20\,\blacksquare = t$ 20

Use the positive square root. The parachute opens after $\blacksquare$ 20 seconds.

2. You drop a ball off a cliff 400 feet high. How much time will it take for the ball to hit the ground?

$$h = -16t^2 + vt + \blacksquare\,^s$$

Find h, v, and s. $0\ h = \blacksquare$, $v = 0$, $s = \blacksquare$ 400

Substitute $0 = -16t^2 + \blacksquare$ 400

Subtract 400 **from both sides.** $-400\,\blacksquare = -16t^2$

Divide both sides by $\blacksquare$. -16 $25\,\blacksquare = t^2$ $5\,\blacksquare = t$ 5

Use the positive square root. The ball will hit the ground after $\blacksquare$ 5 seconds.

Practice

Solve each problem using the vertical motion formula.

1. A shovel drops down a mine shaft 5,000 feet deep. How much time will it take for the shovel to reach 3,400 feet above the bottom of the shaft? 10 seconds

2. A plant falls from a building 256 feet high. When does the plant hit the ground? 4 seconds

3. Possible answer: Find h, v, and s: 3,400, 0, 5,000. Substitute them into the formula: $3{,}400 = -16t^2 + (0)t + 5{,}000$. Simplify: $3{,}400 = -16t^2 + 5{,}000$. Subtract 5,000 from both sides, and then

Cooperative Learning

divide by -16: $100 = t^2$. Take the positive square root of each side: $10 = t$.

3. Explain to a partner how to solve the problem in number **1** in **Practice.** See above.

4. Work with a partner and use the number given in **2** in **Practice.** Find at what time the plant reaches a height of 112 feet.
The plant reaches a height of 112 feet after 3 seconds.

Summary

The standard form of a quadratic function is $y = ax^2 + bx + c$.
You can graph a quadratic function from a table of values.
You can tell the direction of a graph and whether it has a maximum or a minimum by looking at the coefficient of the x^2 term.
You can look at the graph to find the zeros of a quadratic function.
All positive numbers have two square roots. One is positive, and the other is negative. You can use square roots to solve equations.
Use the quadratic formula to find the zeros of quadratic functions.
You can write quadratic equations to solve problems.
Use the vertical motion formula to find the height of a falling object.

More vocabulary review is provided in Exercise 101 of the Classroom Resource Binder.

quadratic function
minimum
maximum
zeros
square
square root
quadratic equation
quadratic formula

Vocabulary Review

Complete the sentences with the words from the box.

1. A number that when multiplied by itself gives the original number is called a _____ of the original number. square root

2. The function $y = ax^2 + bx + c$ is called a _____. quadratic function

3. The values of x, where a quadratic function crosses the x-axis, are called _____. zeros

4. The largest value of y in a quadratic equation is called a _____. maximum

5. An equation with one variable and degree 2 is called a _____. quadratic equation

6. The smallest value of y in a quadratic equation is called a _____. minimum

7. The formula for the solutions of a quadratic equation is called the _____. quadratic formula

8. To _____ a number is to raise it to the second power. square

Chapter Quiz More **assessment** is provided in the Classroom Resource Binder.

Find *a*, *b*, and *c* for each quadratic function.

1. $y = 6x^2 + 8x + 9$ $a = 6, b = 8, c = 9$ **2.** $y = x + 6x^2 - 8$ $a = 6, b = 1, c = -8$

Make a table of values for each function. Then, graph. See Additional Answers, p. 479.
Use $x = 2, 1, 0, -1, -2, -3$.

3. $y = 2x^2$ **4.** $y = x^2 + 2x$ **5.** $y = x^2 + 1$

Tell whether the graph opens upward or downward. Tell whether it has a minimum or maximum.

6. $y = -x^2$
downward; maximum

7. $y = -4x^2 - 2$
downward; maximum

8. $y = 2x^2$
upward; minimum

Find the zeros of each quadratic function from its graph.

9. $y = 3x^2$
0

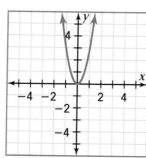

10. $y = x^2 - 9$
3 and −3

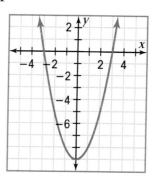

Find each value.

11. square roots of 81
9 and −9

12. $\sqrt{100}$
10

13. $-\sqrt{16}$
−4

Solve each equation. Use the quadratic formula, if necessary.

14. $x^2 = 9$
3 and −3

15. $x^2 + 3 = 28$
5 and −5

16. $0 = x^2 - 9x + 18$
3 and 6

17. The area of a rectangle is 180 square meters. The length is 5 times the width. Find the length and width of the rectangle. The length is 30 meters and width is 6 meters.

Solve using the vertical motion formula: $h = -16t^2 + vt + s$.

18. A pebble falls off a cliff 784 feet high. At what time does it hit the ground?
7 seconds

Additional Practice for this chapter
is provided on p. 423 of this text.

Polynomials and Factoring

Quadratic expressions and polynomials play an important role in engineering and construction. Some arches are based on quadratic formulas. What other curved structures can you think of?

Learning Objectives

- Add, subtract, and multiply polynomials.
- Factor polynomials.
- Solve equations by factoring.
- Use a calculator to check solutions of quadratic equations.
- Solve problems using either factoring or the quadratic formula.
- Apply concepts and skills to using formulas.

Words to Know

polynomial	a term or the sum or difference of terms
monomial	an expression with one term; a number, a variable, or the product of a number and a variable
binomial	a polynomial with two terms
trinomial	a polynomial with three terms
factors	numbers or variables being multiplied
factor	to write an expression as the product of its factors
greatest common factor (GCF)	the largest common factor of two or more terms
Zero Product Property	if the product of two numbers is 0, then one of the numbers must be 0

Arches Project

The graphs of some curves are quadratic functions. These can be seen in parabolic arches in some bridges and buildings. Write a report about arches.

Graph each of the following quadratic equations: $y = -x^2$, $y = -\frac{1}{2}x^2$, $y = -\frac{1}{4}x^2$. To make the table of values, use $-4, -2, 0, 2, 4$ for x. Use a curved line to connect the ordered pairs. How does changing the equation change the shape of the arch?

Project See the Classroom Resource Binder for a scoring rubric to assess this project.

$$y = -x^2$$

$$y = -\frac{1}{2}x^2$$

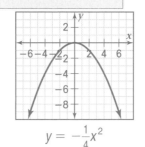

$$y = -\frac{1}{4}x^2$$

As the coefficient of $-x^2$ gets smaller, the arch becomes wider.

Getting Started
To review the meaning of a *term* in an expression, write $5x^2 - 2x + 3$ on the chalkboard. Have students count the number of terms. (3)

| 12·1 | **Polynomials** |

There are special names for some expressions. You can call an expression a **polynomial**. A polynomial is one term or the sum or difference of terms. A **monomial** is a polynomial with one term. A **binomial** has two terms. A **trinomial** has three terms.

Remember
A term is a number, a variable, or the product of a number and a variable.

Expression	Number of Terms	Polynomial Name
$-2x$	1	monomial
$3x + 4$	2	binomial
$5x^2 - x + 3$	3	trinomial

▶ **EXAMPLE 1**

Remember
The constant is the number alone.

Name the type of polynomial and the constant.
$2x^2 + 3x + 7$

Count the terms.
Name the polynomial.
$2x^2 + 3x + 7$ i

$2x^2 + 3x + 7$
↑   ↑   ↑
3 terms

▶ **EXAMPLE 2**

Name the typ
$3x^2 - 8$

Count the terms.
Name the polyn
$3x^2 - 8$ is a b

If you do not

▶ **EXAMPLE 3**

Name the typ
$3x^2$

Count the terms
Name the polynomial.   1 term
$3x^2$ is a monomial. The constant is 0.

Try These

Name the type of polynomial and the constant.

1. $6x^2 + 6xy - 3$

Count the terms.
$$6x^2 + 6xy - 3$$
$\uparrow \quad \uparrow \quad \uparrow$
3 ■ terms
Name the constant. ■ -3
$6x^2 + 6xy - 3$ is a ■. trinomial
The constant is ■. -3

2. $-5n + m$

Count the terms.
$$-5n + m$$
$\uparrow \quad \uparrow$
2 ■ terms
Name the constant. ■ 0
$-5n + m$ is a ■. binomial
The constant is ■. 0

Practice

Name the type of polynomial and the constant.

1. $3x^2 + 3x$
binomial, 0

2. -5
monomial, -5

3. $2x + 6$
binomial, 6

4. $-4pq - 3q$
binomial, 0

5. $y^2 + 4y - 2$
trinomial, -2

6. $5k^2 + 3k + 4$
trinomial, 4

7. $-x^2 + 3xy - 5$
trinomial, -5

8. 3
monomial, 3

9. $-9xy$
monomial, 0

10. $-2a^2 - 5b - 6$
trinomial, -6

11. $3y^2 + y$
binomial, 0

12. $5k^2 - 3k - 6$
trinomial, -6

13. $y^2 - 7y$
binomial, 0

14. $w + 5$
binomial, 5

15. $x^3 + 2x^2y - 4$
trinomial, -4

16. $5b^2$
monomial, 0

17. $-4 + 3x$
binomial, -4

18. $a^2 - 5 - 2a$
trinomial, -5

Cooperative Learning

19. Explain to a partner how to name the type of polynomial in number **7** in **Practice**. Possible answer: Count the terms: $-x^2 \rightarrow$ 1; $3xy \rightarrow$ 2; $-5 \rightarrow$ 3. The polynomial has three terms. It is a trinomial.

20. Write a polynomial with one, two, or three terms. Have a partner count the terms and name the type of polynomial. Check the work. Answers will vary among binomial, monomial, and trinomial.

Getting Started
To review like terms, have students group the like terms in this list: x^2, $3x$, $2x^2$, x^3, $-2x$. (x^3; x^2 and $2x^2$; $3x$ and $-2x$)

12-2 ▶ Adding Polynomials

To add like terms, you add the coefficients. To add polynomials, add like terms from both polynomials.

▶ **EXAMPLE 1**

Math Fact
x^2 means $1x^2$.
x means $1x$.

Add. $2x^2 + 2x + 2$ and $x^2 + x + 4$

Write the polynomials. $2x^2 + 2x + 2$

Line up like terms. $\underline{1x^2 + 1x + 4}$

Add the coefficients of like terms. $3x^2 + 3x + 6$

$$(2x^2 + 2x + 2) + (x^2 + x + 4) = 3x^2 + 3x + 6$$

▶ **EXAMPLE 2**

Add. $3x^2 + 2x - 8$ and $-4x^2 - 2x + 10$

Write the polynomials. $3x^2 + 2x - 8$

Line up like terms. $\underline{-4x^2 - 2x + 10}$

Add the coefficients of like terms. $-1x^2 + 0x + 2$

Simplify. $-x^2 + 2$

$$(3x^2 + 2x - 8) + (-4x^2 - 2x + 10) = -x^2 + 2$$

Be sure to line up like terms when some terms are missing.

▶ **EXAMPLE 3**

Add. $w^2 + 2w - 6$ and $3w^3 + 3$

Write the polynomials. $w^2 + 2w - 6$

Line up like terms. $\underline{3w^3 + 3}$

Add the coefficients of like terms. $3w^3 + w^2 + 2w - 3$

$$(w^2 + 2w - 6) + (3w^3 + 3) = 3w^3 + w^2 + 2w - 3$$

▶ **EXAMPLE 4**

Add. $3p^2 - 1$ and $-3p^2 - 2p - 4$

Write the polynomials. $3p^2 - 1$

Line up like terms. $\underline{-3p^2 - 2p - 4}$

Add the coefficients of like terms. $-2p - 5$

Math Fact
$3p^2 + (-3p^2) = 0p^2 = 0$

$$(3p^2 - 1) + (-3p^2 - 2p - 4) = -2p - 5$$

Practice

Add the polynomials.

1. $3x^2 + 3x + 1$ and $x^2 + x + 5$
$4x^2 + 4x + 6$

2. $k^2 + k + 2$ and $2k^2 + 3k + 1$
$3k^2 + 4k + 3$

3. $4s - 3t$ and $2s + 5t$
$6s + 2t$

4. $-4a - 2b$ and $3a + 4b$
$-a + 2b$

5. $c^2 + 3c - 3$ and $-3c^2 + 3c - 2$
$-2c^2 + 6c - 5$

6. $2x^3 + 4x - 5$ and $-5x^2 + 3x + 1$
$2x^3 - 5x^2 + 7x - 4$

7. $x^2 + 3x - 5$ and $4x + 2$
$x^2 + 7x - 3$

8. $2w^2 + w - 4$ and $3w - 1$
$2w^2 + 4w - 5$

9. $2n^3 - 2$ and $-2n^2 - 3n - 3$
$2n^3 - 2n^2 - 3n - 5$

10. $4z^2 - 3$ and $-2z^2 - 5z - 6$
$2z^2 - 5z - 9$

11. $8r - 3$ and $-r^3 + r + 3$
$-r^3 + 9r$

12. y^2 and $-y^2 + 3y$
$3y$

Cooperative Learning

13. Explain to a partner how to add the polynomials in number **6**
in **Practice.** Possible answer: Write the polynomials and line up the like terms. Then, add
the coefficients of like terms. $(2x^3 + 4x - 5) + (-5x^2 + 3x + 1) \longrightarrow 2x^3 - 5x + 7x - 4$

14. Write two polynomials with no more than three terms each.
Have a partner add the polynomials. Check the work. Answers will vary. Make sure
students only combine like terms.

Getting Started
Review naming
coefficients. Ask
students to name
the coefficient of x in the
following polynomials.
$$x^2 = 49 \ (0)$$
$$4x^2 + x = 32 \ (1)$$
Math Fact
$-2x^2 - 1x + 2$ is the
opposite of $2x^2 + x - 2$.

12-3 ▶ Subtracting Polynomials

You have added polynomials by adding the coefficients of like terms. To subtract a polynomial, you add the opposite of the polynomial.

$$
\begin{array}{ll}
4x^2 + 2x + 5 & \qquad 4x^2 + 2x + 5 \\
-(2x^2 + \ x - 2) \quad \longrightarrow & \quad -2x^2 - 1x + 2 \\
\hline
& \qquad 2x^2 + \ x + 7
\end{array}
$$

▶ **EXAMPLE 1**

Subtract $x^2 + x + 2$ from $3x^2 + 3x + 4$.

Find the opposite of $\quad -(x^2 + x + 2) \longrightarrow -x^2 - x - 2$
$x^2 + x + 2$.

Add the opposite to $3x^2 + 3x + 4$. $\qquad 3x^2 + 3x + 4$

Add the coefficients of like terms. $\qquad \dfrac{-1x^2 - 1x - 2}{2x^2 + 2x + 2}$

$$(3x^2 + 3x + 4) - (x^2 + x + 2) = 2x^2 + 2x + 2$$

▶ **EXAMPLE 2**

Subtract $-s^2 - 3s + 2$ from $5s^2 + 4s - 3$.

Find the opposite of $\quad -(-s^2 - 3s + 2) \longrightarrow +s^2 + 3s - 2$
$-s^2 - 3s + 2$.

Add the opposite to $5s^2 + 4s - 3$. $\qquad 5s^2 + 4s - 3$

Add the coefficients of like terms. $\qquad \dfrac{+1s^2 + 3s - 2}{6s^2 + 7s - 5}$

$$(5s^2 + 4s - 3) - (-s^2 - 3s + 2) = 6s^2 + 7s - 5$$

▶ **EXAMPLE 3**

Subtract $5y^3 + 2$ from $3y^2 + 2y - 4$.

Find the opposite of $5y^3 + 2$. $\quad -(5y^3 + 2) \longrightarrow -5y^3 - 2$

Add the opposite to $3y^2 + 2y - 4$. $\qquad 3y^2 + 2y - 4$

Add the coefficients of like terms. $\quad \dfrac{-5y^3 \qquad\qquad - 2}{-5y^3 + 3y^2 + 2y - 6}$

$$(3y^2 + 2y - 4) - (5y^3 + 2) = -5y^3 + 3y^2 + 2y - 6$$

Subtract.

1. $x^2 + 3x - 5$ from $-3x^2 + 2x - 7$

Find the ■ of $\quad -x^2 - 3x + 5$
opposite
$x^2 + 3x - 5$.

Add the opposite. $\quad -3x^2 + 2x - 7$

Add the coefficients $\quad \underline{-x^2 - 3x + 5}$

of like terms. $\quad -4\,■\,x^2 - ■x - ■\,-2$

$(-3x^2 + 2x - 7) - (x^2 + 3x - 5) = ■$
$\quad\quad\quad\quad\quad\quad\quad\quad\quad -4x^2 - x - 2$

2. $-4p - 2q + 3$ from $2p + 5q$

Find the opposite of $\quad 4p\,■\,2q\,■\,3$
$-4p - 2q + 3$. $\quad\quad\quad\quad + \quad -$

Add the opposite. $\quad 2p + 5q$

Add the coefficients $\quad \underline{4p + 2q - 3}$
of ■ terms. like $\quad 6\,■\,p + ■q - 3$

$(2p + 5q) - (-4p - 2q + 3) = ■$
$\quad\quad\quad\quad\quad\quad\quad\quad\quad 6p + 7q - 3$

Practice

Subtract the polynomials.

1. $4k^2 + 2k + 3$ from $k^2 + k + 6$
$-3k^2 - k + 3$

2. $y^2 + y + 3$ from $3y^2 + 4y + 2$
$2y^2 + 3y - 1$

3. $5m - n$ from $3m + 6n$
$-2m + 7n$

4. $-2a - 3b$ from $3a + b$
$5a + 4b$

5. $w^2 + 2w - 4$ from $-2w^2 + 4w - 6$
$-3w^2 + 2w - 2$

6. $3r^2 + 2r - 7$ from $-4r^3 + 2r + 4$
$-4r^3 - 3r^2 + 11$

7. $z^3 + 4z - 1$ from $5z^2 + 3$
$-z^3 + 5z^2 - 4z + 4$

8. $3x^2 + x - 3$ from $4x - 2$
$-3x^2 + 3x + 1$

9. $3h^2 - 2$ from $3h^2 - 4h - 1$
$-4h + 1$

10. $5s^2 - 2s$ from $-3s^2 - 4s - 5$
$-8s^2 - 2s - 5$

11. $y^2 + y + 2$ from y^2
$-y - 2$

12. $-b^2 - b - 2$ from $3b + 2$
$b^2 + 4b + 4$

13. $3x^3 - 1$ from $3x^3 - x + 1$
$-x + 2$

14. $-2y^2 + 3y$ from y^2
$3y^2 - 3y$

Cooperative Learning

15. Explain to a partner how to subtract the polynomials in number **8** in **Practice.** Possible answer: Add the opposite of each term in the first polynomial. $(4x - 2) - (3x^2 + x - 3) \rightarrow (4x - 2) + (-3x^2 - x + 3) \rightarrow -3x^2 + 3x + 1$

16. Write a subtraction problem using two polynomials with no more than three terms each. Have a partner subtract the first polynomial from the second. Check the work. Answers will vary. Make sure students change all the signs of the polynomial that is being subtracted.

12-4 **Multiplying by a Monomial**

Getting Started
Review the Distributive Property. Ask volunteers to simplify each of the following:
  $5(x + 3)$
  $8(y - 2)$
    $-3(w - 1)$
$(5x + 15; 8y - 16;$
$-3w + 3)$

You have used the Distributive Property to multiply a binomial by a number. You also can use the Distributive Property to multiply a binomial by a monomial.

$$2x(3x + 2)$$
$$2x(3x) + 2x(2)$$
$$6x^2 + 4x$$

▶ **EXAMPLE 1**

Remember
$w \cdot w = w^2$

Simplify. $w(4w + 3)$

$$w(4w + 3)$$

Use the Distributive Property. $w(4w) + w(3)$

Multiply. $4w^2 + 3w$

$$w(4w + 3) = 4w^2 + 3w$$

▶ **EXAMPLE 2**

Math Fact
$-4x(-2x) =$
$(-4)(-2)x \cdot x = 8x^2$

Simplify. $-4x(-2x + 5)$

$$-4x(-2x + 5)$$

Use the Distributive Property. $-4x(-2x) - 4x(5)$

Multiply. $8x^2 - 20x$

$$-4x(-2x + 5) = 8x^2 - 20x$$

You also use the Distributive Property to multiply a trinomial by a monomial.

▶ **EXAMPLE 3**

Simplify. $3k(k^2 - 2k + 4)$

$$3k(k^2 - 2k + 4)$$

Use the Distributive Property. $3k(k^2) + 3k(-2k) + 3k(4)$

Multiply. $3k^3 - 6k^2 + 12k$

$$3k(k^2 - 2k + 4) = 3k^3 - 6k^2 + 12k$$

Try These

Simplify.

1. $-2a(a - 3)$

$$-2a(a - 3)$$

Use the Distributive Property. $\quad -2a(a) - 2a(-3)$

Multiply. $\quad -2a^2 \blacksquare + \blacksquare 6a$

$-2a(a - 3) = \blacksquare -2a^2 + 6a$

2. $3x(x^2 - 2x + 1)$

$$3x(x^2 - 2x + 1)$$

Use the $\blacksquare$ Property. (Distributive) $\quad 3x(\blacksquare)(x^2) + (\blacksquare)(-2x) + (\blacksquare)(1)$

Multiply. $\quad \blacksquare - \blacksquare + \blacksquare$

$3x(x^2 - 2x + 1) = \blacksquare$

$3x^3 - 6x^2 + 3x$

Practice

Simplify.

1. $3b(2b + 4)$ $6b^2 + 12b$

2. $2x(x^2 + 3x + 5)$ $2x^3 + 6x^2 + 10x$

3. $y(3y^2 + y)$ $3y^3 + y^2$

4. $4w(w^2 - 2w - 5)$ $4w^3 - 8w^2 - 20w$

5. $-2s(s - 3)$ $-2s^2 + 6s$

6. $k(k^2 + 2k + 2)$ $k^3 + 2k^2 + 2k$

7. $-4x^2(x - 5)$ $-4x^3 + 20x^2$

8. $-a(2a + 3)$ $-2a^2 - 3a$

9. $p(p^2 - 4p + 1)$ $p^3 - 4p^2 + p$

10. $-2x(x^2 + x + 6)$ $-2x^3 - 2x^2 - 12x$

Cooperative Learning

11. Explain to a partner how to use the Distributive Property in number **4** in **Practice.** Possible answer: Distribute by multiplying $4w$ by each term inside the parentheses: $4w(w^2) + 4w(-2w) + 4w(-5)$. Then, multiply: $4w^3 - 8w^2 - 20w$.

12. Write $(2x + 4)$, and then write a monomial. Have a partner multiply the binomial by the monomial. Check the work. Answers will vary, but all answers should be of the form $2ax + 4a$, where a is the monomial that the student has chosen.

12-5 ▶ **More Multiplication**

Getting Started

On the chalkboard, write $(x + 5)(x + 1)$. Ask a student to shade the second factor.

$(x + 5)\overline{(x +1)}$

Ask another student to use the Distributive Property. Then shade the second factor in each term.

$x\overline{(x +1)} + 5\overline{(x +1)}$

You have used the Distributive Property to multiply a monomial by a binomial or a trinomial. You also can use the Distributive Property to multiply a binomial by a binomial.

$$(x + 2)(x + 3)$$
$$x(x + 3) + 2(x + 3)$$
$$x^2 + \underline{3x + 2x} + 6$$
$$x^2 + 5x + 6$$

Multiply each term in the second set of parentheses by each term in the first set of parentheses. Then, simplify.

▶ **EXAMPLE 1**

Math Fact

$n \bullet 5 = 5n$

Multiply. $(n + 4)(n + 5)$

Multiply each term of $(n + 5)$ by n and 4.
Combine like terms.

$(n + 4)(n + 5)$

$n(n + 5) + 4(n + 5)$
$n^2 + \underline{5n + 4n} + 20$
$n^2 + 9n + 20$

$(n + 4)(n + 5) = n^2 + 9n + 20$

▶ **EXAMPLE 2**

Math Fact

$-3 \bullet -4 = 12$

Multiply. $(y - 3)(y - 4)$

Multiply each term of $(y - 4)$ by y and -3.
Combine like terms.

$(y - 3)(y - 4)$

$y(y - 4) -3(y - 4)$
$y^2 - \underline{4y - 3y} + 12$
$y^2 - 7y + 12$

$(y - 3)(y - 4) = y^2 - 7y + 12$

▶ **EXAMPLE 3**

Multiply. $(k + 2)(k - 2)$

Multiply each term in $(k - 2)$ by k and 2.
Combine like terms.

$(k + 2)(k - 2)$

$k(k - 2) + 2(k - 2)$
$k^2 - \underline{2k + 2k} - 4$
$k^2 + 0 - 4$
$k^2 - 4$

$(k + 2)(k - 2) = k^2 - 4$

Try These

Multiply.

1. $(x + 2)(x - 5)$

Multiply each term in $(x - 5)$ by x and 2.
Combine like terms.

$(x + 2)(x - 5) = \blacksquare\ x^2 - 3x - 10$

$(x + 2)(x - 5)$
$x(x - 5) + 2\blacksquare\ (x - 5)$
$x^2 - 5\blacksquare x + 2x - \blacksquare\ 10$
$x^2 - \blacksquare x - \blacksquare 10$
$\ \ ^3$

2. $(a - 3)(a + 3)$

Multiply each term in $(a + 3)$ by $\overset{a}{\blacksquare}$ and -3.
Combine like terms.

$(a - 3)(a + 3) = \blacksquare\ a^2 - 9$

$(a - 3)(a + 3)$
$a\blacksquare(a + 3) - \blacksquare(a + 3)$
$a^2 + \blacksquare_{\overline{3a}}\ 3a^3 - 9$
$a^2 + \blacksquare - 9$
$\ \ _0$

Practice

1. $(x + 1)(x + 2)$
$x^2 + 3x + 2$

2. $(x + 3)(x + 5)$
$x^2 + 8x + 15$

3. $(y + 4)(y + 2)$
$y^2 + 6y + 8$

4. $(x + 3)(x - 4)$
$x^2 - x - 12$

5. $(a + 4)(a - 2)$
$a^2 + 2a - 8$

6. $(y + 4)(y - 4)$
$y^2 - 16$

7. $(x - 5)(x + 5)$
$x^2 - 25$

8. $(x - 3)(x + 6)$
$x^2 + 3x - 18$

9. $(y + 1)(y - 1)$
$y^2 - 1$

10. $(x - 1)(x + 4)$
$x^2 + 3x - 4$

11. $(a - 2)(a - 2)$
$a^2 - 4a + 4$

12. $(y - 2)(y + 6)$
$y^2 + 4y - 12$

13. $(x + 2)(x + 5)$
$x^2 + 7x + 10$

14. $(a - 4)(a + 6)$
$a^2 + 2a - 24$

15. $(y + 3)(y + 3)$
$y^2 + 6y + 9$

Cooperative Learning

16. Explain to a partner how to do the multiplication in number **2**
in **Practice.** Possible answer: Multiply x and 3 by $(x + 5)$: $x(x + 5) + 3(x + 5) \longrightarrow$
$x^2 + 5x + 3x + 15 \longrightarrow x^2 + 8x + 15$.

17. Write two binomials with the same variable. Have a partner
multiply the binomials. Check the work. Answers will vary. Check the signs in
students' work.

12·6 ▶ Factors

Numbers or variables that you multiply are **factors** of the product.

$$2xy \leftarrow \text{product}$$

$$2 \bullet x \bullet y \leftarrow \text{factors}$$

2, x, and y are all factors of $2xy$. $2x$, $2y$, xy and $2xy$ are also factors. Each factor divides the product.

$$\frac{2xy}{2x} = y \qquad \frac{2xy}{2y} = x \qquad \frac{2xy}{xy} = 2 \qquad \frac{2xy}{2xy} = 1$$

▶ **EXAMPLE 1**

Is 6 a factor of $12ab$?

Write the factors of $12ab$.	$2 \bullet 2 \bullet 3 \bullet a \bullet b$
Write the factors of 6.	$2 \bullet 3$
Look for common factors.	All the factors of 6 are factors of $12ab$.

6 is a factor of $12ab$.

▶ **EXAMPLE 2**

Is $4x^2y$ a factor of $8x^3y^2$?

Write the factors of $8x^3y^2$.	$2 \bullet 2 \bullet 2 \bullet x \bullet x \bullet x \bullet y \bullet y$
Write the factors of $4x^2y$.	$2 \bullet 2 \bullet x \bullet x \bullet \quad y$
Look for common factors.	All the factors of $4x^2y$ are factors of $8x^3y^2$.

$4x^2y$ is a factor of $8x^3y^2$.

▶ **EXAMPLE 3**

Is $2p$ a factor of $7p^2q$?

Write the factors of $7p^2q$.	$7 \bullet p \bullet p \bullet q$
Write the factors of $2p$.	$2 \bullet p$
Look for common factors.	2 is not a factor of $7p^2q$.

$2p$ is not a factor of $7p^2q$.

Try These

1. Is $5x^2$ a factor of $10x^2y$?

Write the factors of $10x^2y$.

Write the factors of $5x^2$.

Look for common factors.

$5x^2$ ∎ a factor of $10x^2y$.
   is

$$\overset{2}{∎} \cdot \overset{5}{∎} \cdot x \cdot x \cdot y$$

$5 ∎ \cdot x \cdot x$

All ∎ the factors of $5x^2$ are factors of $10x^2y$.

2. Is $6xy^2$ a factor of $12xy$?

Write the factors of $12xy$.

Write the factors of $6xy^2$.

Look for common factors.

$6xy^2$ ∎ a factor of $12xy$.
   is not

$$\overset{2}{∎} \cdot 2 \cdot \overset{3}{∎} \cdot \overset{x}{∎} \cdot y$$

$2 ∎ \cdot ∎ \cdot x \cdot y \cdot ∎ y$

$y^2 ∎ \overset{3}{}$ a factor of $12xy$.
   is not

Practice

Tell whether the first expression is a factor of the second expression.

1. 3 a factor of $6k^2$ yes

2. 5 a factor of $5xy$ yes

3. a a factor of $2b^2$ no

4. m a factor of $8mn$ yes

5. $2x$ a factor of $2xy^2$ yes

6. $3w$ a factor of $10w^2$ no

7. x^2 a factor of xy^2 no

8. $3s^2$ a factor of $9s^2t$ yes

9. $8x$ a factor of $8x$ yes

10. $2b$ a factor of $6ab^2$ yes

11. xy a factor of $2y^2$ no

12. mn^2 a factor of $4mn^2$ yes

Cooperative Learning

13. Explain to a partner how to tell whether $3s^2$ is a factor of $9s^2t$
in number **8** in **Practice.** Possible answer: Find the factors of $9s^2t$: 3, 3, s, s, t. Then, find
the factors of $3s^2$: 3, s, s. Since all the factors of $3s^2$ are factors of $9s^2t$, $3s^2$ is a factor of $9s^2t$.

14. Write two monomials. Ask a partner to tell whether one of the
monomials is a factor of the other. Answers will vary.

More practice is provided in Exercise 69 of the Workbook.

12·7 Factoring by Finding the Greatest Common Factor

You **factor** when you write an expression as the product of its factors. To factor a binomial or trinomial, find the **greatest common factor (GCF)** of all of its terms. This is the largest factor of all the terms.

$$\underbrace{6x}_{3 \bullet 2 \bullet x} + \underbrace{3x^2}_{3 \bullet x \bullet x} \quad \leftarrow 3x \text{ is the GCF.}$$

Divide each term by $3x$ to find the other factor.

$$\frac{3 \bullet 2 \bullet x}{3 \bullet x} + \frac{3 \bullet x \bullet x}{3 \bullet x} \rightarrow 2 + x \text{ is the other factor.}$$

So, $6x + 3x^2 = 3x(2 + x)$.

▶ **EXAMPLE 1**

Factor by finding the GCF. $4y^3 - 2y^2 + y$

Find the GCF of all three terms.

$$\underbrace{4y^3}_{2 \bullet 2 \bullet y \bullet y \bullet y} - \underbrace{2y^2}_{2 \bullet y \bullet y} + \underbrace{y}_{y}$$

y is the GCF.

Divide each term by the GCF.

$$\frac{4y^3}{y} - \frac{2y^2}{y} + \frac{y}{y} \rightarrow 4y^2 - 2y + 1$$

Write the product of the factors.

$$y(4y^2 - 2y + 1)$$

$$4y^3 - 2y^2 + y = y(4y^2 - 2y + 1)$$

Check
Multiply. $y(4y^2 - 2y + 1)$
$y \bullet 4y^2 - y \bullet 2y + y \bullet 1$
$4y^3 - 2y^2 + y$

▶ **EXAMPLE 2**

Factor by finding the GCF. $10x^2y - 15xy$

Find the GCF of both terms.

$$\underbrace{10x^2y}_{5 \bullet 2 \bullet x \bullet x \bullet y} - \underbrace{15xy}_{5 \bullet 3 \bullet x \bullet y}$$

$5xy$ is the GCF.

Divide each term by the GCF.

$$\frac{10x^2y}{5xy} - \frac{15xy}{5xy} \rightarrow 2x - 3$$

Write the product of the factors.

$$5xy(2x - 3)$$

$$10x^2y - 15xy = 5xy(2x - 3)$$

Check
Multiply. $5xy(2x - 3)$
$5xy \bullet 2x - 5xy \bullet 3$
$10x^2y - 15xy$

Try These

Factor by finding the GCF.

1. $4x + 8y$

Find the GCF of both terms.

$$4x \quad + \quad 8y$$
$$2 \bullet \blacksquare \bullet x + 2 \bullet \blacksquare \bullet \blacksquare \bullet y$$

The GCF of $4x$ and $8y$ is $\blacksquare$. 4

Find the other factor. Divide each term by the GCF.
$$\frac{4x}{4\blacksquare} + \frac{8y}{\blacksquare 4} \rightarrow \blacksquare + 2y$$

Write the product of the GCF and the other factor. $4\blacksquare (x + 2y)$

$4x + 8y = \blacksquare \ 4(x + 2y)$

2. $6a^2b - 2ab$

Find the GCF of both terms.

$$6a^2b \quad - \quad 2ab$$
$$2 \bullet \blacksquare \bullet a \bullet a \bullet b - 2 \bullet a \bullet b$$

The GCF of $6a^2b$ and $2ab$ is $\blacksquare$. $2ab$

Find the other factor. Divide each term by the GCF.
$$\frac{6a^2b}{2ab\blacksquare} - \frac{2ab}{\blacksquare 2ab} \rightarrow 3a - \blacksquare 1$$

Write the product of the GCF and the other factor. $2ab(\blacksquare - \blacksquare)$

$6a^2b - 2ab = \blacksquare \ 2ab(3a - 1)$

Practice

Factor by finding the GCF.

1. $3x + 9y$
$3(x + 3y)$

2. $10s + 5t$
$5(2s + t)$

3. $3k^2 + 8k$
$k(3k + 8)$

4. $y^2 + 4y$
$y(y + 4)$

5. $a^3 + a^2 - a$
$a(a^2 + a - 1)$

6. $y^3 - 3y$
$y (y^2 - 3)$

7. $8x^2 - 4x^2y$
$4x^2(2 - y)$

8. $12a^3 + 3a^2 + 6a$
$3a(4a^2 + a + 2)$

9. $20m^2n - 5n$
$5n(4m^2 - 1)$

Cooperative Learning

10. Explain to a partner how to factor the binomial in number **9** in **Practice.** Possible answer: Find the GCF of $20m^2n$ and $5n$: $5n$. Divide $20m^2n - 5n$ by $5n$: $4m^2 - 1$. Write $20m^2n - 5n$ as a product: $5n(4m^2 - 1)$.

11. Multiply a monomial by a binomial. Have a partner factor the product. Check the work. Answers will vary.

More practice is provided in Exercise 70 of the Workbook.

12·8 ▶ Factoring Trinomials

Getting Started
Review multiplication of integers. Students can work in teams. One team names two integers less than 10. The other team gives the product.

You can use what you know about multiplying integers to factor some trinomials. If the last term is positive, the signs of its factors are the same.

$$(x + 2)(x + 3) = x^2 + 3x + 2x + 6 = x^2 + 5x + 6$$

same signs   positive product   product of 2 and 3

sum of 2 and 3

▶ **EXAMPLE 1**

Factor. $x^2 + 7x + 10$

Check
Multiply. $(x + 2)(x + 5)$
$x(x + 5) + 2(x + 5)$
$(x^2 + 5x) + (2x + 10)$
$x^2 + 7x + 10$

Factor x^2.
Factor 10.
Find the pair with a sum
Complete t~~...~~

$$x^2 + 7x + 10$$
$(x\quad)(x\quad)$
1 · ~~10~~ or 2 · 5
because $2 + 5 = 7$
$(x + 5)$

nial is negative

sum of
5 and −6

$11x + 30$

product of
−5 and −6

▶ **EXAMPLE 2**

Fac~~...~~

Check
Multiply. $(y - 4)(y - 5)$
$y(y - 5) - 4(y - 5)$
$y^2 - 5y - 4y + 20$
$y^2 - 9y + 20$

Factor
Factor
Find the ~~...~~ with
a sum of −9.
Complete the factors.
$y^2 - 9y + 20 = (y - 4)(y - 5)$

1 · 20, 2 · 10, and 4 · 5

$-4 · -5$ because $-4 + -5 = -9$
$(y - 4)(y - 5)$

Try These

Factor each trinomial.

1. $y^2 + 7y + 12$

Factor y^2.	$(y\quad)(y\quad)$
Factor 12.	$1 \cdot 12; 2 \cdot \blacksquare; 3 \cdot \blacksquare$
Find the pair with a sum of $\blacksquare$. 7	$3 + \blacksquare 4$
Complete the factors.	$(y + \underset{3}{\blacksquare})(y + \underset{4}{\blacksquare})$

the superscripts: $1 \cdot 12; 2 \cdot \underset{6}{\blacksquare}; 3 \cdot \underset{4}{\blacksquare}$

$y^2 + 7y + 12 = \blacksquare\,(y + 3)(y + 4)$

2. $a^2 - 10a + 16$

Factor a^2.	$(\overset{a}{\blacksquare}\quad)(\overset{a}{\blacksquare}\quad)$
Factor 16.	$1 \cdot 16; 2 \cdot \underset{8}{\blacksquare}; \underset{4}{\blacksquare} \cdot \underset{4}{\blacksquare}$
Find the pair with a sum of $\blacksquare$. -10	$-2\blacksquare + \blacksquare -8$
Complete the factors.	$(a - \underset{2}{\blacksquare})(a - \underset{8}{\blacksquare})$

$a^2 - 10a + 16 = \blacksquare\,(a - 2)(a - 8)$

Practice

Factor each trinomial.

1. $x^2 + 5x + 4$
$(x + 1)(x + 4)$

2. $n^2 + 6n + 8$
$(n + 2)(n + 4)$

3. $c^2 + 4c + 4$
$(c + 2)(c + 2)$

4. $y^2 + 9y + 20$
$(y + 4)(y + 5)$

5. $a^2 - 4a + 3$
$(a - 1)(a - 3)$

6. $y^2 - 5y + 6$
$(y - 2)(y - 3)$

7. $x^2 - 7x + 12$
$(x - 3)(x - 4)$

8. $a^2 - 9a + 14$
$(a - 2)(a - 7)$

9. $x^2 + 11x + 30$
$(x + 6)(x + 5)$

Cooperative Learning

10. Explain to a partner how to factor the trinomial in number **4** in **Practice.** See below.

11. Write two binomials. Begin with $(x +\quad)(x +\quad)$. Multiply the binomials. Then, ask a partner to factor the product. Check the work. Answers will vary. All signs should be positive.

10. Possible answer: Factor y^2: $(y + ?)(y + ?)$. Find two numbers that have a sum of 9 and a product of 20: 4, 5. Replace ? with 4 and 5: $(y + 4)(y + 5)$. Check by multiplying the binomials. Make sure the product is the trinomial you factored.

12·9 ▶ More Factoring Trinomials

Getting Started
Ask students to find the product and sum of each pair of numbers.

6 and −1	(−6; 5)
−6 and 1	(−6; −5)
3 and −4	(−12; −1)
−2 and 5	(−10; 3)

Sometimes the last term of a trinomial is negative. The signs of its factors are not the same. One factor is positive. The other factor is negative.

$$(x - 7)(x + 1) = x^2 + 1x - 7x - 7 = x^2 - 6x - 7$$

different signs   negative product   sum of −7 and 1   product of −7 and 1

When the last term is negative, look for a difference and a sum.

▶ **EXAMPLE 1**

Factor. $y^2 + y - 12$

$$y^2 + 1y - 12$$

Check
$(y + 4)(y - 3)$
$y(y + 4) - 3(y + 4)$
$y^2 + 4y - 3y - 12$
$y^2 + y - 12$

Factor y^2. $(y \quad)(y \quad)$

Factor 12. $1 \cdot 12, 2 \cdot 6,$ and $3 \cdot 4$

Find the pair with a difference of 1. $4 - 3 = 1$

Use the pair to make a sum of 1. $+4 - 3 = 1$

Complete the factors. $(y + 4)(y - 3)$

$$y^2 + y - 12 = (y + 4)(y - 3)$$

▶ **EXAMPLE 2**

Factor. $x^2 - 2x - 15$

$$x^2 - 2x - 15$$

Check
$(x - 5)(x + 3)$
$x(x - 5) + 3(x - 5)$
$x^2 - 5x + 3x - 15$
$x^2 - 2x - 15$

Factor x^2. $(x \quad)(x \quad)$

Factor 15. $1 \cdot 15$ and $3 \cdot 5$

Find the pair with a difference of 2. $5 - 3 = 2$

Use the pair to make a sum of −2. $-5 + 3 = -2$

Complete the factors. $(x - 5)(x + 3)$

$$x^2 - 2x - 15 = (x - 5)(x + 3)$$

Try These

Factor each trinomial.

1. $x^2 + 3x - 18$

Factor x^2.
Factor 18.
Find the pair with a difference of $\blacksquare$.3
Use the pair to make a sum of 3.
Complete the factors.
$x^2 + 3x - 18 = \blacksquare (x + 6)(x - 3)$

$x^2 + 3x - 18$
$(x\quad)(x\quad 9)$ 6
$1 \cdot 18; \ 2 \cdot \blacksquare; \ 3 \cdot \blacksquare$
$6 - 3 = \blacksquare 3$
$+6 - 3 = \blacksquare 3$
$(x + \blacksquare)(x - \blacksquare)$
6 3

2. $a^2 - 8a - 20$

Factor a^2.
Factor 20.
Find the pair with a difference of $\blacksquare$.8
Use the pair to make a sum of $\blacksquare$. -8
Complete the factors.
$a^2 - 8a - 20 = \blacksquare (a - 10)(a + 2)$

$a^2 - 8a - 20$
a
$(\blacksquare a\quad)(\blacksquare\ 10\ )$
$1 \cdot 20; \ 2 \cdot \blacksquare; \ 4 \cdot \blacksquare 5$
$10\blacksquare - 2 = \blacksquare 8$
$-10 + 2 = \blacksquare\ -8$
$(a - \blacksquare)(a + \blacksquare)$
10 2

10. Possible answer: Factor a^2: $(a - ?)(a + ?)$. Find two numbers that have a sum of 2 and a product of -24: -4, 6. Replace ? with -4 and $+6$: $(a - 4)(a + 6)$. Check by multiplying the binomials.

Practice
Make sure the product is the trinomial you factored.

Factor each trinomial.

1. $x^2 + 4x - 5$
$(x - 1)(x + 5)$

2. $h^2 + 9h - 10$
$(h - 1)(h + 10)$

3. $y^2 - 5y - 6$
$(y + 1)(y - 6)$

4. $w^2 + w - 6$
$(w - 2)(w + 3)$

5. $a^2 + 2a - 8$
$(a - 2)(a + 4)$

6. $y^2 - 3y - 10$
$(y + 2)(y - 5)$

7. $x^2 - 6x - 16$
$(x + 2)(x - 8)$

8. $a^2 + 2a - 24$
$(a - 4)(a + 6)$

9. $k^2 + 4k - 12$
$(k + 6)(k - 2)$

Cooperative Learning

10. Explain to a partner how to factor the trinomial in number **8** in **Practice.** See above.

11. Write two binomials. Begin with $(x - \quad)(x + \quad)$. Use any two numbers for the second terms. Multiply the binomials. Then, ask a partner to factor the product. Check the work. Answers will vary. Make sure the sign of the last term is negative. The middle term should be the sign of the larger number.

Chapter 12 • Polynomials and Factoring   311

More practice is provided in Exercise 70 of the Workbook.

Factoring the Difference of Two Squares

4	25	64
49	16	81
9	100	36
121	144	

As you point to each number,
have students give the
square root.

Multiplication can show you a way to factor a binomial that is the difference of two squares.

difference of squares
$(x)^2$ and $(4)^2$

sum

$$(x + 4)(x - 4) = x^2 + 4x - 4x - 16 = x^2 - 16$$

difference

► EXAMPLE 1

Factor. $a^2 - 9$

Find the two squares. $a^2 = (a)^2, 9 = (3)^2$

Write the factor as a sum
and difference of a and 3. $(a + 3)(a - 3)$

$a^2 - 9 = (a + 3)(a - 3)$

► EXAMPLE 2

Factor. $x^2 - 1$

Find the two squares. $x^2 = (x)^2, 1^2 = (1)^2$

Write the product of the sum
and difference of x and 1. $(x - 1)(x + 1)$

$x^2 - = (x + 1)(x - 1)$

Sometimes the square of the variable term and the square of the number term are in a different order. Keep this order when you factor.

► EXAMPLE 3

Factor. $25 - n^2$

$25 - n^2$

Find the two squares. $25 = (5)^2, n^2 = (n)^2$

Write the factor as a sum
and difference of 5 and n.   . $(5 + n)(5 - n)$

$25 - n^2 = (5 + n)(5 - n)$

Try These

Factor.

1. $x^2 - 36$

Find the two squares. $x^2 = (x)^2$ $36 = \blacksquare^2$ (6)

Write the factors as a sum and difference. $(x + \blacksquare)(x - \blacksquare)$ (6, 6)

$x^2 - 36 = \blacksquare.\ (x + 6)(x - 6)$

2. $100 - y^2$

Find the two squares. $100 = \blacksquare^2$ (10) $y^2 = (y)^2$

Write the factors as a sum and difference. $(\blacksquare + y)(\blacksquare - y)$ (10, 10)

$100 - y^2 = \blacksquare.\ (10 + y)(10 - y)$

Practice

Factor as the product of two binomials.

1. $x^2 - 64$
$(x + 8)(x - 8)$

2. $n^2 - 4$
$(n + 2)(n - 2)$

3. $49 - c^2$
$(7 + c)(7 - c)$

4. $y^2 - 1$
$(y + 1)(y - 1)$

5. $a^2 - 81$
$(a + 9)(a - 9)$

6. $144 - k^2$
$(12 + k)(12 - k)$

7. $x^2 - 400$
$(x + 20)(x - 20)$

8. $a^2 - 121$
$(a + 11)(a - 11)$

9. $b^2 - 169$
$(b + 13)(b - 13)$

10. $n^2 - 225$
$(n + 15)(n - 15)$

11. $625 - x^2$
$(25 + x)(25 - x)$

12. $c^2 - 256$
$(c + 16)(c - 16)$

Cooperative Learning

13. Possible answer: $y^2 - 1$ Factor y^2: $(y + ?)(y - ?)$.
Find the opposite square roots of 1: $(y + 1)(y - 1)$.

13. Explain to a partner how to factor number **4** in **Practice**. See above.

14. Write a positive number. Find its square. Use the square to write the difference of two squares. Ask a partner to factor as the product of two binomials. Check the work. Answers will vary. All answers should be in the form $(x + a)(x - a)$.

More practice is provided in Exercise 71 of the Workbook.

12-11 ▶ Using the Zero Product Property

If the product of two factors is 0, then one factor must be 0. This is called the **Zero Product Property**.

$$x \bullet y = 0$$
means $x = 0$ or $y = 0$

You can use this property to find the solutions of quadratic equations that equal 0.

$$(x - 2)(x + 4) = 0$$
means $x - 2 = 0$ or $x + 4 = 0$

So, to solve $(x - 2)(x + 4) = 0$, solve:

$x - 2 = 0$	and	$x + 4 = 0$
$x - 2 + 2 = 0 + 2$		$x + 4 - 4 = 0 - 4$
$x = 2$		$x = -4$
Solution: 2		Solution: -4

▶ **EXAMPLE 1**

Check
$(6 - 6)(6 + 5) = 0$
$0(11) = 0$
$0 = 0$ true

$(-5 - 6)(-5 + 5) = 0$
$(-11)0 = 0$
$0 = 0$ true

Solve. Then, check. $(x - 6)(x + 5) = 0$

Let each factor equal 0. $x - 6 = 0$ or $x + 5 = 0$

Solve $x - 6 = 0$. $x - 6 = 0$
$x = 6$

Solve $x + 5 = 0$. $x + 5 = 0$
$x = -5$

The solutions of $(x - 6)(x + 5) = 0$ are 6 and -5.

▶ **EXAMPLE 2**

Check
$0(2 \bullet 0 - 8) = 0$
$0(-8) = 0$
$0 = 0$ true

$4(2 \bullet 4 - 8) = 0$
$4(8 - 8) = 0$
$4(0) = 0$
$0 = 0$ true

Solve. Then, check. $x(2x - 8) = 0$

Let each factor equal 0. $x = 0$ or $2x - 8 = 0$

Solve $x = 0$. $x = 0$

Solve $2x - 8 = 0$. $2x - 8 = 0$
$2x = 8$
$\dfrac{2x}{2} = \dfrac{8}{2}$
$x = 4$

The solutions of $x(2x - 8) = 0$ are 0 and 4.

Try These

Solve. Then check. $(x + 2)(3x + 9) = 0$

Let each factor equal ■. $x + 2\blacksquare = 0$ or $\blacksquare = 0$ *(3x + 9)*
                                0
Solve $x + 2 = 0$. $x + 2 = 0$ $3x + 9 = 0$
                                $x = \blacksquare$ $3x = \blacksquare\ -9$
                                    -2 $x = \blacksquare\ -3$
                                -2 -3
The solutions of $(x + 2)(3x + 9) = 0$ are ■ and ■.

Check: -2	Check: -3
$(x + 2)(3x + 9) = 0$	$(x + 2)(3x + 9) = 0$
$(\blacksquare + 2)(3(\blacksquare) + 9) = 0\ -2$	$(\blacksquare + 2)(3(\blacksquare) + 9) = 0\ -3$
-2 $0\blacksquare\ (\blacksquare + 9) = 0$	-3 $-1\blacksquare\ (\blacksquare + 9) = 0$
-6 $0 = 0$ true	-9 $0 = 0$ true

10. Possible answer: Let $z + 4 = 0$. Solve for z: $z = -4$. Let $4z + 8 = 0$. Solve for z: $z = -2$.
    Check: $(-4 + 4)(4 \bullet -4 + 8) = 0$ true; $(-2 + 4)(4 \bullet -2 + 8) = 0$ true. Solutions are $z = -4$

Practice   and $z = -2$.

Solve. Then, check.

1. $x(x + 3) = 0$
   $x = 0$ and $x = -3$

2. $z(z - 6) = 0$
   $z = 0$ and $z = 6$

3. $2y(y - 7) = 0$
   $y = 0$ and $y = 7$

4. $4x(x + 1) = 0$
   $x = 0$ and $x = -1$

5. $(y + 2)(y - 2) = 0$
   $y = -2$ and $y = 2$

6. $(a - 4)(a + 4) = 0$
   $a = 4$ and $a = -4$

7. $(z + 4)(4z + 8) = 0$
   $z = -4$ and $z = -2$

8. $(3y + 6)(y + 5) = 0$
   $y = -2$ and $y = -5$

9. $(3x - 12)(x - 5) = 0$
   $x = 4$ and $x = 5$

Cooperative Learning

10. Explain to a partner how to solve the equation in number 7
    in **Practice**. See above.

11. Write an equation with the product of two binomials equal to
    zero. Ask a partner to solve the equation. Check the work.
    Answers will vary. Check the signs in the students' work. Students may have 1 or 2 solutions.

12·12 Solving Equations by Factoring

Getting Started
Have students work in groups to make posters on factoring as a display for the classroom.

The equations you have solved were already factored on one side. The other side was 0. Sometimes, one side of the equation is a binomial or trinomial and the other side is 0. Factor the binomial or trinomial. Then, solve.

▶ **EXAMPLE 1**

Solve. $y^2 - 16 = 0$

Factor the difference of two squares.

$$y^2 - 16 = 0$$
$$(y + 4)(y - 4) = 0$$

Check
$(-4)^2 - 16 = 0$
  $16 - 16 = 0$
      $0 = 0$ true

$(4)^2 - 16 = 0$
  $16 - 16 = 0$
      $0 = 0$ true

Let each factor equal 0. $y + 4 = 0$ or $y - 4 = 0$

Solve $y + 4 = 0$.

$$y + 4 = 0$$
$$y = -4$$

Solve $y - 4 = 0$.

$$y - 4 = 0$$
$$y = 4$$

The solutions of $y^2 - 16 = 0$ are -4 and 4.

▶ **EXAMPLE 2**

Solve. $v^2 - 5v - 14 = 0$

Factor the trinomial.

$$v^2 - 5v - 14 = 0$$
$$(v + 2)(v - 7) = 0$$

Check
$(-2)^2 - 5(-2) - 14 = 0$
     $4 + 10 - 14 = 0$
          $14 - 14 = 0$
               $0 = 0$ true

$(7)^2 - 5(7) - 14 = 0$
   $49 - 35 - 14 = 0$
        $14 - 14 = 0$
             $0 = 0$ true

Let each factor equal 0. $v + 2 = 0$ or $v - 7 = 0$

Solve $v + 2 = 0$.

$$v + 2 = 0$$
$$v = -2$$

Solve $v - 7 = 0$.

$$v - 7 = 0$$
$$v = 7$$

Solutions of $v^2 - 5v - 14 = 0$ are -2 and 7.

▶ **EXAMPLE 3**

Solve. $0 = x^2 + 4x + 4$

Factor the trinomial.

$$0 = x^2 + 4x + 4$$

Check
$0 = (-2)^2 + 4(-2) + 4$
$0 = 4 - 8 + 4$
$0 = -4 + 4$
$0 = 0$ true

Both factors are the same.

$$0 = (x + 2)(x + 2)$$

Let either factor equal 0.

$$0 = x + 2$$
$$-2 = x$$

The solution of $0 = x^2 + 4x + 4$ is -2.

Solve.

1. $y^2 + 4y = 0$

Factor.

Let each factor equal 0.

Solve the equations.

$$y^2 + 4y = 0$$
$$y(y + \blacksquare)4$$
$$y = 0 \text{ or } y + \blacksquare = 0$$
$$y = \blacksquare$$
$$4y + \blacksquare = 0$$
$$y = \blacksquare -4$$

The solutions are $\blacksquare$ and $\blacksquare$.

2. $x^2 - 10x + 25 = 0$

Factor.

The factors are the same. Let one factor equal 0.

The solution is $\blacksquare$.

$$x^2 - 10x + 25 = 0$$
$$5(x - \blacksquare)(x - \blacksquare)$$
$$x - \blacksquare = 0$$
$$x = \blacksquare$$

Practice

Solve.

1. $y^2 + 2y + 1 = 0$ $y = -1$

2. $x^2 + 7x + 10 = 0$ $x = -2$ and $x = -5$

3. $y^2 - 8y + 16 = 0$ $y = 4$

4. $x^2 - 9x + 18 = 0$ $x = 3$ and $x = 6$

5. $a^2 - 49 = 0$ $a = 7$ and $a = -7$

6. $y^2 + 6y - 7 = 0$ $y = 1$ and $y = -7$

7. $y^2 + 2y - 15 = 0$ $y = 3$ and $y = -5$

8. $v^2 - 25 = 0$ $v = -5$ and $v = 5$

9. $a^2 - 5a - 36 = 0$ $a = 9$ and $a = -4$

10. $x^2 - 10x + 16 = 0$ $x = 8$ and $x = 2$

11. $n^2 + 3n - 28 = 0$ $n = -7$ and $n = 4$

12. $y^2 + 19y + 48 = 0$ $y = -16$ and $y = -3$

Cooperative Learning

13. Explain to a partner how to solve the equation in number **3** in **Practice.** Possible answer: Factor the trinomial: $(y - 4)(y - 4)$. Let $y - 4 = 0$. Solve for y: $y = 4$. Check: $(4)^2 - 8(4) + 16 = 0$ true. The solution is $y = 4$.

14. Write two binomials and multiply them. Use the product to write an equation equal to 0. Ask a partner to solve your equation. Check the work. Answers will vary. Check students' work.

Getting Started
Write
$x^2 + 5x - 6 = 0$
on the chalkboard.
Ask a volunteer to show that
$x = 1$ is a solution.

12·13 ▶ Calculator: Checking Solutions

You can use your calculator to check solutions of equations that have a binomial or trinomial on one side and 0 on the other.

▶ **EXAMPLE 1**

Tell whether 3.1 is a solution of $x^2 + 2.5x - 17.36 = 0$.

Substitute 3.1 for x. $\qquad (3.1)^2 + 2.5(3.1) - 17.36 = 0$

Use your calculator to simplify each term.   **Display**

Find $(3.1)^2$. Enter 3.1.   [3] [.] [1] | 3.1 |

Multiply by 3.1 by
pressing: [×] [3] [.] [1] [=] | 9.61 |

Write 9.61 on your paper.

Find 2.5(3.1). Enter 2.5. [2] [.] [5] | 2.5 |

Multiply by 3.1 by
pressing: [×] [3] [.] [1] [=] | 7.75 |

Write 7.75 on your paper.

Combine the 3 terms.

Enter 9.61.   [9] [.] [6] [1] | 9.61 |

Add 7.75 by pressing: [+] [7] [.] [7] [5] | 17.36 |

Subtract 17.36 by
pressing: [−] [1] [7] [.] [3] [6] [=] | 0 |

3.1 is a solution of $x^2 + 2.5x - 17.36 = 0$.

▶ **EXAMPLE 2**

Tell whether 2.5 is a solution of $2x^2 - 12.5 = 0$.

Substitute 2.5 for x. $\qquad 2(2.5)^2 - 12.5 = 0$

Use your calculator to simplify the first term.   **Display**

Find $(2.5)^2$. Enter 2.5
by pressing: [2] [.] [5] | 2.5 |

Multiply by 2.5 by
pressing: [×] [2] [.] [5] [=] | 6.25 |

Multiply 6.25 by 2 by
pressing: [×] [2] [=] | 12.5 |

Subtract the two terms. $12.5 - 12.5 = 0$

2.5 is a solution of $2x^2 - 12.5 = 0$.

Practice

Tell whether the number is a solution of the trinomial.

1. $.08; v^2 - 2.08v + .16 = 0$ yes

2. $4.2; x^2 + 5.1x + 3.78 = 0$ no

3. $1.6; a^2 - 4.2a + 4.16 = 0$ yes

4. $.15; x^2 + .85x - .15 = 0$ yes

5. $.9; x^2 + 56.1x - 51.3 = 0$ yes

6. $7.9; y^2 + 9.83y - .693 = 0$ no

People in Math

MUHAMMAD IBN MUSA AL-KHWARIZMI

Muhammad ibn Musa Al-Khwarizmi was a very famous mathematician. He wrote about algebra. He lived during the 800s in the city of Baghdad. People at that time went to this city to learn math and astronomy.

Al-Khwarizmi wrote two important books on arithmetic and algebra. The title of one book is *Hisab al-jabr w' al-muqa-bilah*. This means "the science of putting together and taking apart." We get the word *algebra* from the word *al-jabr*.

Studying astronomy in Baghdad

Some of his books were copied into Latin. This helped people in Europe study his work centuries later. The word *algebra* came to mean the science of equations.

We also get the word *algorithm* from his name, Al-Khwarizmi. A Latin translator called him Algoritmi. This became the word *algorithm*. Algorithm means a rule for solving a problem. One example is the Order of Operations.

More practice is provided in Exercise 71 of the Workbook.

Problem Solving: Choosing the Best Method

12·14

You have learned two ways to solve quadratic equations. You can use factoring, or you can use the quadratic formula. For both methods, the equation must be written in standard form.

To solve $ax^2 + bx + c = 0$, factor the polynomial. Or, use the quadratic formula:

$$x = \frac{-b \pm \sqrt{b^2 - 4ac}}{2a}$$

You can choose the method you find easier. You do not have to use the same method all the time.

▶ **EXAMPLE**

Solve. $3x^2 - 6x = 0$

READ   **What do you need to find out?**
You need to find which values of x are solutions to the quadratic equation.

PLAN   **What do you need to do?**
You need to use factoring to solve for x.

DO   **Follow the plan.**

Look for common factors in the terms of the polynomial. $3x^2 - 6x = 0$

Factor out $3x$. $3x(x - 2) = 0$

Let each factor equal 0. $3x = 0$ or $x - 2 = 0$

Solve $3x = 0$. $3x = 0 \;\rightarrow\; x = 0$

Solve $x - 2 = 0$. $x - 2 = 0 \;\rightarrow\; x = 2$

CHECK   **Does your answer make sense?**
Substitute both solutions into the original equation. ✓

The solutions of $3x^2 - 6x = 0$ are 2 and 0.

Try These

Solve each equation. Use factoring or the quadratic formula.

1. $x^2 + 5x + 6 = 0$

What two numbers give a product of
6 and a sum of 5?

$3 \cdot 2 = 6$ and $2 + 3 = 5$

Let each factor equal 0.

Solve each equation.

The solutions of $x^2 + 5x + 6 = 0$ are -2 and -3.

$x^2 + 5x + 6 = 0$

$(x + 2)(x + 3) = 0$

$x + 2 = 0$ or $x + 3 = 0$

$x = -2$ or $x = -3$

2. $x^2 - 19x - 120 = 0$

What two numbers give a product
of 120 and a difference of 19?

Use the quadratic formula.

$x^2 - 19x - 120 = 0$

$x = \dfrac{-(-19) \pm \sqrt{(-19)^2 - 4(1)(-120)}}{2(1)}$

$x = \dfrac{19 \pm \sqrt{361 + 480}}{2}$

$x = \dfrac{19 \pm 29}{2} = \dfrac{48}{2}$ or $\dfrac{-10}{2}$

$x = 24$ or -5

Practice

Solve each equation. Use factoring or the quadratic formula.
Tell which method you used.

1. $x^2 + 15x - 54 = 0$
$x = -18$ or 3; factoring

2. $2x^2 - 8x = 0$
$x = 0$ or 4; quadratic formula

3. $x^2 - 19x + 48 = 0$
$x = 16$ or 3; factoring

4. $2x^2 + 2x - 4 = 0$
$x = -2$ or 1; quadratic formula

5. $3x^2 - 45x = 0$
$x = 0$ or 15; quadratic formula

6. $x^2 + 1x - 72 = 0$
$x = -9$ or 8; factoring

Cooperative Learning

7. Explain to a partner how to choose which method to use to solve
number 4 in Practice. Possible answer: Student uses the quadratic formula since they don't
know how to factor when $a = 2$.

8. Work with a partner to solve $0 = x^2 + 8x - 65$. First, try to solve
by factoring. Then, use the quadratic formula. $(x + 13)(x - 5) = 0$; $x = -13$ or 5.

12·15 Application: Using a Formula

Getting Started
Review that the volume of a gas is $v = \frac{5}{3}t + 450$ where t is temperature. Ask a volunteer to show how to find the volume of a gas at 30°C. ($v = \frac{5}{3}(30) + 450$; $v = 500$ cc)

Formulas can help you solve problems. You can use what you know about exponents to use formulas with degree 2.

You can use a formula to find the height of an object thrown upward if you know the amount of time in the air. The formula is $h = 40t - 5t^2$, where h means height in meters and t means time.

▶ **EXAMPLE 1**

At what height is a ball 4 seconds after it is thrown up in the air?

Write the formula.	$h = 40t - 5t^2$
Substitute 4 for t.	$h = 40(4) - 5(4)^2$
Multiply.	$h = 160 - 80$
Subtract.	$h = 80$

Math Fact
$-5(4)^2 = -5 \bullet 4 \bullet 4$

The ball is 80 meters high 4 seconds after it is thrown up in the air.

You can use a formula to find the number of diagonals in a polygon. The formula is $d = \frac{s^2 - 3s}{2}$. Here, d means diagonals and s means sides.

▶ **EXAMPLE 2**

Find the number of diagonals in a polygon with 6 sides.

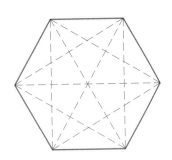

Write the formula.	$d = \dfrac{s^2 - 3s}{2}$
Substitute 6 for s.	$d = \dfrac{6^2 - 3(6)}{2}$
Multiply.	$d = \dfrac{36 - 18}{2}$
Subtract.	$d = \dfrac{18}{2}$
Divide.	$d = 9$

A polygon with 6 sides has 9 diagonals.

Try These

Meteorologists find formulas that can be used to predict the average monthly high temperature in a city. Such a formula is $t = -m^2 + 19m + 19$. The variable t stands for the temperature in degrees Fahrenheit. The variable m stands for the month of the year.

1. Find the average monthly high temperature for February.

$$t = -m^2 + 19m + 19$$

Substitute 2 for m. $\quad t = -(2)^2 + 19\blacksquare_2 + 19$

Multiply. $\quad t = \blacksquare_{-4} + \blacksquare_{38} + \blacksquare 19$

Add. $\quad t = \blacksquare 53$

The average monthly high temperature is $\blacksquare_{53}$ °F.

2. Find the average monthly high temperature for May.

$$t = -m^2 + 19m + 19$$

Substitute 5 for m. $\quad t = -(\blacksquare_5)^2 + 19\blacksquare_5 + 19$

Multiply. $\quad t = \blacksquare_{-25} + \blacksquare_{95} + \blacksquare 19$

Add. $\quad t = \blacksquare 89$

The average monthly high temperature is $\blacksquare_{89}$ °F.

Practice

Use the formulas in this lesson to answer each question.

1. Find the height of a ball 2 seconds after it has been thrown. 60 meters

2. Find the height of a ball 7 seconds after it has been thrown. 35 meters

3. Find the average monthly high temperature for January. 37°F

4. Find the number of diagonals in a polygon with 8 sides. 20 diagonals

5. Find the number of diagonals in a polygon with 9 sides. 27 diagonals

Cooperative Learning

6. Explain to a partner how to use the formula to solve number 1 in **Practice**. Possible answer: Substitute 2 for t: $h = 40(2) - 5(2)^2$. Multiply : $80 - 20$. Subtract: 60. The ball is 60 meters high 2 seconds after it is thrown upward.

7. Choose a number between 3 and 7. Have a partner find the number of diagonals for a polygon with that number of sides. Check the work. Possible answers: 2, 5, 9.

Summary

You can name a monomial, binomial, or trinomial by counting the terms.
To add polynomials, line up the like terms and add their coefficients.
To subtract polynomials, add the opposite of the polynomial.
Use the Distributive Property to multiply a binomial by a monomial.
Use the Distributive Property to multiply two binomials. Multiply each term in one binomial by each term in the other binomial.
The factors of a monomial are the numbers or variables that divide the monomial.
You can factor some polynomials by finding the greatest common factor of the terms.
You can factor some trinomials as the product of two binomials. Factor the first term. Then, find two numbers that have a sum or difference equal to the middle term and a product equal to the last term.
Solve quadratic equations by factoring and by letting each factor equal zero.
You can use factoring or the quadratic formula to solve problems that have a quadratic equation.
Formulas can help you solve problems.

More vocabulary review is provided in Exercise 111 of the Classroom Resource Binder.

polynomial

monomial

binomial

trinomial

factors

Zero Product Property

greatest common factor

Vocabulary Review

Complete the sentences with words from the box.

1. A polynomial with three terms is called a ____. trinomial

2. The ____ means that if the product of two numbers is 0, then one of the numbers must be 0. Zero Product Property

3. An expression with one term is called a ____. monomial

4. A ____ is a polynomial with two terms. binomial

5. A monomial or the sum or difference of monomials is called a ____. polynomial

6. Numbers or variables being multiplied are ____. factors

7. The largest common factor of two or more terms is the ____. greatest common factor

Chapter Quiz More **assessment** is provided in the Classroom Resource Binder.

Name the type of polynomial.

1. $-10xy$ monomial   **2.** $-3x^2 - xy - 8y^2$ trinomial   **3.** $-4a + b$ binomial

Combine each pair of polynomials.

4. Add $x^2 + 5x - 8$ and $2x + 6$.
$x^2 + 7x - 2$

5. Subtract $4x^2 - 8$ from $3x^2 + 4x + 1$.
$-x^2 + 4x + 9$

Multiply.

6. $x(3x + 2)$
$3x^2 + 2x$

7. $-2x(x^2 + x)$
$-2x^3 - 2x^2$

8. $x(x^2 + 3y + 4)$
$x^3 + 3xy + 4x$

9. $(y + 3)(y + 9)$
$y^2 + 12y + 27$

10. $(a - 2)(a - 8)$
$a^2 - 10a + 16$

11. $(x - 5)(x + 7)$
$x^2 + 2x - 35$

Tell whether the first expression is a factor of the second expression.

12. Is xy a factor of $5x^2$? no

13. Is $2xy$ a factor of $8xy^2$? yes

Factor by finding the greatest common factor.

14. $a^2 + 4ab$ $a(a + 4b)$ **15.** $2k^3 + 4k$ $2k(k^2 + 2)$ **16.** $10x^2y - 5xy$ $5xy(2x - 1)$

Factor as the product of two binomials.

17. $x^2 + 9x + 8$
$(x + 1)(x + 8)$

18. $x^2 + 8x - 9$
$(x - 1)(x + 9)$

19. $y^2 - y - 12$
$(y + 3)(y - 4)$

20. $y^2 - 12y + 20$
$(y - 2)(y - 10)$

21. $x^2 - 25$
$(x + 5)(x - 5)$

22. $n^2 + 8n + 16$
$(n + 4)(n + 4)$

Solve each equation. Use factoring or the quadratic formula.

23. $6x(x + 4) = 0$
$x = 0$ and $x = -4$

24. $(3a - 12)(a + 5) = 0$
$a = 4$ and $a = -5$

25. $x^2 + 6x + 5 = 0$
$x = -1$ and $x = -5$

26. $x^2 - 49 = 0$
$x = 7$ and $x = -7$

27. $2x^2 - 16x = 0$
$x = 0$ and $x = 8$

28. $x^2 - 18x + 80 = 0$
$x = 10$ and $x = 8$

29. Use the formula $h = 40t - 5t^2$ to find the height in meters of a ball 5 seconds after it is thrown. 75 meters

Additional Practice for this chapter is provided on page 424 of this text.

Chapter 12 • Polynomials and Factoring   325

Unit 4 Review

Use the graph to answer Questions 1 and 2.

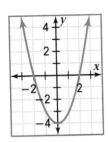

1. Which number or numbers are the zeros of the quadratic function? C

   A. 4
   B. 4 and 2
   C. 2 and −2
   D. −4

2. Which statement is true about the graph? A

   A. It has a minimum at (0, −4).
   B. It has a maximum at (2, 0).
   C. It opens downward.
   D. It has a maximum at (0, −4).

3. The area of a sign is 18 square feet. The length is 2 times the width. What is the width of the sign? C

   A. 6 ft
   B. 12 ft
   C. 3 ft
   D. 18 ft

Critical Thinking See the Classroom Resource Binder for a scoring rubric to assess this Critical Thinking question.

4. What are the solutions of the equation $x^2 - 3x - 10 = 0$? B

   A. −5 and 2
   B. 5 and −2
   C. 7 and 3
   D. not given

5. $80 is deposited into a savings account. The rate of interest is 5% a year, compounded yearly. What is the total after 3 years? A

   A. $92.61
   B. $102.10
   C. $85.15
   D. $270.00

6. A tennis ball is dropped from a building 784 feet high. When does the ball hit the ground? (Use the formula $h = -16t^2 + vt + s$) B

   A. 5 seconds
   B. 7 seconds
   C. 9 seconds
   D. 10 seconds

Critical Thinking

Tom makes posters for class. He has a choice of white, yellow, or blue paper. He also has a choice of black or red pen. How many different ways can Tom make the posters? 6 ways

CHALLENGE Paper comes in 2 shapes (square, rectangle). Draw a tree diagram to show how many different posters Tom can now make.
See Additional Answers, p. 479.

Unit Five

Radicals and Geometry

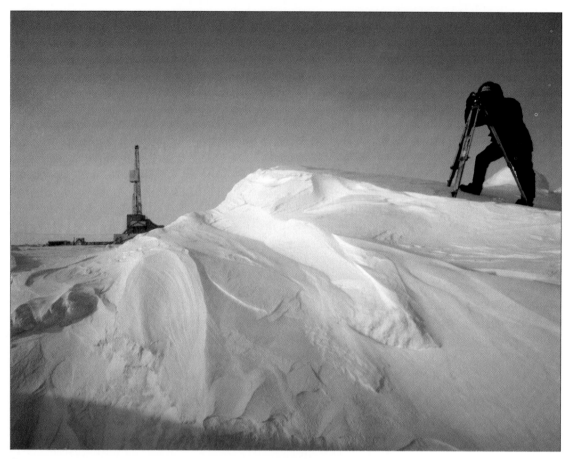

Surveyors measure the land. They use right triangles and radical equations to find heights and distances. What tools does a surveyor use?

Learning Objectives

- Simplify radicals.
- Solve radical equations.
- Identify the sides and angles of a right triangle.
- Use the Pythagorean Theorem.
- Use a calculator to check radical equations.
- Solve problems by identifying right triangles.
- Apply concepts and skills to finding distance in the coordinate plane.

Words to Know

radical	square root written as a number under a radical sign
irrational number	numbers with decimals that do not end and do not repeat
radical equation	an equation that has a variable under a radical sign
right triangle	a triangle with one right angle and two acute angles
hypotenuse	the side across from the right angle of a right triangle
Pythagorean Theorem	a formula for finding the length of a side of a right triangle when you know the lengths of the other sides; $a^2 + b^2 = c^2$
45°−45°−90° triangle	a right triangle whose acute angles both measure 45°
30°−60°−90° triangle	a right triangle whose acute angles measure 30° and 60°
Pythagorean triple	three positive whole numbers that satisfy the Pythagorean Theorem; the numbers can be the measures of the sides of a right triangle
Distance Formula	a way to find the distance between two points using the Pythagorean Theorem

Box Kite Project

Make a kite in the shape of a box like the drawing on the right. You can use crepe paper and straws to make the kite. Four sides are rectangles. Two sides are squares. Measure a side of the square.

Then use the Pythagorean theorem, (see Lesson 13.7), to find the length of the diagonal brace. Then, use the shortcut in Lesson 13.8 to check. Measure the brace. How close is your measurement to the actual length?

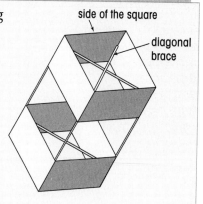

side of the square

diagonal brace

Project See the Classroom Resource Binder for a scoring rubric to assess this project.

More practice is provided in Exercise 73 of the Workbook.

13·1 Radicals and the Number Line

Getting Started
Review square roots. Have students match the numbers in each column.

You have learned about squares and square roots. Square roots are also known as **radicals.**

$\sqrt{3}$ is a radical number.
$\sqrt{}$ is the radical sign. In $\sqrt{3}$, 3 is the radicand.

Radicals can be the square roots of perfect squares, or they can be **irrational numbers.**

4 is a perfect square. Its square root is $\sqrt{4} = 2$.
9 is a perfect square. Its square root is $\sqrt{9} = 3$.

If the radicand is not a perfect square, the radical is an irrational number. The decimal form of an irrational number does not repeat and does not end.

$\sqrt{2} = 1.414\ldots$ $\sqrt{3} = 1.732\ldots$ $\sqrt{5} = 2.336\ldots$

All the numbers shown on the number line are radicals. Notice that $\sqrt{2}$ is between the radicals of two perfect squares, $\sqrt{1}$ and $\sqrt{4}$.

▶ **EXAMPLE 1**

$\sqrt{7}$ is between what two whole numbers?

Find the closest perfect square less than 7.	4
Find its square root.	$\sqrt{4} = 2$
Find the closest perfect square greater than 7.	9
Find its square root.	$\sqrt{9} = 3$

$\sqrt{7}$ is between 2 and 3.

▶ **EXAMPLE 2**

$\sqrt{3}$ is between what two whole numbers?

Find the closest perfect square less than 3.	1
Find its square root.	$\sqrt{1} = 1$
Find the closest perfect square greater than 3.	4
Find its square root.	$\sqrt{4} = 2$

$\sqrt{3}$ is between 1 and 2.

Try These

1. $\sqrt{6}$ is between what two whole numbers?

Find the closest perfect square less than 6.   4

Find its square root. $\sqrt{4} = \blacksquare\ 2$

Find the closest perfect square $\blacksquare$ than 6. *greater* $\blacksquare\ 9$

Find its square root. $\sqrt{\blacksquare} = \blacksquare$
                          9   3

$\sqrt{6}$ is between $\blacksquare$ and $\blacksquare$.
            2   3

2. $\sqrt{11}$ is between what two whole numbers?

Find the closest perfect square $\blacksquare$ than 11. *less* $\blacksquare\ 9$

Find its square root. $\sqrt{\blacksquare} = \blacksquare$
                          9   3

Find the closest perfect square greater than 11.   16

Find its square root. $\sqrt{16} = \blacksquare\ 4$

$\sqrt{11}$ is between $\blacksquare$ and $\blacksquare$.
            3   4

Practice

Locate each square root between two whole numbers.

1. $\sqrt{5}$ is between what two whole numbers?   2 and 3

2. $\sqrt{14}$ is between what two whole numbers?   3 and 4

3. $\sqrt{19}$ is between what two whole numbers?   4 and 5

4. $\sqrt{10}$ is between what two whole numbers?   3 and 4

5. $\sqrt{8}$ is between what two whole numbers?   2 and 3

6. $\sqrt{17}$ is between what two whole numbers?   4 and 5

7. $\sqrt{13}$ is between what two whole numbers?   3 and 4

8. $\sqrt{26}$ is between what two whole numbers?   5 and 6

9. Possible answer: The closest perfect square less than 17 is 16: $\sqrt{16} = 4$. The closest perfect square greater than 17 is 25: $\sqrt{25} = 5$. $\sqrt{17}$ is between 4 and 5.

Cooperative Learning

9. Explain to a partner how to locate the radical between two whole numbers in number **6** in **Practice**.   See above.

10. Write a radical whose radicand is not a perfect square. Ask a partner to locate the square root between two whole numbers.
Answers will vary. Make sure that once students have located the radicand between two perfect square radicands, they take the square root of the perfect squares.

Getting Started
To prepare
students to
simplify radicals,
have them identify the perfect
square factor in each number
below.

13·2 ▶ Simplifying Radicals

8 (4 • 2)
18 (9 • 2)
12 (4 • 3)
27 (9 • 3)

You can simplify radicals that are not perfect squares.
Write the radicand as a product of a perfect square and
another factor. Then, find the square root of the
perfect square.

$$\sqrt{8} = \sqrt{4 \cdot 2} = \sqrt{4} \cdot \sqrt{2} = 2 \cdot \sqrt{2} = 2\sqrt{2}$$

▶ **EXAMPLE 1**

Math Fact
$12 = 1 \cdot 12$
$12 = 2 \cdot 6$
$12 = 3 \cdot 4$

Simplify. $\sqrt{12}$

$\sqrt{12}$

Write 12 as the product of a perfect $\sqrt{4 \cdot 3}$
square and another factor. Use 4 • 3.

Simplify. $\sqrt{4} \cdot \sqrt{3}$

Take the square root of the perfect square. $2 \cdot \sqrt{3}$

$\sqrt{12} = 2\sqrt{3}$

▶ **EXAMPLE 2**

Math Fact
$27 = 1 \cdot 27$
$27 = 3 \cdot 9$

Simplify. $\sqrt{27}$

$\sqrt{27}$

Write 27 as the product of a perfect square $\sqrt{9 \cdot 3}$
and another factor. Use 9 • 3.

Simplify. $\sqrt{9} \cdot \sqrt{3}$

Take the square root of the perfect square. $3 \cdot \sqrt{3}$

$\sqrt{27} = 3\sqrt{3}$

▶ **EXAMPLE 3**

Math Fact
$48 = 1 \cdot 48$
$48 = 2 \cdot 24$
$48 = 3 \cdot 16$
$48 = 4 \cdot 12$
$48 = 6 \cdot 8$

Simplify. $\sqrt{48}$

$\sqrt{48}$

Write 48 as the product of a perfect square $\sqrt{16 \cdot 3}$
and another factor. Use 16 • 3.

Simplify. $\sqrt{16} \cdot \sqrt{3}$

Take the square root of the perfect square. $4 \cdot \sqrt{3}$

$\sqrt{48} = 4\sqrt{3}$

Practice

Simplify.

1. $\sqrt{24}$ $2\sqrt{6}$ **2.** $\sqrt{40}$ $2\sqrt{10}$ **3.** $\sqrt{28}$ $2\sqrt{7}$

4. $\sqrt{50}$ $5\sqrt{2}$ **5.** $\sqrt{60}$ $2\sqrt{15}$ **6.** $\sqrt{54}$ $3\sqrt{6}$

7. $\sqrt{44}$ $2\sqrt{11}$ **8.** $\sqrt{72}$ $6\sqrt{2}$ **9.** $\sqrt{52}$ $2\sqrt{13}$

10. $\sqrt{63}$ $3\sqrt{7}$ **11.** $\sqrt{80}$ $4\sqrt{5}$ **12.** $\sqrt{75}$ $5\sqrt{3}$

13. $\sqrt{90}$ $3\sqrt{10}$ **14.** $\sqrt{56}$ $2\sqrt{14}$ **15.** $\sqrt{96}$ $4\sqrt{6}$

Cooperative Learning

16. Explain to a partner how to simplify the radical in number **2**
in **Practice.** Possible answer: $\sqrt{40} = \sqrt{4 \cdot 10} = \sqrt{4} \cdot \sqrt{10} = 2 \cdot \sqrt{10} = 2\sqrt{10}$

17. Choose a perfect square and multiply it by 5. Use the product
to write a radical. Ask a partner to simplify the radical. Check
the work. Answers will vary. All answers should be in the form $a\sqrt{5}$, where a is a whole number.

13·3 ▶ Adding and Subtracting Radicals

Getting Started

To review like and unlike terms, write $3x^2 + 5x - x^2 + 9$ on the chalkboard. Have a student circle the like terms. ($3x^2$ and $-x^2$)

You add and subtract to simplify radicals the same way you combine like terms.

Like radicals	**Unlike radicals**
$2\sqrt{3}$ and $4\sqrt{3}$	$\sqrt{3}$ and $\sqrt{5}$
$\sqrt{2}$ and $3\sqrt{2}$	$7\sqrt{2}$ and $2\sqrt{7}$

To add or subtract like radicals, add or subtract the numbers in front of the radicals.

$$2\sqrt{3} + 4\sqrt{3} = (2 + 4)\sqrt{3} = 6\sqrt{3}$$

▶ **EXAMPLE 1**

Simplify. $2\sqrt{5} + 3\sqrt{5}$

Add the numbers in front of $2\sqrt{5} + 3\sqrt{5}$
the like radicals. $5\sqrt{5}$

$$2\sqrt{5} + 3\sqrt{5} = 5\sqrt{5}$$

A sum or difference may have unlike radicals. First, group like radicals together. Then, add or subtract the like radicals.

▶ **EXAMPLE 2**

Remember
$\sqrt{3} = 1\sqrt{3}$

Simplify. $3\sqrt{3} - 4\sqrt{2} + \sqrt{3} + 7\sqrt{2}$

Group like radicals. $3\sqrt{3} - 4\sqrt{2} + \sqrt{3} + 7\sqrt{2}$

Add the numbers in front of $3\sqrt{3} + 1\sqrt{3} - 4\sqrt{2} + 7\sqrt{2}$
the like radicals. $4\sqrt{3} + 3\sqrt{2}$

$$3\sqrt{3} - 4\sqrt{2} + \sqrt{3} + 7\sqrt{2} = 4\sqrt{3} + 3\sqrt{2}$$

Sometimes, you need to simplify a radical before you can add or subtract.

▶ **EXAMPLE 3**

Math Fact
$\sqrt{8} = \sqrt{4} \cdot \sqrt{2} = 2\sqrt{2}$

Simplify. $\sqrt{8} - \sqrt{5} + 4\sqrt{2}$

Simplify $\sqrt{8}$. $\sqrt{8} - \sqrt{5} + 4\sqrt{2}$

Group like radicals. $2\sqrt{2} - \sqrt{5} + 4\sqrt{2}$

Add the numbers in front of $2\sqrt{2} + 4\sqrt{2} - \sqrt{5}$
like radicals. $6\sqrt{2} - \sqrt{5}$

$$\sqrt{8} - \sqrt{5} + 4\sqrt{2} = 6\sqrt{2} - \sqrt{5}$$

Try These

Simplify.

1. $5\sqrt{6} + 3\sqrt{7} - 2\sqrt{6} + \sqrt{7}$

Group like radicals. $\qquad$ $5\sqrt{6} + 3\sqrt{7} - 2\sqrt{6} + \sqrt{7}$

Add. $\qquad$ $2\sqrt{6}\ 5\sqrt{6} - \blacksquare + 3\sqrt{7} + \blacksquare\ \sqrt{7}$

$\qquad\qquad\qquad 3\sqrt{6}\ \blacksquare + 4\sqrt{7}$

$5\sqrt{6} + 3\sqrt{7} - 2\sqrt{6} + \sqrt{7} = \blacksquare\ 3\sqrt{6} + 4\sqrt{7}$

2. $\sqrt{12} - \sqrt{2} + 4\sqrt{3}$

Simplify $\sqrt{12}$. $\qquad$ $\sqrt{12} - \sqrt{2} + 4\sqrt{3}$

Group like radicals. $\qquad$ $2\sqrt{3}\ \blacksquare - \sqrt{2} + 4\sqrt{3}$

Add. $\qquad$ $2\sqrt{3}\ \blacksquare + 4\sqrt{3} - \sqrt{2}$

$\qquad\qquad\qquad 6\sqrt{3}\ \blacksquare - \blacksquare\ \sqrt{2}$

$\sqrt{12} - \sqrt{2} + 4\sqrt{3} = \blacksquare\ 6\sqrt{3} - \sqrt{2}$

Practice

Simplify.

1. $7\sqrt{2} + 3\sqrt{2}$ $10\sqrt{2}$

2. $5\sqrt{3} - 2\sqrt{3}$ $3\sqrt{3}$

3. $2\sqrt{5} - \sqrt{6} + 4\sqrt{5} + 9\sqrt{6}$
$6\sqrt{5} + 8\sqrt{6}$

4. $\sqrt{7} + 2\sqrt{7} - 2\sqrt{7}$ $\sqrt{7}$

5. $5\sqrt{2} - 2\sqrt{2} + 3\sqrt{6}$ $3\sqrt{2} + 3\sqrt{6}$

6. $\sqrt{11} + 2\sqrt{11} + 6\sqrt{11}$ $9\sqrt{11}$

7. $\sqrt{8} - \sqrt{2}$ $\sqrt{2}$

8. $7\sqrt{13} + 3\sqrt{7} - 5\sqrt{13} - 4\sqrt{7}$
$2\sqrt{13} - \sqrt{7}$

9. $\sqrt{20} + \sqrt{5} + 3\sqrt{5}$ $6\sqrt{5}$

10. $\sqrt{18} + \sqrt{2} - \sqrt{3}$ $4\sqrt{2} - \sqrt{3}$

11. $\sqrt{7} + \sqrt{24} - \sqrt{6}$ $\sqrt{7} + \sqrt{6}$

12. $4\sqrt{13} - \sqrt{2} + \sqrt{18}$ $4\sqrt{13} + 2\sqrt{2}$

13. Possible answer: $\sqrt{7} + \sqrt{24} - \sqrt{6}$. Simplify $\sqrt{24}$: $\sqrt{7} + 2\sqrt{6} - \sqrt{6}$; Combine like radicals by adding the coefficients: $\sqrt{7} + \sqrt{6}$.

Cooperative Learning

13. Explain to a partner how to simplify number **11** in **Practice**. See above.

14. Write an expression with like and unlike radicals. Ask a partner to simplify it. Check the work. Answers will vary. The answers should have at least 2 terms with different radicals.

More practice is provided in Exercise 74 of the Workbook.

13·4 ▶ Multiplying and Dividing Radicals

Getting Started
Review with students how to find the product of terms such as $3x^2 \cdot 4x^4$. $(12x^6)$.

You can multiply radicals by first multiplying the numbers outside the radicals. Then, multiply the radicands. Be sure to simplify the radical if possible.

▶ **EXAMPLE 1**

Simplify. $5\sqrt{2} \cdot 3\sqrt{6}$

$5\sqrt{2} \cdot 3\sqrt{6}$

Multiply the numbers outside the radicals, $15 \cdot \sqrt{12}$
and multiply the radicands.

Simplify the radical. $15 \cdot \sqrt{4} \cdot \sqrt{3}$

Multiply. $15 \cdot 2\sqrt{3}$

$30\sqrt{3}$

$5\sqrt{2} \cdot 3\sqrt{6} = 30\sqrt{3}$

To divide radicals, divide the numbers in front of the radicals. Then, divide the radicands.

▶ **EXAMPLE 2**

Simplify. $\dfrac{18\sqrt{10}}{3\sqrt{2}}$

Divide the numbers outside the radicals, $\dfrac{18}{3} \cdot \dfrac{\sqrt{10}}{\sqrt{2}}$
and divide the radicands.

$6 \cdot \sqrt{5}$

$\dfrac{18\sqrt{10}}{3\sqrt{2}} = 6\sqrt{5}$

Sometimes, you cannot divide the radicals. Do not leave a radical in the denominator. Multiply the numerator and denominator by the radical in the denominator.

▶ **EXAMPLE 3**

Simplify. $\dfrac{\sqrt{2}}{\sqrt{3}}$

Multiply the numerator and denominator by $\sqrt{3}$. Then, simplify.

$\dfrac{\sqrt{2}}{\sqrt{3}} \cdot \dfrac{\sqrt{3}}{\sqrt{3}}$

$\dfrac{\sqrt{6}}{\sqrt{9}} = \dfrac{\sqrt{6}}{3}$

$\dfrac{\sqrt{2}}{\sqrt{3}} = \dfrac{\sqrt{6}}{3}$

Try These

Simplify.

1. $2\sqrt{15} \cdot 4\sqrt{3}$

$2\sqrt{15} \cdot 4\sqrt{3}$

Multiply. $(2 \cdot 4) \cdot (\blacksquare \cdot \blacksquare)$
$\qquad\qquad\qquad \sqrt{15} \quad \sqrt{3}$

Simplify the $\quad 45\,8 \cdot \sqrt{\blacksquare}$
radical. $\qquad 8 \cdot \sqrt{9} \cdot \sqrt{\blacksquare}5$
$\qquad\qquad\qquad\quad ^3$

Multiply. $\qquad 8 \cdot \blacksquare \cdot \sqrt{\blacksquare}5$

$\qquad\qquad 24\,\blacksquare \cdot \sqrt{\blacksquare}5$

$2\sqrt{15} \cdot 4\sqrt{3} = \blacksquare\ 24\sqrt{5}$

2. $\dfrac{\sqrt{3}}{\sqrt{48}}$

$\dfrac{\sqrt{3}}{\sqrt{48}}$

$\dfrac{\sqrt{3}}{\sqrt{16} \cdot \sqrt{3}}$

Cannot divide.
So, simplify the
denominator.

Divide. $\qquad \dfrac{1}{\blacksquare}\sqrt{16}$

Simplify. $\qquad \dfrac{1}{\blacksquare}\,4$

$\dfrac{\sqrt{3}}{\sqrt{48}} = \blacksquare\ \dfrac{1}{4}$

Practice

Simplify.

1. $3\sqrt{5} \cdot \sqrt{18}$ $9\sqrt{10}$

2. $\dfrac{\sqrt{14}}{\sqrt{21}}$ $\dfrac{\sqrt{6}}{3}$

3. $\dfrac{10\sqrt{2}}{\sqrt{8}}$ 5

4. $\sqrt{6} \cdot 4\sqrt{2}$ $8\sqrt{3}$

5. $\sqrt{12} \cdot \sqrt{18}$ $6\sqrt{6}$

6. $\dfrac{2\sqrt{45}}{6}$ $\sqrt{5}$

7. $\sqrt{3} \cdot 3\sqrt{21}$ $9\sqrt{7}$

8. $\dfrac{4\sqrt{12}}{2\sqrt{3}}$ 4

9. $2\sqrt{10} \cdot 3\sqrt{2}$ $12\sqrt{5}$

10. $2\sqrt{7} \cdot \sqrt{14}$ $14\sqrt{2}$

11. $\dfrac{2\sqrt{75}}{5\sqrt{3}}$ 2

12. $\dfrac{2}{\sqrt{27}}$ $\dfrac{2\sqrt{3}}{9}$

13. Possible answer: Student chooses number 3: $\dfrac{10\sqrt{2}}{\sqrt{8}}$;
Simplify $\sqrt{8}$: $\dfrac{10\sqrt{2}}{2\sqrt{2}}$; Divide: 5.

Cooperative Learning

13. Choose one of the division problems in **Practice**. Ask a partner
to explain how to solve the problem. See above.

14. Write a multiplication problem with radicals. Ask a partner to
simplify. Check the work. Answers will vary. Make sure that students do not leave perfect
square factors under the radical.

13·5 ▶ Radical Equations

Getting Started
To help students recognize that $(\sqrt{x})^2 = x$, have students simplify $(\sqrt{4})^2$, $(\sqrt{9})^2$, $(\sqrt{25})^2$. (4; 9; 25)

An equation that contains a variable in the radical is called a **radical equation.** To solve this equation, get the radical alone on one side. Square both sides of the equation. Then, solve the equation. Check your solution.

▶ **EXAMPLE 1**

Solve. $2\sqrt{y} = 8$

$$2\sqrt{y} = 8$$

Check

$2\sqrt{y} = 8$

$2\sqrt{16} = 8$

$2 \bullet 4 = 8$

$8 = 8$ true

Get the radical alone. Divide both sides by 2.

Simplify.

Square both sides.

$$\frac{2\sqrt{y}}{2} = \frac{8}{2}$$

$$\sqrt{y} = 4$$

$$(\sqrt{y})^2 = 4^2$$

$$y = 16$$

The solution of $2\sqrt{y} = 8$ is 16.

▶ **EXAMPLE 2**

Solve. $\sqrt{5b} + 3 = 8$

$$\sqrt{5b} + 3 = 8$$

Get the radical alone. Subtract 3 from both sides.

$$5b + 3 - 3 = 8 - 3$$

Check

$\sqrt{5b} + 3 = 8$

$\sqrt{5 \bullet 5} + 3 = 8$

$\sqrt{25} + 3 = 8$

$5 + 3 = 8$

$8 = 8$ true

Square both sides.

Solve for b.

$$\sqrt{5b} = 5$$

$$(\sqrt{5b})^2 = 5^2$$

$$5b = 25$$

$$b = 5$$

The solution of $\sqrt{5b} + 3 = 8$ is 5.

▶ **EXAMPLE 3**

Solve. $\sqrt{2m - 1} = 7$

Check

$\sqrt{2m - 1} = 7$

$\sqrt{2 \bullet 25 - 1} = 7$

$\sqrt{50 - 1} = 7$

$\sqrt{49} = 7$

$7 = 7$ true

Square both sides.

Solve for m.

$$\sqrt{2m - 1} = 7$$

$$(\sqrt{2m - 1})^2 = 7^2$$

$$2m - 1 = 49$$

$$2m = 50$$

$$m = 25$$

The solution of $\sqrt{2m - 1} = 7$ is 25.

Try These

Solve.

1. $3\sqrt{2n} = 12$

Get the radical alone.
Divide both sides by 3.

Square both sides.

Solve for n.

$3\sqrt{2n} = 12$

$\dfrac{3\sqrt{2n}}{3} = \dfrac{12}{3}$

$\sqrt{2n}\ \blacksquare = 4$

$(\sqrt{2n})^2 = 4^2$

$2n\ \blacksquare = 16$

$\dfrac{2n}{2\ \blacksquare} = \dfrac{16}{2\ \blacksquare}$

$n = \blacksquare$
$\qquad 8$

$\overset{8}{\blacksquare}$ is the solution of
$3\sqrt{2n} = 12$.

2. $\sqrt{5t + 1} = 4$

Square both sides.

Solve for t.

$\sqrt{5t + 1} = 4$

$(\sqrt{5t + 1})^2 = 4^2$

$5t + 1\ \blacksquare = 16$

$5t + 1 - \overset{1}{\blacksquare} = 16 - \overset{1}{\blacksquare}$

$5t = 15$

$\dfrac{5t}{5\ \blacksquare} = \dfrac{15}{\blacksquare 5}$

$t = \blacksquare 3$

$\overset{3}{\blacksquare}$ is the solution of
$\sqrt{5t + 1} = 4$.

Practice

Solve.

1. $3\sqrt{x} = 6$ $x = 4$

2. $5\sqrt{n} + 1 = 6$ $n = 1$

3. $3\sqrt{3x} = 9$ $x = 3$

4. $\sqrt{b} = 3$ $b = 9$

5. $\sqrt{n + 2} = 2$ $n = 2$

6. $\sqrt{4x} = 8$ $x = 16$

7. $\sqrt{2p - 6} = 4$ $p = 11$

8. $\sqrt{6a} - 2 = 4$ $a = 6$

9. $\sqrt{6k + 4} = 4$ $k = 2$

10. $\sqrt{3y} = 3$ $y = 3$

11. $\sqrt{9x} = 6$ $x = 4$

12. $\sqrt{2a} + 5 = 13$ $a = 32$

13. $\sqrt{3w + 4} = 5$ $w = 7$

14. $6\sqrt{3a} = 18$ $a = 3$

15. $\sqrt{3t} = 6$ $t = 12$

16. Possible answer: $\sqrt{2p - 6} = 4$; square both sides:
$(\sqrt{2p - 6})^2 = 4^2$; $2p - 6 = 16$; add 6 to both sides: $2p = 22$;
divide both sides by 2: $p = 11$.

Cooperative Learning

16. Explain to a partner how to solve number **7** in **Practice.** See above.

17. Choose a number between 5 and 10. Substitute the number for r
in this equation: $\sqrt{x} = r$. Ask a partner to solve the equation.
Answers will vary. All answers should be a perfect square between 25 and 100.

More practice is provided in Exercises 76 and 77 of the Workbook.

13·6 ▸ Parts of Right Triangles

A right angle measures 90°. **Right triangles** have one right angle. Each of the other two angles in a right triangle measure less than 90°. The sum of the measures of all three angles in any triangle is 180°.

The sides of right triangles have special names.

The side opposite the right angle is the **hypotenuse**. The hypotenuse is always the longest side. The sides that form the right angle are the legs.

▶ **EXAMPLE 1**

Name the hypotenuse and the legs.

Find the right angle. The hypotenuse is the side opposite.

The other sides are the legs.

The hypotenuse is c. The legs are a and b.

▶ **EXAMPLE 2**

Name the longest side.

The hypotenuse is always the longest side.

Find the right angle. The hypotenuse is the side opposite.

The longest side is p.

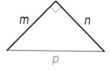

▶ **EXAMPLE 3**

Which two sides form the right angle?

Find the right angle.

Name the sides that form the right angle.

Sides p and q form the right angle.

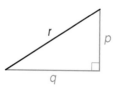

Try These

1. Name the legs and the hypotenuse.

Find the right angle. The hypotenuse is the side opposite.

The other sides are the legs.

$$\overset{t}{} \quad \overset{r}{} \quad \overset{s}{}$$

The hypotenuse is ■. The legs are ■ and ■.

2. Which two sides form the right angle?

Find the right angle.

Name the sides that form the right angle.

$$\overset{x}{} \quad \overset{y}{}$$

Sides ■ and ■ form the right angle.

Practice

Name the hypotenuse and the legs of each triangle.

1.

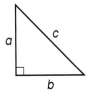

legs: *a*, *b*; hypotenuse: *c*

2.

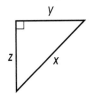

legs: *y*, *z*; hypotenuse: *x*

3.

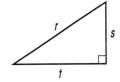

legs: *s*, *t*; hypotenuse: *r*

4.

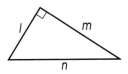

legs: *l*, *m*; hypotenuse: *n*

5.

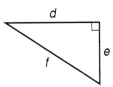

legs: *d*, *e*; hypotenuse: *f*

6.

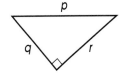

legs: *q*, *r*; hypotenuse: *p*

Cooperative Learning

7. Explain to a partner how to name the sides in number **3** in **Practice.** Possible answer: Find the right angle. The side opposite the right angle is the hypotenuse. The two sides that form the right angle are the legs.

8. Draw a right triangle and label the sides with letters. Have a partner name the legs and the hypotenuse of your triangle.
Answers will vary. Check students' drawings to make sure the longest side is the hypotenuse.

13·7 The Pythagorean Theorem

Getting Started

Review how to use a formula. On the chalkboard, show the following:

5

3

Ask a volunteer to use the formula to find the perimeter. (16)

You have identified the sides of a right triangle. When you know the lengths of two sides of a right triangle, you can find the length of the third. Use the formula known as the **Pythagorean Theorem** to find the length of the third side.

$$a^2 + b^2 = c^2$$
$$\text{leg}^2 + \text{leg}^2 = \text{hypotenuse}^2$$

▶ EXAMPLE 1

6 ft

c

8 ft

Math Fact
Length is positive, so you do not need to find the negative square root.

Find c.

Write the Pythagorean Theorem.	$a^2 + b^2 = c^2$
Find a and b.	a is 6, b is 8
Substitute 6 for a and 8 for b.	$6^2 + 8^2 = c^2$
Simplify.	$36 + 64 = c^2$
	$100 = c^2$
Take the square root of both sides.	$\sqrt{100} = \sqrt{c^2}$
Simplify.	$10 = c$

c is 10 feet long.

▶ EXAMPLE 2

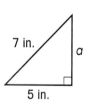

7 in.

a

5 in.

Math Fact
$\sqrt{24} = \sqrt{4} \cdot \sqrt{6} = 2\sqrt{6}$

Find a.

Write the Pythagorean Theorem.	$a^2 + b^2 = c^2$
Find c and b.	c is 7, b is 5
Substitute 5 for b and 7 for c.	$a^2 + 5^2 = 7^2$
Simplify.	$a^2 + 25 = 49$
Subtract 25 from both sides.	$a^2 + 25 - 25 = 49 - 25$
	$a^2 = 24$
Take the square root of both sides.	$\sqrt{a^2} = \sqrt{24}$
Simplify.	$a = 2\sqrt{6}$

a is $2\sqrt{6}$ inches long.

Try These

Find the length of each missing side.

1.

Write the Pythagorean Theorem.	$a^2 + b^2 = c^2$
Substitute 2 for a and ■ for b.	$2^2 + ■^2 = c^2$ 3
Simplify.	$4 + ■ = c^2$ 9
	$13 = c^2$
Take the square root of both sides	$\sqrt{13} = \sqrt{c^2}$
Simplify as much as possible.	$\sqrt{13} = ■\ c$
c is ■ meters long. $\sqrt{13}$	

2.

Write the Pythagorean Theorem.	$■\ a^2 + b^2 = c^2$
Substitute ■ for a and ■ for c.	$9^2 + b^2 = ■^2$ 15
9 15	
Simplify.	$81 ■ + b^2 = 225$
Subtract ■ from both sides.	$■ + b^2 - ■ = 225 - ■$ 81
81	81 81
square root	$b^2 = 144$
Take the ■ of both sides.	$\sqrt{b^2} = \sqrt{144}$
Simplify.	$■ = ■$
b is ■ yards long.	b 12
12	

Practice

Find the length of each missing side.

1.

2. $\sqrt{61}$ ft

3.

4. Possible answer: Write the Pythagorean Theorem and substitute the legs for a and b and the hypotenuse for c: $5^2 + 6^2 = c^2$. Simplify: $61 = c^2$. Take the square root of both sides: $\sqrt{61} = c$.

Cooperative Learning

4. Explain to a partner how to find the length of the missing side in number **2** in **Practice**. See above.

5. Draw a right triangle. Give lengths of two of the sides. Have a partner find the third side. Answers will vary. Check the work.

More practice is provided in Exercises 76 and 77 of the Workbook.

13·8 ► Special Right Triangles: 45°–45°–90°

Getting Started
Review simplifying radicals, such as $\frac{5}{\sqrt{2}}$.

(See Lesson 13.4.)

Math Fact
The lengths of the legs of a 45°–45°–90° triangle are equal.

A right triangle with two equal angles is a **45°–45°–90° triangle.** If you know one side of this triangle, you can find the other two sides using a shortcut.

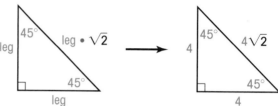

$$\text{leg} = \text{leg}$$
$$\text{hypotenuse} = \text{leg} \bullet \sqrt{2}$$

► **EXAMPLE 1**

Find the lengths of the missing sides.

Write an equation for the side you know.   leg = 5
Write the equation for the hypotenuse.   hypotenuse = leg$\sqrt{2}$
Substitute 5 for the leg.   hypotenuse = 5$\sqrt{2}$
$q = 5$ meters and $r = 5\sqrt{2}$ meters.

► **EXAMPLE 2**

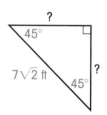

Find the lengths of the legs.

Write an equation for the side you know.   hypotenuse = leg$\sqrt{2}$
Substitute $7\sqrt{2}$ for the hypotenuse. $7\sqrt{2} = \text{leg}\sqrt{2}$
Solve for the leg. $\dfrac{7\sqrt{2}}{\sqrt{2}} = \dfrac{\text{leg}\sqrt{2}}{\sqrt{2}}$
   $7 = \text{leg}$

The legs are 7 feet each.

► **EXAMPLE 3**

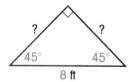

Find the lengths of the legs.

Write the equation for the side you know.   hypotenuse = leg$\sqrt{2}$
Substitute 8 for the hypotenuse. $8 = \text{leg}\sqrt{2}$
Solve for the leg. $\dfrac{8}{\sqrt{2}} = \dfrac{\text{leg}\sqrt{2}}{\sqrt{2}}$

Simplify. Multiply numerator and denominator by $\sqrt{2}$. $\dfrac{8}{\sqrt{2}} \bullet \dfrac{\sqrt{2}}{\sqrt{2}} = \text{leg}$
   $4\sqrt{2} = \text{leg}$

The legs are $4\sqrt{2}$ feet each.

Try These

Find the lengths of the missing sides.

1.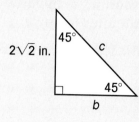

Write the equation for the side you know.

$leg = \blacksquare \; 2\sqrt{2}$

Write the equation for the hypotenuse.

$hypotenuse = leg\sqrt{2}$

Substitute $2\sqrt{2}$ for $\blacksquare$. leg

$hypotenuse = \dfrac{\blacksquare}{2\sqrt{2} \cdot \sqrt{2}}$

$b = \underset{2\sqrt{2}}{\blacksquare}$ inches and $c = \underset{4}{\blacksquare}$ inches.

$\blacksquare = leg\sqrt{2}$ hypotenuse

2.

Write the equation for the side you know.

$\underset{12}{\blacksquare}$

Substitute $\blacksquare$ for hypotenuse.

$12 \; \blacksquare = leg\sqrt{2}$

Divide both sides by $\dfrac{\blacksquare}{\sqrt{2}}$.

$\dfrac{12 \; \blacksquare}{\sqrt{2} \blacksquare} = \dfrac{leg\sqrt{2}}{\blacksquare \; \sqrt{2}}$

Simplify.

$\underset{6\sqrt{2}}{\blacksquare} = leg$

The lengths of the legs are $\underset{6\sqrt{2}}{\blacksquare}$.

$g = \underset{6\sqrt{2}}{\blacksquare}$ centimeters and $h = \underset{6\sqrt{2}}{\blacksquare}$ centimeters.

Practice

Find the lengths of the missing sides.

1.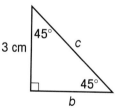

$b = 3$ cm; $c = 3\sqrt{2}$ cm

2.

$a = 9$ ft; $b = 9$ ft

3.

$a = 5\sqrt{2}$ in.; $b = 5\sqrt{2}$ in.

Cooperative Learning

4. Explain to a partner how to find the legs in number 3 in **Practice.** Possible answer: Write the equation for the given side: hypotenuse = leg$\sqrt{2}$. Substitute 10 for hypotenuse: 10 = leg$\sqrt{2}$. Divide both sides by $\sqrt{2}$ and simplify to get leg = 5$\sqrt{2}$.

5. Draw a 45°–45°–90° triangle like the ones in **Practice.** Label the length of one leg. Ask a partner to find the measurements of the other two sides. Answers will vary. The legs should be equal and the hypotenuse should be the length of a leg times $\sqrt{2}$.

13-9 **Special Right Triangles: 30°–60°–90°**

Getting Started

Help students to identify the parts of a 30°–60°–90° triangle. On the chalkboard, use green chalk to draw the short side and the label for the 30° angle. Then use different colors for the other two sides and angles.

In a **30°–60°–90° triangle**, the short leg is opposite the 30° angle. The long leg is opposite the 60° angle.

You can use a shortcut to find the length of one side.

$$\text{long leg} = \text{short leg} \cdot \sqrt{3}$$
$$\text{hypotenuse} = 2 \cdot \text{short leg}$$

▶ **EXAMPLE 1**

Find the lengths of the sides.

Write an equation for the side you know.	$\text{long leg} = \text{short leg } \sqrt{3}$
Substitute 5 for the short leg.	$\text{long leg} = 5\sqrt{3}$
Write the equation for the hypotenuse.	$\text{hypotenuse} = 2 \cdot \text{short leg}$
Substitute 5 for the short leg.	$\text{hypotenuse} = 2 \cdot 5$
Simplify.	$\text{hypotenuse} = 10$

$m = 5\sqrt{3}$ feet and $n = 10$ feet.

▶ **EXAMPLE 2**

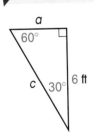

Find the lengths of the sides.

Write an equation for the side you know.	$\text{long leg} = \text{short leg } \sqrt{3}$
Substitute 6 for the long leg.	$6 = \text{short leg } \sqrt{3}$
Solve for the short leg: divide both sides by $\sqrt{3}$.	$\dfrac{6}{\sqrt{3}} = \dfrac{\text{short leg } \sqrt{3}}{\sqrt{3}}$
Simplify.	$2\sqrt{3} = \text{short leg}$
The hypotenuse is 2 times the short leg.	$\text{hypotenuse} = 2 \cdot 2\sqrt{3}$
	$\text{hypotenuse} = 4\sqrt{3}$

The missing sides are $a = 2\sqrt{3}$ feet and $c = 4\sqrt{3}$ feet.

Try These

Find the missing sides.

1. Find the length of the short leg.

   Find the side you know. $\qquad$ hypotenuse = ■

   Write the equation for the short leg. hypotenuse = 2 • short leg

   Divide by ■. 2 $\qquad$ 5 ■ = short leg

   The length of the short leg is ■ meters. 5

   short leg / long leg
   60°   30°
   10 m

2. Find the length of the long leg. $\qquad$ short leg

   Write the equation for the long leg. long leg = ■√3

   Substitute ■ for the short leg. 5 $\qquad$ long leg = ■√3 5

   The length of the long leg is ■ meters. 5√3

7. Possible answer: Write the equation for the given side.
hypotenuse = 2 • short leg. Substitute 14 for the hypotenuse:
14 = 2 • short leg; short leg = 7. Write the equation for the missing
leg: long leg = short leg√3. Substitute 7 for short leg: long leg = 7√3.

Practice

Find the missing sides.

1.

4 in. 60° hypotenuse
30°
long leg

long leg = 4√3 in.;
hypotenuse = 8 in.

2.

hypotenuse 60° short leg
30°
3√3 ft

short leg = 3 ft;
hypotenuse = 6 ft

3.
long leg
30°
short leg 60° 14 m

short leg = 7 m;
long leg = 7√3 m

4.

short leg   9 yd
60°
30°
hypotenuse

short leg = 3√3 yd; hypotenuse = 6√3 yd

5.
hypotenuse
4√3 yd 60°
30°
long leg

long leg = 12 yd;
hypotenuse = 8√3 yd

6.
6√2 in.
60°   30°
short leg   long leg

short leg = 3√2 in.;
long leg = 3√6 in.

Cooperative Learning

7. Explain to a partner how to find the long leg in number 3
   in **Practice.** See above.

8. Draw a 30°−60°−90° triangle like the ones in **Practice.** Label the
   hypotenuse with a measurement between 10 and 20. Ask a
   partner to find the lengths of the two legs. Answers will vary. The short leg should
   be half the hypotenuse, so it should be between 5 and 10. The long leg should be the short leg
   times √3.

Chapter 13 • Radicals and Geometry   347

You can use your calculator to check solutions to radical equations. The calculator display is very close to the exact value of the radical.

▶ **EXAMPLE 1**

Getting Started
Ask students to round the following numbers to two decimal places: 0.2489, 0.3910, 0.5980, 0.3458. (0.25, 0.39, 0.60, 0.35)

Tell whether 4.47 is a solution of the equation $x = \sqrt{20}$.

Substitute **4.47** for *x*. $\qquad\qquad 4.47 = \sqrt{20}$

Use your calculator to simplify.

		Display
Enter 20 by pressing:	[2] [0]	20
Find the square root by pressing:	[√]	4.472135

4.47 is a solution of $x = \sqrt{20}$.

▶ **EXAMPLE 2**

Tell whether 9.01 is a solution of $\sqrt{3x} = 5.2$.

Substitute **9.01** for *x*. $\quad \sqrt{3 \cdot 9.01} = 5.2$

Simplify the radicand first.

		Display
Enter 3 by pressing:	[3]	3
Multiply by 9.01 by pressing:	[×] [9] [.] [0] [1] [=]	27.03
Find the square root by pressing:	[√]	5.19903

Math Fact
5.19903 is close to 5.2.

9.01 is a solution of $\sqrt{3x} = 5.2$.

▶ **EXAMPLE 3**

Tell whether 20 is a solution of $\sqrt{x} + 12 = 18.93$.

Substitute **20** for *x*. $\qquad \sqrt{20} + 12 = 18.93$

Find the square root before adding.

		Display
Enter 20 by pressing:	[2] [0]	20
Find the square root by pressing:	[√]	4.47213
Add 12 by pressing:	[+] [1] [2] [=]	16.47213

Math Fact
16.47 is not close to 18.93.

20 is not a solution of $\sqrt{x} + 12 = 18.93$.

Practice

Tell whether the number is a solution of the equation.

1. .39; $\sqrt{50x} = 4.42$ yes

2. 62.8; $\sqrt{x - 7.2} = 7.46$ yes

3. 96; $\sqrt{x} + 18 = 27.8$ yes

4. 5.4; $\sqrt{3.6x} = 10.41$ no

5. 2.1; $\sqrt{x + 3.82} = 2.43$ yes

6. 43; $\sqrt{x} - 2.84 = 1.65$ no

On-the-Job Math

BUILDING WITH BLUEPRINTS

Skyscrapers, bridges, tunnels, and houses all have something in common. They are all planned before they are built. Large structures are complicated. Before a builder can start, an architect or engineer must make a plan.

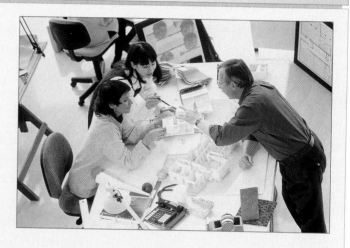

Plans for buildings are called blueprints. They show every part, such as the walls, floors, doors, and windows. All the measurements for each part are there too. Builders use the plans to make and put together the parts. Both the builders and planners need to know math. Geometric formulas like the Pythagorean Theorem can help them plan and measure the parts.

Architects do not just think about the buildings. They think about the purpose of each structure when it is done. Will the inside need elevators or stairs? Does it need heating and cooling systems? What safety features are needed? Will people be comfortable? Will the building look attractive from the outside? The blueprints will have the answers to all of these questions.

13·11 Problem Solving: Pythagorean Triples

Getting Started
Review the Pythagorean Theorem, $a^2 + b^2 = c^2$.
Have students find c in each of the following:
$$3^2 + 4^2 = c^2$$
$$5^2 + 12^2 = c^2$$
$$8^2 + 15^2 = c^2$$
(5; 13; 17)

Special groups of three positive whole numbers are called **Pythagorean triples.** When these three numbers are substituted into the Pythagorean Theorem, you get a true equation.

$$\text{Pythagorean Theorem } a^2 + b^2 = c^2$$
$$\downarrow \quad \downarrow \quad \downarrow$$
$$3^2 + 4^2 = 5^2$$
$$9 + 16 = 25$$
$$25 \quad = 25 \quad \text{true}$$

The numbers 3, 4, and 5 make a Pythagorean triple. So, a triangle with sides of 3 in., 4 in., and 5 in. is a right triangle.

▶ **EXAMPLE**

Tell whether a triangle with sides 4 cm, 10 cm, and 12 cm is a right triangle.

READ **What do you need to find out?**
You need to determine if the three given numbers are measures of a right triangle.

Math Fact
The hypotenuse is the longest side of a right triangle. So, substitute the largest number of the triple for c.

PLAN **What do you need to do?**
You need to substitute these numbers into the Pythagorean Theorem to see if the result is a true statement.

DO **Follow the plan.**

Write the Pythagorean Theorem.	$a^2 + b^2 = c^2$
Substitute 4 for a, 10 for b, and 12 for c.	$4^2 + 10^2 \, ? \, 12^2$
Simplify.	$16 + 100 \, ? \, 144$
	$116 \quad ? \, 144$

CHECK **Does your answer make sense?**
$4^2 + 10^2$ does not equal 12^2 ✓

A triangle with the sides 4 cm, 10 cm, and 12 cm is not a right triangle.

Try These

Tell whether the three numbers are measures of the sides of a right triangle.

1. 5, 12, 13

Write the Pythagorean $a^2 + b^2 = c^2$
Theorem.

Substitute ■ for a,
12 ■ for b, and 13 for c. $5^2 + 12^2 = 13^2$

Simplify. $25 + 144 = 169$

$169\ ■\ =\ ■\ 169$

The numbers 5, 12, and 13
are ■ measures of the sides
of a right triangle.

2. 50, 120, 130

Write the ■. $a^2 + b^2 = c^2$
Pythagorean Theorem
Substitute ■ for a, 50 $■^2 + ■^2 = ■^2$
■ for b, and ■ for c. 50 120 130

Simplify. $2{,}500 + ■ = ■$ 14,400
16,900

$16{,}900\ ■\ =\ ■$ 16,900
16,900

The numbers 50, 120, and
are 130 ■ measures of the
sides of a right triangle.

Practice

Tell whether the three lengths are measures of the sides of a right triangle.

1. 6 ft, 8 ft, 10 ft yes

2. 10 cm, 24 cm, 26 cm yes

3. 4 m, 8 m, 10 m no

4. 30 yd, 40 yd, 50 yd yes

5. 10 in., 20 in., 35 in. no

6. 15 mm, 20 mm, 25 mm yes

7. 15 ft, 36 ft, 39 ft yes

8. 12 m, 16 m, 20 m yes

9. 6 cm, 8 cm, 12 cm no

10. 21 in., 28 in., 35 in. yes

Cooperative Learning

11. Explain to a partner how to tell whether the lengths in number 6
in **Practice** are the sides of a right triangle. Substitute 15, 20, and 25 into the
Pythagorean Theorem. Simplify. $15^2 + 20^2 = 25^2$; $225 + 400 = 625$, true.

12. Work with a partner to find another set of three positive whole
numbers that is a Pythagorean triple. Use the Pythagorean
Theorem to check your work. Answers will vary. Make sure students substitute the longest
side for c.

13·12 ▸ Application: Finding Distance

Getting Started
Point out that the coordinate grid is made up of squares. Draw a square and its diagonal on the chalkboard. Ask students if the triangles formed are right triangles.

Math Facts
The line between the points (1, 2) and (4, 2) is
$4 - 1 = 3$ units long.
The line between the points (1, 6) and (1, 2) is
$6 - 2 = 4$ units long.

You can use the Pythagorean Theorem to find the distance between any two points. Draw the two points on the coordinate plane. The line between them is the hypotenuse of a right triangle. When you use the Pythagorean Theorem this way, it is called the **Distance Formula**. Label the hypotenuse d for distance.

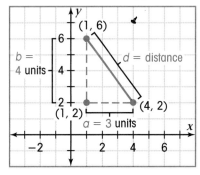

$$a^2 + b^2 = d^2$$
$$3^2 + 4^2 = d^2$$
$$9 + 16 = d^2$$
$$25 = d^2$$
$$5 = d$$

▶ **EXAMPLE 1**

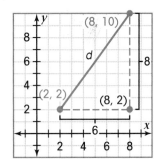

Find the distance between points (8, 10) and (2, 2).

Graph the points. Draw a right triangle.

Substitute 6 and 8 for a and b.

$$a^2 + b^2 = d^2$$
$$6^2 + 8^2 = d^2$$

Solve for d.

$$36 + 64 = d^2$$
$$100 = d^2 \rightarrow 10 = d$$

The distance between (8, 10) and (2, 2) is 10 units.

▶ **EXAMPLE 2**

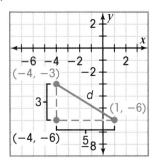

Find the distance between points $(-4, -3)$ and $(1, -6)$.

Graph the points. Draw a right triangle.

Substitute the 5 and 3 for a and b.

$$a^2 + b^2 = d^2$$
$$5^2 + 3^2 = d^2$$

Solve for d.

$$25 + 9 = d^2$$
$$34 = d^2 \rightarrow \sqrt{34} = d$$

The distance between $(-4, -3)$ and $(1, -6)$ is $\sqrt{34}$ units.

Try These

1. Find the distance between $(-4, 5)$ and $(0, 3)$.
Graph the points.

Draw a right triangle.

Find the legs of the triangle. $4\blacksquare, 2$

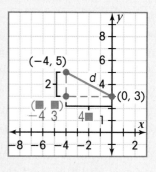

Substitute the legs into
the Pythagorean Theorem.

$$a^2 + b^2 = d^2$$
$$4\blacksquare^2 + \blacksquare^2 = d^2 \quad 2$$

Solve for d.

$$20\blacksquare = d^2$$
$$2\sqrt{5}\blacksquare = d \qquad 2\sqrt{5}$$

The distance between $(-4, 5)$ and $(0, 3)$ is $\blacksquare$ units.

2. Find the distance between $(-3, 7)$ and $(2, 3)$.
Graph the points.

Draw a right triangle.

Find the legs of the triangle. $5\blacksquare, 4$

Substitute the legs into
the Pythagorean Theorem.

$$a^2 + b^2 = d^2$$
$$5\blacksquare^2 + \blacksquare^2 = d^2 \quad 4$$

Solve for d.

$$41\blacksquare = d^2$$
$$\sqrt{41}\blacksquare = d \qquad \sqrt{41}$$

The distance between $(-3, 7)$ and $(2, 3)$ is $\blacksquare$ units.

5. Graph the points and draw a right triangle. The lengths of the legs are 4 and 8. Use the Pythagorean Theorem and substitute 4 and 8 for a and b. The distance between $(1, 4)$ and $(5, -4)$ is $4\sqrt{5}$ units.

Practice

Graph each pair of points. Then, find the distance between the points.

1. $(4, 2)$ and $(-3, 4)$ $\sqrt{53}$ units

2. $(-3, -3)$ and $(3, 5)$ 10 units

3. $(1, 4)$ and $(5, -4)$ $4\sqrt{5}$ units

4. $(8, 3)$ and $(5, 7)$ 5 units

Cooperative Learning

5. Explain to a partner how to find the distance between the points in number **3** in **Practice**. See above.

6. Draw two points on a coordinate plane. Have a partner find the distance between the two points. Check the work. Answers will vary. Check students' substitution and calculations.

Summary

You can simplify a radical by rewriting it as a product of a perfect square and another factor.

To add or subtract radicals, group the numbers with the same radical and add or subtract the numbers in front of the radical.

To multiply or divide radicals, multiply or divide the numbers outside the radicals and then multiply or divide the radicands.

To solve radical equations, get the radical alone on one side of the equation.

Use the Pythagorean Theorem to find the length of a missing side of a right triangle.

Recognize $45°-45°-90°$ or $30°-60°-90°$ triangles.

If you substitute three numbers into the equation $a^2 + b^2 = c^2$ and get a true equation, the three numbers can be the sides of a right triangle.

Use the Pythagorean Theorem to find the distance between two points.

More vocabulary review is provided in Exercise 121 of the Classroom Resource Binder.

radicals
radical equation
right triangle
hypotenuse
Pythagorean Theorem
$45°-45°-90°$ triangle
$30°-60°-90°$ triangle
Pythagorean triples

Vocabulary Review

Complete the sentences with words from the box.

1. A _____ has acute angles measuring 30° and 60°. 30°-60°-90° triangle

2. In a right triangle, the _____ is opposite the right angle. hypotenuse

3. A _____ equation has a variable under a radical. radical equation

4. The _____ is used to find a missing side of a right triangle. Pythagorean Theorem

5. Square roots written with a radical sign are called _____. radicals

6. A _____ has two acute angles measuring 45°. 45°-45°-90° triangle

7. Groups of three whole numbers that satisfy the Pythagorean Theorem are called _____. Pythagorean triples

8. A triangle that has a 90°angle is called a _____. right triangle

Chapter Quiz
More assessment is provided in the Classroom Resource Binder.

Between what two whole numbers is each radical?

1. $\sqrt{6}$ 2 and 3

2. $\sqrt{85}$ 9 and 10

3. $\sqrt{38}$ 6 and 7

Simplify.

4. $\sqrt{20}$ $2\sqrt{5}$

5. $\sqrt{27}$ $3\sqrt{3}$

6. $5\sqrt{7} - 4\sqrt{2} + 3\sqrt{7}$ $8\sqrt{7} - 4\sqrt{2}$

7. $4\sqrt{2} \cdot 9\sqrt{5}$ $36\sqrt{10}$

8. $\dfrac{3\sqrt{20}}{2}$ $3\sqrt{5}$

9. $\dfrac{12\sqrt{18}}{3\sqrt{9}}$ $4\sqrt{2}$

10. $3\sqrt{6} \cdot \sqrt{24}$ 36

11. $\sqrt{48} + \sqrt{27}$ $7\sqrt{3}$

12. $\dfrac{5\sqrt{3}}{\sqrt{2}}$ $\dfrac{5\sqrt{6}}{2}$

Solve.

13. $2\sqrt{x} = 8$ $x = 16$

14. $\sqrt{a} + 2 = 7$ $a = 25$

15. $\sqrt{4x} = 3$ $x = \dfrac{9}{4}$

16. $4\sqrt{n + 2} = 20$ $n = 23$

17. $\sqrt{5x} - 2 = 8$ $x = 20$

18. $\sqrt{2y + 3} = 5$ $y = 11$

Find the length of each missing side.

19.

$m = 5$ in.

20.
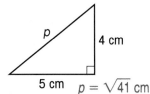
$p = \sqrt{41}$ cm

21.
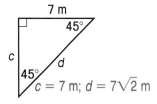
$c = 7$ m; $d = 7\sqrt{2}$ m

22.
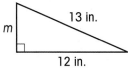
$j = 4\sqrt{3}$ cm; $k = 8$ cm

23.
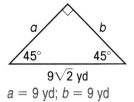
$a = 9$ yd; $b = 9$ yd

24.
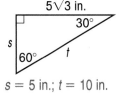
$s = 5$ in.; $t = 10$ in.

25. Tell whether a triangle with sides 27 m, 36 m, and 54 m is a right triangle. no

26. Graph the points $(6, -5)$ and $(-6, 4)$. Then, find the distance between the two points. 15 units

Additional Practice for this chapter is provided on p. 425 of this text.

The amount of current that flows through electrical lines is found by using a rational equation. This current goes through the lines into your home. What are some uses of electrical current in your home?

Learning Objectives

- Evaluate rational expressions.
- Add, subtract, multiply, and divide rational expressions.
- Solve rational equations.
- Solve proportions by finding the cross products.
- Use a calculator to check solutions to a proportion.
- Use proportions to solve problems.
- Apply concepts and skills to using inverse variation.

Words to Know

rational number	a number that can be written as a fraction
rational expression	the quotient of two variable expressions; can be written as a fraction
undefined	when a rational expression has zero as the denominator; has no value
least common multiple (LCM)	the smallest positive common multiple of two or more numbers or polynomials
least common denominator (LCD)	the LCM of two denominators
rational equation	an equation that contains rational expressions
proportion	a statement that two ratios are equal
cross products	the products of numbers or expressions diagonally across from each other in a proportion
inverse variation	a rational equation in the form $y = \frac{k}{x}$ where k is a positive constant

Model School Project

Model railroads come in different sizes. The scale tells you the size of the model compared to the actual size of the train. One scale is the HO scale. The model train is $\frac{1}{87}$ the size of the real train.

Make a model of your school for a model railroad set. Find out the measurements of your school—the length, width, and height. Use the HO scale to determine the size of the model. You will need to use the proportion $\frac{1}{87} = \frac{\text{model size}}{\text{actual size}}$. You can use cardboard or light wood to make the model.

Project See the Classroom Resource Binder for a scoring rubric to assess this project.

More practice is provided in Exercises 80 and 83 of the Workbook.

14·1 ▶ Rational Numbers and Expressions

Getting Started
Review evaluating expressions. Write the following on the chalkboard.

$x + 6$ $\qquad$ $2x - y$

Have students evaluate the expressions for $x = 5$ and $y = -2$. (11; 12)

A **rational number** is any number that can be written as a fraction. A **rational expression** is a variable expression that can be written as a fraction. It is the quotient of the numerator and the denominator.

Rational numbers	Rational expressions
$3 \quad \frac{1}{4} \quad .79 \quad 2\frac{1}{2}$	$2x \quad \frac{x}{5} \quad \frac{2y}{5x^2 - 4}$

You evaluate rational expressions the same way you evaluate variable expressions. Substitute a value for the variable.

▶ **EXAMPLE 1**

Evaluate $\frac{2x}{x + 6}$ when x is 4.

Substitute 4 for x.

Simplify.

Write the fraction in lowest terms.

The value of $\frac{2x}{x + 6}$ is $\frac{4}{5}$ when x is 4.

$\dfrac{2x}{x + 6}$

$\dfrac{2 \cdot 4}{4 + 6}$

$\dfrac{8}{10}$

$\dfrac{4}{5}$

▶ **EXAMPLE 2**

Evaluate $\frac{11}{2x^2 - 2}$ when x is -3.

Substitute -3 for x.

Simplify.

The value of $\frac{11}{2x^2 - 2}$ is $\frac{11}{16}$ when x is -3.

$\dfrac{11}{2x^2 - 2}$

$\dfrac{11}{2(-3)^2 - 2}$

$\dfrac{11}{16}$

▶ **EXAMPLE 3**

Evaluate $\frac{x - y}{y + 2x}$ when x is 3 and y is -2.

Substitute 3 for x and -2 for y.

Simplify.

The value of $\frac{x - y}{y + 2x}$ is $\frac{5}{4}$ when x is 3 and y is -2.

$\dfrac{x - y}{y + 2x}$

$\dfrac{3 - (-2)}{-2 + 2(3)}$

$\dfrac{5}{4}$

Try These

Evaluate each expression.

1. $\frac{x + 3}{x^2 - 2}$ when x is 4

Substitute ■ for x.

$\frac{4 \; ■ + 3}{4 \; ■^2 - 2}$

Simplify.

$\frac{7 \; ■}{14 \; ■}$

Write the fraction in lowest terms.

$■ \frac{1}{2}$

The value of $\frac{x + 3}{x^2 - 2}$ is $■ \frac{1}{2}$ when x is 4.

2. $\frac{2a}{3a + 2b}$ when a is 4 and b is -4

Substitute ■ for a and -4 ■ for b.

$\frac{2(■) \, 4}{3(■) + 2(■)} \; \overset{4}{\underset{-4}{}}$

Simplify.

$\frac{8 \; ■}{4 \; ■}$

Write the fraction in lowest terms.

$■ \; 2$

The value of $\frac{2a}{3a + 2b}$ is $■ \, 2$ when a is 4 and b is -4.

Practice

Evaluate each expression.

1. $\frac{6}{y + 3}$ when y is 9 $\frac{1}{2}$

2. $\frac{z - 5}{8}$ when z is 21 2

3. $\frac{x}{x + 7}$ when x is 4 $\frac{4}{11}$

4. $\frac{2k}{k - 2}$ when k is 6 3

5. $\frac{2x}{3x + 4}$ when x is 5 $\frac{10}{19}$

6. $\frac{y + 1}{2y^2 - 3}$ when y is -2 $-\frac{1}{5}$

7. $\frac{2 + m}{6q}$ when m is 4 and q is -1 -1

8. $\frac{4}{a + b}$ when a is 3 and b is 5 $\frac{1}{2}$

9. $\frac{4x}{3x + 2y}$ when x is 3 and y is -4 12

10. $\frac{x - 4}{y^2 + 5y + 6}$ when x is 8 and y is -4 2

Cooperative Learning

11. Possible answer: Substitute 3 for x and -4 for y: $\frac{4 \cdot 3}{3(3) + 2(-4)}$. Then, simplify: $\frac{12}{9 + (-8)} = \frac{12}{1} = 12$.

11. Explain to a partner how to find the value of the rational expression in number **9** in **Practice**. See above.

12. Pick three integers between -4 and 4 for x. Ask a partner to evaluate $\frac{2x}{x^2 + 2}$ for each of the integers. Check the work.

Possible answers include $\pm\frac{4}{9}, \pm\frac{6}{11}, \pm\frac{2}{3},$ and 0.

More practice is provided in Exercise 80 of the Workbook.

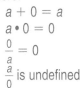

14-2 Zero in the Denominator

$a + 0 = a$

$a \cdot 0 = 0$

$\dfrac{0}{a} = 0$

$\dfrac{a}{0}$ is undefined

Some values of the variable make the denominator 0. You cannot divide by 0. So, the rational expression is **undefined** when the denominator is 0. You can find the values that make this happen. Let the denominator equal 0. Then, solve this equation.

▶ **EXAMPLE 1**

Find the value that makes $\dfrac{7}{a + 5}$ undefined.

Let the denominator equal 0.	$a + 5 = 0$
Solve for a.	$a = -5$

Solution: **−5**

$\dfrac{7}{a + 5}$ is undefined when a is -5.

Sometimes, the denominator has two factors. Let each factor equal 0 to solve this equation.

▶ **EXAMPLE 2**

Find the values that make $\dfrac{x + 3}{2x(x - 2)}$ undefined.

Let the denominator equal 0.	$2x(x - 2) = 0$
The denominator has two factors. Let each factor equal 0.	$2x = 0$ or $x - 2 = 0$
Solve each factor for x.	$x = 0$ or $x = 2$

Solution: **0 or 2**

$\dfrac{x + 3}{2x(x - 2)}$ is undefined when x is 0 or 2.

Sometimes, you need to factor the denominator.

▶ **EXAMPLE 3**

Remember
Find two numbers that have a sum of 3 and a product of 2.
$1 + 2 = 3$; $1 \cdot 2 = 2$.

Find the values that make $\dfrac{y + 4}{y^2 + 3y + 2}$ undefined.

Let the denominator equal 0.	$y^2 + 3y + 2 = 0$
Factor.	$(y + 1)(y + 2) = 0$
Let each factor equal 0.	$y + 1 = 0$ or $y + 2 = 0$
Solve each factor for y.	$y = -1$ or $y = -2$

Solution: **−1 or −2**

$\dfrac{y + 4}{y^2 + 3y + 2}$ is undefined when y is -1 or -2.

Try These

Find the value or values that make each rational expression undefined.

1. $\dfrac{a^2 - 6}{2a - 6}$

Let the ■ equal 0.   ■ = 0
denominator $2a - 6$

Solve for ■. $2a = ■\,6$
    a

                 $a = ■\,3$

$\dfrac{a^2 - 2}{2a - 6}$ is undefined when a is ■. 3

2. $\dfrac{y + 1}{3y^2 - 12y}$

Let the ■ equal 0. $3y^2 - 12y = 0$
denominator

Factor. $3y(y - 4) = 0$

Let each factor   ■ = 0   or   ■ = 0
equal 0. $3y$ $y - 4$
                   0   4

Solve for ■. y $y = ■$ or $y = ■$
                   0   4

$\dfrac{y + 1}{3y^2 - 12y}$ is undefined when y is
■ or ■.
0   4

Practice

Find the value or values that make each rational expression undefined.

1. $\dfrac{8}{y + 6}$ -6

2. $\dfrac{2x}{x - 3}$ 3

3. $\dfrac{5(a + 3)}{4a}$ 0

4. $\dfrac{2y(y - 4)}{3y + 12}$ -4

5. $\dfrac{x^2 + 3}{x(x + 5)}$ 0 or -5

6. $\dfrac{4}{5p(p - 7)}$ 0 or 7

7. $\dfrac{9}{y^2 + 5y}$ 0 or -5

8. $\dfrac{4v}{v^2 - 6v + 8}$ 2 or 4

Cooperative Learning

9. Explain to a partner how to find the values that make number **5** in **Practice** undefined. Possible answer: Let the denominator equal 0. Then, solve for x: $x = 0$ or $x = -5$.

10. Write a rational expression with two factors in the denominator. Have a partner find the values that make the expression undefined. Check the work. Answers will vary. Answers could have 1 or 2 values, depending on the student's expression.

Getting Started
Review factoring.
Have students
factor the following:
6   $(2 \cdot 3)$
x^2 $(x \cdot x)$
$6x^2$ $(2 \cdot 3 \cdot x \cdot x)$

14-3 Simplifying Rational Expressions

To simplify rational expressions, factor the numerator and denominator. Then, divide the numerator and denominator by their common factors.

▶ **EXAMPLE 1**

Math Facts
$9 = 3 \cdot 3$
$12 = 2 \cdot 2 \cdot 3$

Simplify. $\dfrac{9}{12}$

Factor 9 and 12.

$\dfrac{3 \cdot 3}{2 \cdot 2 \cdot 3}$

Divide numerator and denominator by the common factors.

$\dfrac{3 \cdot \cancel{3}^{1}}{2 \cdot 2 \cdot \cancel{3}_{1}}$

Simplify.

$\dfrac{3}{4}$

$\dfrac{9}{12} = \dfrac{3}{4}$

▶ **EXAMPLE 2**

Math Facts
$4x^2 = 2 \cdot 2 \cdot x \cdot x$
$6x = 2 \cdot 3 \cdot x$

Simplify. $\dfrac{4x^2}{6x}$

Factor $4x^2$ and $6x$.

$\dfrac{2 \cdot 2 \cdot x \cdot x}{3 \cdot 2 \cdot x}$

Divide the numerator and denominator by the common factors.

$\dfrac{2 \cdot \cancel{2}^{1} \cdot \cancel{x}^{1} \cdot x}{3 \cdot \cancel{2}_{1} \cdot \cancel{x}_{1}}$

Simplify.

$\dfrac{2x}{3}$

$\dfrac{4x^2}{6x} = \dfrac{2x}{3}$

Sometimes, you need to factor polynomials before you can divide by common factors.

▶ **EXAMPLE 3**

Remember
Find two numbers that have a
sum of 5 and a product of 4.
$(1 + 4 = 5; 1 \cdot 4 = 4.)$

Simplify. $\dfrac{2y + 2}{y^2 + 5y + 4}$

Factor the numerator and the denominator.

$\dfrac{2(y + 1)}{(y + 1)(y + 4)}$

Divide the numerator and denominator by $(y + 1)$.

$\dfrac{2\cancel{(y + 1)}^{1}}{\cancel{(y + 1)}_{1}(y + 4)}$

Simplify.

$\dfrac{2}{y + 4}$

$\dfrac{2y + 2}{y^2 + 5y + 4} = \dfrac{2}{y + 4}$

Try These

Simplify each rational expression.

1. $\dfrac{10}{15}$

Factor 10 and 15.
the common factors

Divide by ■.

$3\ \dfrac{2 \cdot 5}{■ \cdot ■\ 5}$

$3\ \dfrac{2 \cdot \cancel{5}}{■ \cdot \cancel{5}}$

Simplify.

$\dfrac{10}{15} = ■\dfrac{2}{3}$

$\dfrac{■2}{■3}$

2. $\dfrac{2a}{2a^2 - 4a}$

Factor the
denominator.

$\dfrac{2a}{2a\ ■(a - 2)}$

Divide by the
common factors.

$\dfrac{2\cancel{a}}{2a\ \cancel{■}(a - 2)}$

Simplify.

$\dfrac{2a}{2a^2 - 4a} = ■\dfrac{1}{a - 2}$

$\dfrac{1}{■\,a - 2}$

Practice

Simplify each rational expression.

1. $\dfrac{4}{16}\quad \dfrac{1}{4}$

2. $\dfrac{8}{24}\quad \dfrac{1}{3}$

3. $\dfrac{14}{20}\quad \dfrac{7}{10}$

4. $\dfrac{6b^2}{9b}\quad \dfrac{2b}{3}$

5. $\dfrac{2y}{8y^2}\quad \dfrac{1}{4y}$

6. $\dfrac{3y^3}{18y^2}\quad \dfrac{y}{6}$

7. $\dfrac{(a - 1)(a + 2)}{a(a + 2)}\quad \dfrac{a - 1}{a}$

8. $\dfrac{3x(x - 3)}{(x - 3)(x + 3)}\quad \dfrac{3x}{x + 3}$

9. $\dfrac{(p + 5)(p - 5)}{(p - 5)(p - 5)}\quad \dfrac{p + 5}{p - 5}$

10. $\dfrac{3y}{3y^2 - 6y}\quad \dfrac{1}{y - 2}$

11. $\dfrac{2x + 4}{5x^2 + 10x}\quad \dfrac{2}{5x}$

12. $\dfrac{2m^2 - 8m}{4m}\quad \dfrac{m - 4}{2}$

13. $\dfrac{a + 1}{a^2 + 3a + 2}\quad \dfrac{1}{a + 2}$

14. $\dfrac{4y + 8}{y^2 + 7y + 10}\quad \dfrac{4}{y + 5}$

15. $\dfrac{x^2 - 5x + 6}{2x - 4}\quad \dfrac{x - 3}{2}$

Cooperative Learning

16. Possible answer: Find the common factor: $x - 3$. Divide the fraction by $\dfrac{x - 3}{x - 3}$. The result is $\dfrac{3x}{x + 3}$.

16. Explain to a partner how to simplify number **8** in **Practice**. See above.

17. Ask a partner to simplify $\dfrac{4x}{2x^2 + x}$. Check the work. $\dfrac{4}{2x + 1}$

More practice is provided in Exercise 81 of the Workbook.

14·4 Finding the Least Common Multiple

Getting Started
Review multiples. Call out a number, such as 3. Have a volunteer list some multiples of 3 on the chalkboard. (0, 3, 6, 9, 12)

The **least common multiple (LCM)** is the smallest non-zero multiple numbers have in common.

Multiples of 4 → 0, 4, 8, 12, 16
Multiples of 6 → 0, 6, 12, 18, 24
The LCM of 4 and 6 is 12.

▶ **EXAMPLE 1**

Find the LCM of 6 and 8.

Find multiples of 6.   0, 6, 12, 18, 24, 30
Find multiples of 8.   0, 8, 16, 24, 32, 40

The LCM of 6 and 8 is 24.

To find the LCM of variable expressions, first find the LCM of the coefficients. Then, use the higher power of each variable.

▶ **EXAMPLE 2**

Find the LCM of x^3y and xy^2.

Math Fact
The LCM of 1 and 1 is 1.

Find the larger power of x. x^3

Find the larger power of y. y^2

The LCM of x^3y and xy^2 is x^3y^2.

▶ **EXAMPLE 3**

Find the LCM of $3a^2$ and $6ab$.

Multiples
3: 0, 3, 6, 9, 12
6: 0, 6, 12, 18, 24

Find the LCM of 3 and 6.   6

Find the larger power of a. a^2

Find the larger power of b.   b

The LCM of $3a^2$ and $6ab$ is $6a^2b$.

The LCM of two polynomials with no common factors is the product of the two polynomials.

▶ **EXAMPLE 4**

Find the LCM of $x - 6$ and $x + 5$.

$x - 6$ and $x + 5$ have no common factors. So, use their product. $(x - 6)(x + 5)$

The LCM of $x - 6$ and $x + 5$ is $(x - 6)(x + 5)$.

Try These

Find the LCM of each pair of polynomials.

1. $4x^2y$ and $10xy$

$4x^2y$ and $10xy$

Find the LCM of 4 and 10. ■ 20

Find the larger power of x. ■ x^2

Find the larger power of y. ■ y

The LCM of $4x^2y$ and $10xy$ is ■. $20x^2y$

2. a and $a + 1$

a and $a + 1$

a and $a + 1$ have no common factors.

The LCM of a and $a + 1$ is ■. $a(a + 1)$

Practice

Find the LCM of each pair of numbers or polynomials.

1. 4 and 6 12

2. 5 and 15 15

3. x^2 and x x^2

4. $3a$ and $6a^2$ $6a^2$

5. $2x^2$ and $2xy$ $2x^2y$

6. b^2 and a ab^2

7. x and $x + 6$ $x(x + 6)$

8. $a - 5$ and $3a$ $3a(a - 5)$

9. $6x^2$ and $9x$ $18x^2$

10. $5ab$ and $6b^2$ $30ab^2$

11. $x - 1$ and $x + 1$ $(x - 1)(x + 1)$

12. $z - 3$ and $z + 5$ $(z - 3)(z + 5)$

Cooperative Learning

13. Explain to a partner how to find the LCM in number 9
in **Practice.** Possible answer: Find the LCM of 6 and 9: 18. Find the highest power of x: x^2. Take the product: $18x^2$.

14. Write two variable expressions. Ask a partner to find the LCM.
Answers will vary. Check students' work.

Getting Started
Have students
list multiples of
3 and of 4. Have
them circle the LCM. (12)

14·5 Addition and Subtraction

Remember
LCM means least common
multiple.

You add or subtract like fractions by adding the numerators and using the same denominator. To add or subtract fractions with unlike denominators, first find a common denominator. Use the LCM as the **least common denominator (LCD)**.

▶ EXAMPLE 1

Math Fact
The LCM of 3 and 4 is 12.

Add. $\dfrac{2}{3} + \dfrac{3}{4}$

Use 12 for the LCD.

Rewrite each fraction with 12 as the denominator.

Add the numerators.

Simplify.

$\dfrac{2}{3} + \dfrac{3}{4} = \dfrac{17}{12}$

$\dfrac{2}{3} + \dfrac{3}{4}$

$\dfrac{2 \cdot 4}{3 \cdot 4} + \dfrac{3 \cdot 3}{4 \cdot 3}$

$\dfrac{8 + 9}{12}$

$\dfrac{17}{12}$

▶ EXAMPLE 2

Add. $\dfrac{3x}{5} + \dfrac{x}{15}$

Use 15 for the LCD.

Rewrite each fraction with 15 as the denominator.

Add the numerators.

Simplify.

$\dfrac{3x}{5} + \dfrac{x}{15} = \dfrac{2x}{3}$

$\dfrac{3x}{5} + \dfrac{x}{15}$

$\dfrac{3x \cdot 3}{5 \cdot 3} + \dfrac{x \cdot 1}{15 \cdot 1}$

$\dfrac{9x + 1x}{15}$

$\dfrac{10x}{15} = \dfrac{2x}{3}$

The denominator may contain variables.

▶ EXAMPLE 3

Math Fact
The LCM of $4a^2$ and $8a$ is $8a^2$.

Subtract. $\dfrac{5}{4a^2} - \dfrac{3}{8a}$

Use $8a^2$ for the LCD.

Rewrite each fraction with $8a^2$ as the denominator.

Subtract the numerators.

$\dfrac{5}{4a^2} - \dfrac{3}{8a} = \dfrac{10 - 3a}{8a^2}$

$\dfrac{5}{4a^2} - \dfrac{3}{8a}$

$\dfrac{5 \cdot 2}{4a^2 \cdot 2} - \dfrac{3 \cdot a}{8a \cdot a}$

$\dfrac{10 - 3a}{8a^2}$

Try These

Add or subtract.

1. $\dfrac{1}{3x} + \dfrac{4}{3x}$

The denominators are the same.

Add the numerators.

$\dfrac{1}{3x} + \dfrac{4}{3x} = \blacksquare\,\dfrac{5}{3x}$

$\dfrac{1}{3x} + \dfrac{4}{3x}$

$\blacksquare\,\dfrac{5}{3x}$

2. $\dfrac{4x}{y^2} - \dfrac{3x}{y}$

y^2 Use $\blacksquare$ as the LCD.

Rewrite each fraction y^2 with $\blacksquare$ as the denominator.

Subtract the numerators.

$\dfrac{4x}{y^2} - \dfrac{3x}{y}$

$\dfrac{4x \cdot 1}{y^2 \cdot 1} - \dfrac{3x \cdot \blacksquare\, y}{y \cdot \blacksquare\, y}$

$\dfrac{4x\,\blacksquare}{y^2\,\blacksquare} - \dfrac{\blacksquare\, 3xy}{\blacksquare\, y^2}$

$\dfrac{4x\,\blacksquare - \blacksquare\, 3xy}{\blacksquare}$

$\dfrac{4x}{y^2} - \dfrac{3x}{y} = \blacksquare\,\dfrac{4x - 3xy}{y^2}\ \ y^2$

Practice

Add or subtract.

1. $\dfrac{1}{2} + \dfrac{2}{5}\ \ \dfrac{9}{10}$ **2.** $\dfrac{2}{3} - \dfrac{5}{12}\ \ \dfrac{1}{4}$ **3.** $\dfrac{5}{6} - \dfrac{1}{8}\ \ \dfrac{17}{24}$ **4.** $\dfrac{2}{9} + \dfrac{5}{6}\ \ 1\dfrac{1}{18}$

5. $\dfrac{2a}{7} + \dfrac{a}{14}\ \ \dfrac{5a}{14}$ **6.** $\dfrac{3y}{5} - \dfrac{7y}{20}\ \ \dfrac{y}{4}$ **7.** $\dfrac{b}{10} + \dfrac{5b}{15}\ \ \dfrac{13b}{30}$ **8.** $\dfrac{3m}{4} - \dfrac{m}{2}\ \ \dfrac{m}{4}$

9. $\dfrac{4}{x} - \dfrac{6}{y}\ \ \dfrac{4y - 6x}{xy}$ **10.** $\dfrac{5}{ab} + \dfrac{3}{b}\ \ \dfrac{5 + 3a}{ab}$ **11.** $\dfrac{2}{m} + \dfrac{7}{p}\ \ \dfrac{2p + 7m}{mp}$ **12.** $\dfrac{1}{r} - \dfrac{8}{dr}\ \ \dfrac{d - 8}{dr}$

13. $\dfrac{2}{xy^2} + \dfrac{8}{x^2y}\ \ \dfrac{2x + 8y}{x^2y^2}$ **14.** $\dfrac{x}{6} - \dfrac{1}{3x}\ \ \dfrac{x^2 - 2}{6x}$ **15.** $\dfrac{5a}{b^2} - \dfrac{6a}{b}\ \ \dfrac{5a - 6ab}{b^2}$ **16.** $\dfrac{3x}{y} - \dfrac{2x}{y^2}\ \ \dfrac{3xy - 2x}{y^2}$

Cooperative Learning

17. Possible answer: Find the LCD: 6x. Write equivalent fractions: $\dfrac{x^2}{6x} - \dfrac{2}{6x}$. Subtract: $\dfrac{x^2 - 2}{6x}$.

17. Explain to a partner how to subtract the rational expressions in number **14** in **Practice.** See above.

18. Ask a partner to add $\dfrac{4x}{y} + \dfrac{2x^2}{y^2}$. Check the work.

$\dfrac{4xy + 2x^2}{y^2}$

More practice is provided in Exercise 82 of the Workbook.

Getting Started
Ask a volunteer
to explain how to
use the Distributive
Property to find the product
of a and $a + 4$.
$(a(a + 4) = a^2 + 4a)$

14-6 **More Addition and Subtraction**

Sometimes, the denominator has more than one term. After you multiply by the LCD, you can use the Distributive Property to help simplify the problem.

▶ **EXAMPLE 1**

Add. $\dfrac{5}{x} + \dfrac{3}{x + 2}$

The LCD of x and $x + 2$ is $x(x + 2)$.

$$\dfrac{5}{x} + \dfrac{3}{x + 2}$$

Write equivalent fractions with $x(x + 2)$ as the denominator.

$$\dfrac{5(x + 2)}{x(x + 2)} + \dfrac{3x}{x(x + 2)}$$

Use the Distributive Property to simplify $5(x + 2)$.

$$\dfrac{5x + 10}{x(x + 2)} + \dfrac{3x}{x(x + 2)}$$

Add the numerators.

$$\dfrac{5x + 10 + 3x}{x(x + 2)} = \dfrac{8x + 10}{x(x + 2)}$$

$$\dfrac{5}{x} + \dfrac{3}{x + 2} = \dfrac{8x + 10}{x(x + 2)}$$

▶ **EXAMPLE 2**

Subtract. $\dfrac{2}{a + 3} - \dfrac{5}{a + 5}$

The LCD of $a + 3$ and $a + 5$ is $(a + 3)(a + 5)$.

$$\dfrac{2}{a + 3} - \dfrac{5}{a + 5}$$

Write equivalent fractions with $(a + 3)(a + 5)$ as the denominator.

$$\dfrac{2(a + 5)}{(a + 3)(a + 5)} - \dfrac{5(a + 3)}{(a + 3)(a + 5)}$$

Use the Distributive Property to simplify $2(a + 5)$ and $5(a + 3)$.

$$\dfrac{2a + 10}{(a + 3)(a + 5)} - \dfrac{5a + 15}{(a + 3)(a + 5)}$$

Remember
$-(5a + 15) = -5a - 15$

Subtract the numerators.

$$\dfrac{2a + 10 - (5a + 15)}{(a + 3)(a + 5)}$$

$$\dfrac{2a + 10 - 5a - 15}{(a + 3)(a + 5)} = \dfrac{-3a - 5}{(a + 3)(a + 5)}$$

$$\dfrac{2}{a + 3} - \dfrac{5}{a + 5} = \dfrac{-3a - 5}{(a + 3)(a + 5)}$$

Try These

Add or subtract.

1. $\dfrac{x}{4} - \dfrac{4}{x}$

The LCD of 4 and x is ■. $4x$

$\dfrac{x}{4} - \dfrac{4}{x}$

Write equivalent fractions
with ■ as the denominator.
$4x$

$\dfrac{x(■)x}{4(■)x} - \dfrac{4(■)4}{x(■)4} \rightarrow \dfrac{x^2}{4x} - \dfrac{■16}{4x}$

Subtract the numerators.

$\dfrac{x^2 - ■16}{4x}$

$\dfrac{x}{4} - \dfrac{4}{x} = ■ \dfrac{x^2 - 16}{4x}$

2. $\dfrac{4}{x+3} + \dfrac{6}{x-3}$

The LCD of $x + 3$ and $x - 3$
is $(x + 3)(x - 3)$.

$\dfrac{4}{x+3} + \dfrac{6}{x-3}$

Write equivalent fractions with
$(x + 3)(x - 3)$ as the denominator.

$\dfrac{4(x-3)}{(x+3)(x-3)} + \dfrac{6(x+3)}{(x+3)(x-3)}$

Use the Distributive Property
to simplify $4(x - 3)$ and $6(x + 3)$.

$\dfrac{4x\,■ - ■12}{(x+3)(x-3)} + \dfrac{6x\,■ + ■18}{(x+3)(x-3)}$
$\quad 4x \qquad\qquad\qquad 6x$

Add the numerators.

$\dfrac{■ - 12 + ■ + 18}{(x+3)(x-3)} = \dfrac{10x + ■6}{(x+3)(x-3)}$

$\dfrac{4}{x+3} + \dfrac{6}{x-3} = ■\dfrac{10x + 6}{(x+3)(x-3)}$

Practice

Add or subtract.

1. $\dfrac{8y + 18}{y(y+3)}$ **2.** $\dfrac{16x + 10}{2x(x+5)}$ **3.** $\dfrac{7y + 15}{(y+1)(y+3)}$ **4.** $\dfrac{9a}{(a-2)(a+4)}$

1. $\dfrac{6}{y} + \dfrac{2}{y+3}$ **2.** $\dfrac{2}{2x} + \dfrac{7}{x+5}$ **3.** $\dfrac{4}{y+1} + \dfrac{3}{y+3}$ **4.** $\dfrac{3}{a-2} + \dfrac{6}{a+4}$

5. $\dfrac{2a}{a+2} + \dfrac{5}{a-2}$ **6.** $\dfrac{3x}{x-4} + \dfrac{4}{x+4}$ **7.** $\dfrac{5}{x-3} - \dfrac{6}{x}$ **8.** $\dfrac{8}{a-5} - \dfrac{3}{a}$

5. $\dfrac{2a^2 + a + 10}{(a+2)(a-2)}$ **6.** $\dfrac{3x^2 + 16x - 16}{(x-4)(x+4)}$ **7.** $\dfrac{-x + 18}{x(x-3)}$ **8.** $\dfrac{5a + 15}{a(a-5)}$

Cooperative Learning

9. Explain to a partner how to add the expressions in number **3**
in **Practice**. Possible answer: Find the LCD: $(y + 1)(y + 3)$. Write equivalent fractions. Use the
Distributive Property in the numerator. Add the fractions. Combine like terms.

10. Ask a partner to subtract $\dfrac{4}{y+1} - \dfrac{3}{y-1}$. Check the work.

$\dfrac{y - 7}{(y+1)(y-1)}$

More practice is provided in Exercise 82 of the Workbook.

14·7 Multiplication and Division

Getting Started
Review simplifying rational expressions. (See Lesson 14.3.)

You multiply rational expressions the same way you multiply fractions with numbers. Multiply the numerators, and multiply the denominators.

► EXAMPLE 1

Multiply. $\dfrac{2}{5} \cdot \dfrac{5}{6}$

Multiply numerators and multiply denominators.

$$\dfrac{2 \cdot 5}{5 \cdot 6}$$

Divide by common factors.

$$\dfrac{2 \cdot \cancel{5}}{\cancel{5} \cdot \cancel{6}}_{3}$$
$$\dfrac{1}{3}$$

Simplify.

$$\dfrac{2}{5} \cdot \dfrac{5}{6} = \dfrac{1}{3}$$

► EXAMPLE 2

Multiply. $\dfrac{3x}{4} \cdot \dfrac{2}{x}$

Multiply numerators and multiply denominators.

$$\dfrac{3x \cdot 2}{4 \cdot x}$$

Divide by common factors.

$$\dfrac{3\cancel{x} \cdot \cancel{2}}{\underset{2}{\cancel{4}} \cdot \cancel{x}}$$
$$\dfrac{3}{2}$$

Simplify.

$$\dfrac{3x}{4} \cdot \dfrac{2}{x} = \dfrac{3}{2}$$

To divide by a fraction, you multiply by its reciprocal. You divide rational expressions the same way.

► EXAMPLE 3

Divide. $\dfrac{3x}{y} \div \dfrac{9}{y}$

Multiply by the reciprocal.

$$\dfrac{3x}{y} \cdot \dfrac{y}{9}$$

Multiply numerators and multiply denominators.

$$\dfrac{3x \cdot y}{y \cdot 9}$$

Divide by common factors.

$$\dfrac{3x\cancel{y}}{\underset{3}{\cancel{9}}\cancel{y}}$$
$$\dfrac{x}{3}$$

Simplify.

$$\dfrac{3x}{y} \div \dfrac{9}{y} = \dfrac{x}{3}$$

Try These

Multiply or divide.

1. $\dfrac{6}{3a} \cdot \dfrac{2a}{5a}$

$$\dfrac{6}{3a} \cdot \dfrac{2a}{5a}$$

Multiply numerators and multiply denominators. $\dfrac{6 \cdot 2a}{3a \cdot 5a}$

Divide by common factors. $\dfrac{\overset{2}{6} \cdot 2\cancel{a}}{3\cancel{a} \cdot 5a}$

Simplify. $\dfrac{4}{5a}\ \blacksquare$

$\dfrac{6}{3a} \cdot \dfrac{2a}{5a} = \blacksquare \dfrac{4}{5a}$

2. $\dfrac{x}{y} \div \dfrac{3x^2}{4}$

$$\dfrac{x}{y} \div \dfrac{3x^2}{4}$$

Multiply by the $\blacksquare$. reciprocal $\dfrac{x}{y} \cdot \dfrac{\blacksquare\ 4}{\blacksquare\ 3x^2}$

Multiply numerators and multiply denominators. $\dfrac{x\ \blacksquare \cdot \blacksquare\ 4}{y\ \blacksquare \cdot \blacksquare\ 3x^2}$

Divide by common factors. $\dfrac{\cancel{x} \cdot 4}{y \cdot 3\cancel{x^2}\ x}$

Simplify. $\dfrac{\blacksquare\ 4}{\blacksquare\ 3xy}$

$\dfrac{x}{y} \div \dfrac{3x^2}{4} = \blacksquare \dfrac{4}{3xy}$

Practice

Multiply or divide.

1. $\dfrac{2}{7} \cdot \dfrac{7}{8}\ \ \dfrac{1}{4}$

2. $\dfrac{1}{3} \cdot \dfrac{9}{10}\ \ \dfrac{3}{10}$

3. $\dfrac{6}{7} \cdot \dfrac{14}{15}\ \ \dfrac{4}{5}$

4. $\dfrac{2}{3} \div \dfrac{4}{9}\ \ \dfrac{3}{2}$ or $1\dfrac{1}{2}$

5. $\dfrac{5}{8} \div \dfrac{3}{4}\ \ \dfrac{5}{6}$

6. $\dfrac{7}{10} \div \dfrac{14}{25}\ \ \dfrac{5}{4}$ or $1\dfrac{1}{4}$

7. $\dfrac{2y}{5} \cdot \dfrac{3y}{8}\ \ \dfrac{3y^2}{20}$

8. $\dfrac{4}{5x} \cdot \dfrac{1}{5x}\ \ \dfrac{4}{25x^2}$

9. $\dfrac{3m}{4} \cdot \dfrac{8m}{9}\ \ \dfrac{2m^2}{3}$

10. $\dfrac{7}{3x} \cdot \dfrac{3x}{2x}\ \ \dfrac{7}{2x}$

11. $\dfrac{8a}{3a} \cdot \dfrac{a}{6a^2}\ \ \dfrac{4}{9a}$

12. $\dfrac{5p^2}{2p} \cdot \dfrac{6}{10p}\ \ \dfrac{3}{2}$ or $1\dfrac{1}{2}$

13. $\dfrac{a^2}{10} \div \dfrac{4a}{5}\ \ \dfrac{a}{8}$

14. $\dfrac{x}{3} \div \dfrac{5x^2}{10}\ \ \dfrac{2}{3x}$

15. $\dfrac{7}{y^2} \div \dfrac{8y}{2y^2}\ \ \dfrac{7}{4y}$

16. $\dfrac{4y}{x} \div \dfrac{8}{x}\ \ \dfrac{y}{2}$

Cooperative Learning

17. Explain to a partner how to multiply the rational expressions in number **11** in **Practice.** Possible answer: Multiply the numerators and denominators: $\dfrac{8a(a)}{(3a)(6a^2)}$. Divide by their common factors and simplify: $\dfrac{4}{9a}$.

18. Write two rational expressions. Have a partner divide the rational expressions. Check the work. Answers will vary. Check students' work.

More practice is provided in Exercise 82 of the Workbook.

Getting Started
To help students
identify like
binomials, write
on the chalkboard:
   $3(x + 1)$
   $4(x - 2)$
   $2(x + 1)$
Have a volunteer circle the
like binomial. $(x + 1)$

14·8 ▶ More Multiplication and Division

Sometimes, you can factor polynomials before multiplying and dividing. Then, multiply numerators and multiply denominators.

$$\frac{2x + 4}{x - 2} \cdot \frac{3x - 6}{x + 2} \longrightarrow \frac{2(x + 2)}{x - 2} \cdot \frac{3(x - 2)}{x + 2} \longrightarrow \frac{2(x + 2) \cdot 3(x - 2)}{(x - 2)(x + 2)} = \frac{6}{1} = 6$$

▶ **EXAMPLE 1**

Divide. $\dfrac{3m}{3m + 6} \div \dfrac{9m}{m + 2}$

$$\frac{3m}{3m + 6} \div \frac{9m}{m + 2}$$

Multiply by the reciprocal.

$$\frac{3m}{3m + 6} \cdot \frac{m + 2}{9m}$$

Factor the denominator.

$$\frac{3m}{3(m + 2)} \cdot \frac{m + 2}{9m}$$

Multiply.

$$\frac{3m \cdot (m + 2)}{3(m + 2) \cdot 9m}$$

Divide by common factors.

$$\frac{3m \cdot (m + 2)}{3(m + 2) \cdot 9m}$$

Simplify.

$$\frac{1}{9}$$

$$\frac{3m}{3m + 6} \div \frac{9m}{m + 2} = \frac{1}{9}$$

▶ **EXAMPLE 2**

Multiply. $\dfrac{4x + 4}{x^2 + 3x + 2} \cdot \dfrac{x + 2}{3x}$

$$\frac{4x + 4}{x^2 + 3x + 2} \cdot \frac{x + 2}{3x}$$

Factor the numerator
and denominator.

$$\frac{4(x + 1)}{(x + 1)(x + 2)} \cdot \frac{x + 2}{3x}$$

Multiply.

$$\frac{4(x + 1)(x + 2)}{(x + 1)(x + 2)3x}$$

Divide by common factors.

$$\frac{4(x + 1)(x + 2)}{(x + 1)(x + 2)3x}$$

Simplify.

$$\frac{4}{3x}$$

$$\frac{4x + 4}{x^2 + 3x + 2} \cdot \frac{x + 2}{3x} = \frac{4}{3x}$$

Try These

Multiply or divide.

1. $\dfrac{8}{4a-8} \cdot \dfrac{a-2}{9a}$

$\dfrac{8}{4a-8} \cdot \dfrac{a-2}{9a}$

Factor. $\dfrac{8}{a \, 4(\blacksquare - 2)} \cdot \dfrac{a-2}{9a}$

Multiply. Divide by common factors. $\dfrac{8 \cdot (a-2)}{a \, 4(\blacksquare - 2) \cdot 9a}$

Simplify. $\dfrac{\blacksquare \, 2}{\blacksquare \, 9a}$

$\dfrac{8}{4a-8} \cdot \dfrac{a-2}{9a} = \blacksquare \dfrac{2}{9a}$

2. $\dfrac{5x+10}{x} \div \dfrac{x^2+5x+6}{5}$

$\dfrac{5x+10}{x} \div \dfrac{x^2+5x+6}{5}$

Multiply by the ■. reciprocal Factor. $\dfrac{5x+10}{x} \cdot \dfrac{\blacksquare \, 5}{\blacksquare \, x^2+5x+6}$

$\dfrac{5(x+\blacksquare)}{x} \cdot \dfrac{5}{(x+\blacksquare)(x+3)}$ with small 2's

Multiply. Divide by common factors. $\dfrac{\overset{2}{5(x+\blacksquare)} \cdot 5}{x(x+\blacksquare)(x+3)}$

Simplify. $\dfrac{\blacksquare \, 25}{\blacksquare \, x(x+3)}$

$\dfrac{5x+10}{x} \div \dfrac{x^2+5x+6}{5} = \blacksquare \dfrac{25}{x(x+3)}$

Practice

Multiply or divide.

1. $\dfrac{3y+6}{5} \cdot \dfrac{4y}{y+2}$ $\dfrac{12y}{5}$

2. $\dfrac{y}{6y+8} \cdot \dfrac{3y+4}{3y}$ $\dfrac{1}{6}$

3. $\dfrac{6}{5x-10} \cdot \dfrac{x-2}{7x}$ $\dfrac{6}{35x}$

4. $\dfrac{10a}{a-3} \cdot \dfrac{4a-12}{2}$ $20a$

5. $\dfrac{6b+18}{b} \div \dfrac{b+3}{b}$ 6

6. $\dfrac{2x+4}{x} \div \dfrac{3x+6}{2}$ $\dfrac{4}{3x}$

7. $\dfrac{5y}{5y+15} \div \dfrac{15y}{y+3}$ $\dfrac{1}{15}$

8. $\dfrac{12}{m+6} \div \dfrac{9m}{2m+12}$ $\dfrac{8}{3m}$

9. $\dfrac{3}{x^2+4x+3} \cdot \dfrac{x+3}{5}$ $\dfrac{3}{5(x+1)}$

Cooperative Learning

10. Explain to a partner how to divide the rational expressions in number **5** in **Practice.**   Possible answer: Multiply by the reciprocal: $\dfrac{b}{b+3}$. Factor $6b+18$. Multiply the numerators and denominators. Divide the common factors ($b+3$ and b) and simplify.

11. Write a rational expression with $x+1$ as the numerator and another rational expression with $2x+2$ as the denominator. Have a partner multiply the rational expressions. Check the work. Answers will vary. If a and b were the rational expressions a student chose for the numerator and denominator, then the answer should be $\dfrac{a}{2b}$.

More practice is provided in Exercise 83 of the Workbook.

14·9 **Solving Rational Equations**

A **rational equation** contains rational expressions. To solve a rational equation, you change it to one you know how to solve. To do this, you multiply each term by the least common denominator of all the denominators in the equation. Then, solve the remaining equation.

▶ **EXAMPLE 1**

Check
$$\frac{x}{3} + \frac{x}{2} = 10$$
$$\frac{12}{3} + \frac{12}{2} = 10$$
$$4 + 6 = 10$$
$$10 = 10 \quad \text{true}$$

Solve. $\quad \dfrac{x}{3} + \dfrac{x}{2} = 10$

The LCD of 3 and 2 is 6.

Multiply each term by 6.

Simplify.

Solve for x.

$$\frac{x}{3} + \frac{x}{2} = 10$$
$$(6)\frac{x}{3} + (6)\frac{x}{2} = (6)10$$
$$2x + 3x = 60$$
$$5x = 60$$
$$x = 12$$

The solution of $\frac{x}{3} + \frac{x}{2} = 10$ is 12.

▶ **EXAMPLE 2**

Check
$$\frac{2}{n} + \frac{1}{3} = \frac{4}{n}$$
$$\frac{2}{6} + \frac{1}{3} = \frac{4}{6}$$
$$\frac{2}{6} + \frac{2}{6} = \frac{4}{6}$$
$$\frac{4}{6} = \frac{4}{6} \quad \text{true}$$

Solve. $\quad \dfrac{2}{n} + \dfrac{1}{3} = \dfrac{4}{n}$

The LCD for n and 3 is $3n$.

Multiply each term by $3n$.

Simplify.

Solve for n.

$$\frac{2}{n} + \frac{1}{3} = \frac{4}{n}$$
$$(3n)\frac{2}{n} + (3n)\frac{1}{3} = (3n)\frac{4}{n}$$
$$6 + n = 12$$
$$n = 6$$

The solution of $\frac{2}{n} + \frac{1}{3} = \frac{4}{n}$ is 6.

▶ **EXAMPLE 3**

Check
$$\frac{4}{x} + \frac{3}{2x} = \frac{11}{6}$$
$$\frac{4}{3} + \frac{3}{2 \cdot 3} = \frac{11}{6}$$
$$\frac{4}{3} + \frac{3}{6} = \frac{11}{6}$$
$$\frac{8}{6} + \frac{3}{6} = \frac{11}{6}$$
$$\frac{11}{6} = \frac{11}{6} \quad \text{true}$$

Solve. $\quad \dfrac{4}{x} + \dfrac{3}{2x} = \dfrac{11}{6}$

The LCD for x, $2x$, and 6 is $6x$.

Multiply each term by $6x$.

Simplify.

Add.

Solve for x.

$$\frac{4}{x} + \frac{3}{2x} = \frac{11}{6}$$
$$(6x)\frac{4}{x} + (6x)\frac{3}{2x} = (6x)\frac{11}{6}$$
$$24 + 9 = 11x$$
$$33 = 11x$$
$$3 = x$$

The solution of $\frac{4}{x} + \frac{3}{2x} = \frac{11}{6}$ is 3.

Solve.

1. $\dfrac{1}{3} - \dfrac{2}{3a} = \dfrac{1}{a}$

The LCD is ■.3a $\dfrac{1}{3} - \dfrac{2}{3a} = \dfrac{1}{a}$

Multiply each term by ■.3a $3a\dfrac{1}{3} - 3a\dfrac{2}{3a} = 3a\dfrac{1}{a}$

Simplify. $a■ - 2 = ■ \, 3$

Solve for a. $a = ■ \, 5$

The solution of $\dfrac{1}{3} - \dfrac{2}{3a} = \dfrac{1}{a}$ is ■.5

2. $\dfrac{3y}{5} - \dfrac{3}{2} = \dfrac{7y}{10}$

The LCD is ■. 10 $\dfrac{3y}{5} - \dfrac{3}{2} = \dfrac{7y}{10}$

Multiply each term by ■. 10 $10\dfrac{3y}{5} - 10\dfrac{3}{2} = 10\dfrac{7y}{10}$

Simplify. $6■y - 15 = ■y \, 7$

Solve for y. $y = ■ \, -15$

The solution of $\dfrac{3y}{5} - \dfrac{3}{2} = \dfrac{7y}{10}$ is ■. -15

Practice

Solve each rational equation.

1. $\dfrac{y}{3} + \dfrac{y}{6} = 1$ $y = 2$

2. $\dfrac{b}{4} - \dfrac{b}{5} = 2$ $b = 40$

3. $\dfrac{m}{3} - \dfrac{m}{4} = 3$ $m = 36$

4. $\dfrac{4}{x} + \dfrac{2}{3} = \dfrac{8}{x}$ $x = 6$

5. $\dfrac{1}{4} + \dfrac{3}{n} = \dfrac{4}{n}$ $n = 4$

6. $\dfrac{3}{p} - \dfrac{1}{p} = \dfrac{1}{5}$ $p = 10$

7. $\dfrac{1}{5} - \dfrac{2}{5n} = \dfrac{1}{n}$ $n = 7$

8. $\dfrac{2}{7} - \dfrac{4}{7a} = \dfrac{2}{a}$ $a = 9$

9. $\dfrac{1}{8b} + \dfrac{3}{8} = \dfrac{2}{b}$ $b = 5$

10. $\dfrac{2x}{5} - \dfrac{5}{2} = \dfrac{3x}{10}$ $x = 25$

11. $\dfrac{6}{3} - \dfrac{3v}{5} = \dfrac{6v}{15}$ $v = 2$

12. $\dfrac{2y}{3} + \dfrac{5}{2} = \dfrac{7y}{6}$ $y = 5$

13. $\dfrac{4}{n} + \dfrac{6}{4n} = \dfrac{11}{8}$ $n = 4$

14. $\dfrac{1}{2x} + \dfrac{5}{6} = \dfrac{9}{3x}$ $x = 3$

15. $\dfrac{1}{z} - \dfrac{3}{8} = \dfrac{1}{4z}$ $z = 2$

Cooperative Learning

16. Explain to a partner how to solve the rational equation in number **10** in **Practice**.
Possible answer: Find the LCD: 10. Multiply each term by 10 to simplify. Solve for x.

17. Write a rational equation. Ask a partner to solve your equation. Check the work. Answers will vary. Check students' work.

14-10 Solving Proportions

A **proportion** states that two ratios are equal. In a proportion, the **cross products** are equal.

$$\frac{5}{x} \diagdown \diagup \frac{4}{8}$$

You can solve a proportion by finding the cross products. The cross products are $5 \cdot 8$ and $x \cdot 4$. Then, solve the equation.

$$5 \cdot 8 = x \cdot 4$$

$$40 = 4x$$

$$10 = x$$

▶ **EXAMPLE 1**

Solve. $\dfrac{2}{n + 1} = \dfrac{4}{n}$

Find the cross products. $2 \cdot n = 4(n + 1)$

Simplify. $2n = 4n + 4$

Solve for n. $-2n = 4$

                                        $n = -2$

The solution of $\dfrac{2}{n + 1} = \dfrac{4}{n}$ is -2.

Sometimes, the cross products are quadratic expressions. You can solve the equation by factoring or by using the quadratic formula.

▶ **EXAMPLE 2**

Solve. $\dfrac{y}{y + 1} = \dfrac{10}{y + 7}$

Find the cross products. $y(y + 7) = 10(y + 1)$

Simplify. $y^2 + 7y = 10y + 10$

The equation is quadratic. Get all the terms on one side. $y^2 - 3y - 10 = 0$

Factor. $(y - 5)(y + 2) = 0$

Let each factor equal 0. $y - 5 = 0 \quad y + 2 = 0$

Solve for y. $y = 5 \qquad y = -2$

The solutions of $\dfrac{y}{y + 1} = \dfrac{10}{y + 7}$ are 5 or -2.

Try These

Solve.

1. $\dfrac{b-2}{b+3} = \dfrac{3}{8}$

$$8 \; \dfrac{b-2}{b+3} = \dfrac{3}{8}$$

Find the cross products. $\blacksquare(b-2) = \blacksquare(b+3)$

Simplify. $8b - \overset{16}{\blacksquare} = 3b + \overset{9}{\blacksquare}$

Get the variables on one side. $5b - 16 = 9$

Solve for b.

$$5b = \blacksquare\, 25$$
$$b = \blacksquare\, 5$$

The solution of $\dfrac{b-2}{b+3} = \dfrac{3}{8}$ is $\blacksquare.5$

2. $\dfrac{7}{y-4} = \dfrac{5}{y-2}$

$$\dfrac{7}{y - \overset{2}{4}} = \dfrac{5}{y - \overset{4}{2}}$$

cross product
Find the $\blacksquare$. $7(y - \blacksquare) = 5(y - \blacksquare)$

Simplify. $7y - \overset{14}{\blacksquare} = 5y - \overset{20}{\blacksquare}$

Get the variables on one side. $2\blacksquare y - 14 = -20$

Solve for y.

$$2y\,\blacksquare = -6$$
$$y = \blacksquare\, -3$$

The solution of $\dfrac{7}{y-4} = \dfrac{5}{y-2}$ is $\blacksquare.\;-3$

Practice

Solve.

1. $\dfrac{6}{x} = \dfrac{4}{8}$ $x = 12$

2. $\dfrac{6}{3} = \dfrac{x}{5}$ $x = 10$

3. $\dfrac{3}{n+1} = \dfrac{6}{n}$ $n = -2$

4. $\dfrac{x}{5} = \dfrac{x-2}{15}$ $x = -1$

5. $\dfrac{y-3}{y+1} = \dfrac{6}{8}$ $y = 15$

6. $\dfrac{1}{5} = \dfrac{a-2}{a-6}$ $a = 1$

7. $\dfrac{3}{x-4} = \dfrac{6}{x-6}$ $x = 2$

8. $\dfrac{y-1}{2} = \dfrac{y+2}{3}$ $y = 7$

9. $\dfrac{n}{5n+6} = \dfrac{1}{n}$
$n = 6$ or $n = -1$

Cooperative Learning

10. Explain to a partner how to solve the rational equation in number **9** in **Practice.** See below.

11. Write an equation with a proportion. Have a partner solve the equation. Check the work. Answers will vary. Check students' work.

10. Possible answer: Find the cross products: $n^2 = 5n + 6$. Get all terms on the left side: $n^2 - 5n - 6 = 0$. Factor the trinomial: $(n - 6)(n + 1)$. Let each factor equal zero. Solve for n. Check by replacing n with 6 and -1 in the original equation.

Calculator: Checking Solutions

Some proportions have large numbers or decimals. You can use a calculator to work with proportions.

EXAMPLE 1

Getting Started
To review, have students write the cross products for this proportion.

$$\frac{3}{5} = \frac{15}{25}$$

$(3 \cdot 25 = 5 \cdot 15)$

Tell whether the proportion is true. $\dfrac{.29}{1.45} = \dfrac{2.61}{13.05}$

Write the cross products. $.29 \cdot 13.05 = 2.61 \cdot 1.45$

Simplify the left side.   **Display**

| Enter .29. | . 2 9 | .29 |
| Multiply by 13.05. | × 1 3 . 0 5 = | 3.7845 |

Simplify the right side.   **Display**

| Enter 2.61. | 2 . 6 1 | 2.61 |
| Multiply by 1.45. | × 1 . 4 5 = | 3.7845 |

Compare the results.   3.7845 = 3.7845

$\dfrac{.29}{1.45} = \dfrac{2.61}{13.05}$ is a true proportion.

EXAMPLE 2

Tell whether 12 is a solution of $\dfrac{35}{7u + 56} = \dfrac{7}{28}$.

Substitute 12 for u. $\dfrac{35}{7(12) + 56} = \dfrac{7}{28}$

Simplify the denominator first.   **Display**

Enter 7.	7	7
Multiply by 12.	× 1 2 =	84
Add 56.	+ 5 6 =	140

Then, divide the numerator by the denominator.

| Enter 35. | 3 5 | 35 |
| Divide by 140. | ÷ 1 4 0 = | .25 |

Simplify the right side.   **Display**

| Enter 7. | 7 | 7 |
| Divide by 28. | ÷ 2 8 = | .25 |

Compare the results.   .25 = .25   true

Yes, 12 is a solution of $\dfrac{35}{7u + 56} = \dfrac{7}{28}$.

Practice

Tell whether the number is a solution of the proportion.

1. 6; $\dfrac{11x}{11x + 66} = \dfrac{33}{11x}$ yes

2. 4; $\dfrac{15.3}{3.4} = \dfrac{30.6}{1.7y}$ yes

3. 6; $\dfrac{15x}{75x + 90} = \dfrac{15}{15x}$ yes

4. 2; $\dfrac{3.12}{.52x + 1.04} = \dfrac{.52x + .52}{.52}$ no

5. 537.2; $\dfrac{x}{31.6} = \dfrac{68}{4}$ yes

6. −2; $\dfrac{20x}{20x + 20} = \dfrac{200}{20x + 140}$ yes

7. 9; $\dfrac{7x - 4.9}{.7x + 1.4} = \dfrac{.7}{2.8}$ no

8. −3; $\dfrac{56}{8x - 32} = \dfrac{40}{8x - 16}$ yes

Math Connection

CURRENCY EXCHANGE

Perhaps you plan to travel to a foreign country. To pay your expenses while you travel, you may need that country's money. You can change United States dollars into the money of that country. This is called currency exchange. Currency is a form of money.

Every day, banks set exchange rates. The exchange rate tells you the amounts of each currency that are equal to each other. For example, in May, you might exchange $100 for 63 British pounds. Exchange rates change as time goes by. In September, you might only get 61 British pounds for $100.

The words *strong* and *weak* describe changes in currency exchange. Sometimes the dollar is strong compared to the British pound. That means you can exchange dollars for more pounds than usual. If the dollar is weak, that means you get fewer pounds for your dollar.

More practice is provided in Exercise 84 of the Workbook.

Getting Started
Have students
bring in maps with
different scales.
Help students read
the scales.

14·12 ▶ Problem Solving: Using Proportions

Proportions are helpful in solving many types of problems, such as problems involving scale or percents.

▶ **EXAMPLE**

On a map, 5 centimeters stands for 9 miles. On this scale, how many centimeters stand for 36 miles?

READ **What do you need to find out?**
You need to find how many centimeters on the map represent 36 miles.

PLAN **What do you need to do?**
You need to set up a proportion and solve for the unknown number.

DO **Follow the plan.**

Set up a proportion. $\dfrac{5 \text{ cm}}{9 \text{ mi}} = \dfrac{x \text{ cm}}{36 \text{ mi}}$

Cross multiply. $5 \cdot 36 = 9x$

Simplify. $180 = 9x$

Solve for x. $20 = x$

CHECK **Does your answer make sense?**
Substitute 20 into the proportion.

$$\frac{5 \text{ cm}}{9 \text{ mi}} = \frac{20 \text{ cm}}{36 \text{ mi}}$$

$$5 \cdot 36 = 9 \cdot 20$$

$$180 = 180 \checkmark$$

20 centimeters stands for 36 miles on the map.

Try These

1. Only 1 out of 4 of Terry's tomato plants survived a drought. Terry started with a total of 20 plants. How many survived the drought?

Set up a proportion. $\dfrac{1\ \blacksquare\ \text{survived}}{4\ \text{total}} = \dfrac{x\ \text{survived}}{20\ \blacksquare\ \text{total}}$

Find the cross products. $1\blacksquare \cdot \blacksquare = \blacksquare x$
$\qquad\qquad\qquad\quad\ 20 \qquad 4$

Simplify. $20\ \blacksquare = \blacksquare x\ 4$

Solve for x. $5\ \blacksquare = x$

$5\blacksquare$ of Terry's tomato plants survived.

2. A scuba diver can get 12 feet under water in 8 seconds. Find how many seconds it will take to get 36 feet under water.

Set up a proportion ■. $\dfrac{12\ \text{feet}\ \blacksquare}{8\ \text{seconds}\ \blacksquare} = \dfrac{\blacksquare\ 36\ \text{feet}}{\blacksquare\ x\ \text{seconds}}$

Find the cross products. $\blacksquare x = \blacksquare \cdot \blacksquare$
$\qquad\qquad\qquad\ \ 12 \qquad 36\ \ 8$

Simplify. $12\ \blacksquare x = \blacksquare\ 288$

Solve for x. $x = \blacksquare\ 24$

It will take ■ to get 36 feet under water. 24 s

Practice

Use a proportion to solve each problem.

1. A map scale uses 8 cm to represent 28 miles. How many miles would 2 cm represent on the map?   7 miles

2. At Park High School, 3 out of 4 seniors have part-time jobs. There are 75 seniors with part-time jobs. Find the total number of seniors.   100 total seniors

3. Sandy has band practice 3 out of 5 school days each week. Find the number of days she has band practice in 40 school days.
   24 days of band

4. A scuba diver can get 6 yards under water in 30 seconds. Find how many yards the diver can go under water in 10 seconds at the same rate.   2 yd

Cooperative Learning

5. Possible answer: Set up a proportion: $\dfrac{6\ \text{yd}}{30\ \text{s}} = \dfrac{x\ \text{yd}}{10\ \text{s}}$. Cross multiply: $60 = 30x$. Divide by 30: $x = 2$.

5. Explain to a partner how you solve number 4 in **Practice**. See above.

6. Write a proportion to show how many days a week you exercise. Ask a partner to find out how many days you exercise in 28 days. Check the work.   Answers will vary. All answers should be a multiple of 4.

More practice is provided in Exercise 85 of the Workbook.

14·13 Application: Inverse Variation

Getting Started
Explain that in direct variation, if one variable increases, the second increases. For example, the bigger the object, the more force is needed to move it.

Contrast this with inverse variation. As one variable increases, the other decreases. For example, the faster a runner runs, the less time it takes to finish the race.

You can solve problems in which the value of one variable increases as the other decreases. This is called **inverse variation.** Inverse variation is a rational equation in the form $y = \frac{k}{x}$. k is a positive constant.

In the table below, the variable x represents the number of people painting a house, and y represents the number of days it takes.

People	x	1	2	4	8	16
Days	y	16	8	4	2	1

The equation $y = \frac{16}{x}$ shows how the number of days is related to the number of people.

▶ **EXAMPLE 1**

How many days will it take for 32 people to paint the house?

$$y = \frac{16}{x}$$

Math Fact
$\frac{16 \div 16}{32 \div 16} = \frac{1}{2}$

Substitute 32 for x.

$$y = \frac{16}{32}$$

Simplify.

$$y = \frac{1}{2}$$

It takes $\frac{1}{2}$ of a day for 32 people to paint the house.

You can use $y = \frac{60}{x}$ to find the time it takes to make a trip 60 miles long. x represents the rate (mph), and y represents the time (h).

▶ **EXAMPLE 2**

How long will the trip take if you travel 30 mph?

$$y = \frac{60}{x}$$

Substitute 30 for x.

$$y = \frac{60}{30}$$

Simplify.

$$y = 2$$

The trip will take 2 hours if you travel 30 mph.

Try These

Use $y = \frac{24}{x}$ to find the width of a rectangle with area of 24 cm². x represents the length, and y represents the width.

1. What is the width of the rectangle if the length is 8 cm?

$$y = \frac{24}{x}$$

8

Substitute ■ for x.

$$y = \frac{24}{■\,8}$$

Simplify.

$$y = ■\,3$$

The width of the rectangle is ■ if the length is 8 cm.

3 cm

2. What is the width of the rectangle if the length is 12 cm?

$$y = \frac{24}{x}$$

12

Substitute ■ for x.

$$y = \frac{24}{■\,12}$$

Simplify.

$$y = ■\,2$$

The width of the rectangle is ■ if the length is 12 cm.

2 cm

Practice

Use $t = \frac{90}{r}$ to solve each problem. r is the rate (mph), and t is the time (hours) for a 90 mile trip.

1. How long will the trip take if you travel 10 mph?   9 h

2. How long will the trip take if you travel 50 mph? $1\frac{4}{5}$ h

Use $h = \frac{48}{b}$ to solve each problem. b represents the base of a triangle of area 24, and h represents the height.

3. What is the height of the triangle if the base is 6 centimeters?   8 cm

4. What is the height of the triangle if the base is 12 centimeters?   4 cm

Cooperative Learning

5. Explain to a partner how to find the height of the triangle in number **4** in **Practice.** Possible answer: Substitute 12 for b and simplify: $h = \frac{48}{12} = 4.$

6. Write a problem that can be solved using the inverse variation in **Try These.** Ask a partner to solve the problem. Check the work.
All possible answers are between 1 and 24 cm.

Summary

To evaluate rational expressions, substitute values for variables.

A rational expression is undefined when the denominator is zero.

You can simplify rational expressions by factoring. Then, divide by common factors.

To find the LCM of two polynomials, list the multiples.

You find the LCD to add or subtract rational expressions.

You multiply numerator by numerator then denominator by denominator to multiply rational expressions. You multiply by the reciprocal to divide rational expressions.

You multiply each term in a rational equation by the LCD to get rid of the denominator. Then, you solve the equation.

You solve proportions by cross multiplying.

You can use proportions to solve different kinds of problems.

Inverse variation is a rational equation you can use to solve problems.

More vocabulary review is provided in Exercise 131 of the Classroom Resource Binder.

rational number
undefined
least common multiple (LCM)
rational equation
proportion
inverse variation

Vocabulary Review

Complete the sentences with the words from the box.

1. The smallest positive common multiple of two or more numbers or polynomials is called the $\underline{\text{least common multiple (LCM)}}$.

2. A _____ is an equation that contains rational expressions.   rational equation

3. A rational equation in the form $y = \frac{k}{x}$ is an _____.   inverse variation

4. A _____ is a number that can be written as a fraction.   rational number

5. A rational expression is _____ when the denominator is zero.   undefined

6. A statement that two ratios are equal is called a _____.   proportion

Chapter Quiz   More assessment is provided in the Classroom Resource Binder.

Evaluate each expression.

1. $\frac{y + 3}{y^2 - 1}$ when y is -2 $\frac{1}{3}$

2. $\frac{a^2 - 3}{a + 4}$ when a is 4 $\frac{13}{8}$

Find the values that make the rational expression undefined.

3. $\frac{3y + 2}{4y(y - 5)}$ 0 or 5

4. $\frac{b - 5}{(b + 5)(b + 6)}$ -5 or -6

Simplify each rational expression.

5. $\frac{(x - 5)(x + 3)}{x(x + 3)}$ $\frac{x - 5}{x}$

6. $\frac{2x - 10}{x^2 - 10x + 25}$ $\frac{2}{x - 5}$

Find the least common multiple for each pair of expressions.

7. $4xy$ and $12y$ $12xy$

8. $2ab^2$ and $4ab$ $4ab^2$

9. $x - 3$ and $4x$ $4x(x - 3)$

Add, subtract, multiply, or divide.

10. $\frac{2}{7} + \frac{1}{2}$ $\frac{11}{14}$

11. $\frac{4}{xy} + \frac{7}{y}$ $\frac{4 + 7x}{xy}$

12. $\frac{y}{9} + \frac{5}{y}$ $\frac{y^2 + 45}{9y}$

13. $\frac{x}{8} - \frac{3}{4x}$ $\frac{x^2 - 6}{8x}$

14. $\frac{a - 2}{6} \cdot \frac{2}{3a - 6}$ $\frac{1}{9}$

15. $\frac{5x - 15}{x} \cdot \frac{x^2}{5}$ $x(x-3)$

16. $\frac{4x - 12}{x^2} \div \frac{4}{x}$ $\frac{x-3}{x}$

17. $\frac{3x - 9}{x^2 - 9} \cdot \frac{6x + 18}{x}$ $\frac{18}{x}$

Solve.

18. $\frac{1}{2} + \frac{5}{n} = \frac{6}{n}$ $n = 2$

19. $\frac{1}{6} - \frac{2}{6n} = \frac{1}{n}$ $n = 8$

20. $\frac{3}{9} - \frac{5}{3a} = 2$ $a = -1$

21. $\frac{6}{n + 1} = \frac{9}{n}$ $n = -3$

22. $\frac{x}{6} = \frac{x - 2}{18}$ $x = -1$

23. $\frac{y + 1}{y - 3} = \frac{4}{3}$ $y = 15$

Use a proportion to solve the problem.

24. A map scale shows that 3 centimeters stands for 5 miles. Find how many centimeters represent 25 miles.   15 cm

Use $y = \frac{18}{x}$ to solve the problem. y is the number of days it takes to fix a sidewalk, and x is the number of people fixing the sidewalk.

25. How many days will it take for 3 people to fix the sidewalk?   6 days

Additional Practice for this chapter is provided on p. 426 of this text.

Probability tells how likely
something is to happen.
A tan puppy in the same
litter with black puppies
is a low probability. What
colors do you think the
parents of these puppies
might be?

Learning Objectives

- Find the number of permutations.
- Find the number of combinations.
- Find the probability of an event.
- Find the probability of compound events.
- Use a calculator to find the number of permutations and combinations.
- Solve problems using empirical probability.
- Apply concepts and skills to making a prediction.

Words to Know

permutations	ways of putting a group of objects in order; there are six permutations for three letters: ABC, ACB, BAC, BCA, CAB, CBA
combination	a group of objects in which order does not matter; In counting combinations, ABC is the same as CAB
at random	each outcome is equally likely to happen
outcomes	the results of an activity, experiment, or game
event	an outcome or group of outcomes that you are looking for
probability	value from 0 to 1 that tells how likely an event is to happen
complementary events	events that are opposites; if winning is the event, then losing is the complementary event
independent events	events whose outcomes do not affect each other
compound event	two or more events
dependent events	events for which the outcome of one affects the outcome of the other
empirical probability	probability based on what has already happened

Number Cubes Project

Project See the Classroom Resource Binder for a scoring rubric to assess this project.

Probability measures how likely something is to happen. Conduct a probability experiment. Toss two number cubes. Record the sum of the numbers that land face up.

Toss	Cube 1	Cube 2	Sum
1	2	4	6
2	3	4	7
3	2	5	7

Toss the two number cubes 10 times. How many times did the sum of 7 occur in 10 tosses? Repeat this experiment. This time count the number of times the sum of 2 occurs in 10 tosses. What do you notice?

More practice is provided in Exercise 87 of the Workbook.

15·1 ▶ Counting

You can draw a tree diagram to show choices. The diagram below shows the different choices for sandwiches when you have two kinds of bread and three kinds of filling.

2 breads	3 fillings	sandwiches
rye	turkey	turkey and rye
	tuna	tuna and rye
	cheese	cheese and rye
wheat	turkey	turkey and wheat
	tuna	tuna and wheat
	cheese	cheese and wheat

You can multiply to find the total number of choices.

choice of   choice of   total choices
bread   filling   sandwich

$$2 \times 3 = 6$$

▶ **EXAMPLE 1**

Dennis can take 1 of 3 language classes and 1 of 4 science classes. How many ways can he choose a language class and a science class?

Find the number of languages.   3 choices
Find the number of science classes.   4 choices
Multiply. $3 \times 4 = 12$

There are 12 ways Dennis can choose a language and a science class.

▶ **EXAMPLE 2**

You can either bike or drive from A to C. There are 4 roads from A to B. There are 3 roads from B to C. How many ways can you ride from A to C through B?

Find the number of vehicles.   2 choices
Find the number of roads from A to B.   4 choices
Find the number of roads from B to C.   3 choices
Multiply. $2 \times 4 \times 3 = 24$

There are 24 possible ways to go from A to C through B.

Try These

Find the total number of choices.

1. Karl has 5 pairs of pants and 6 shirts. How many choices does Karl have for a pair of pants and a shirt?

Find the number of pants. ■ 5

Find the number of shirts. 6

Multiply. ■ × ■ = ■
 5 6 30

Karl has ■ choices.
 30

2. Liv has pens with red, blue, green, and purple ink. She has yellow, blue, and white paper. How many combinations of ink and paper does Liv have?

Find the number of inks. ■ 4

Find the number of colors of paper. ■ 3

Multiply. ■ × ■ = ■
 4 3 12

Liv has ■ choices.
 12

Practice

Find the total number of choices.

1. Stephanie has 8 T-shirts and 2 pairs of jeans. How many choices does she have to pick a T-shirt and a pair of jeans? 16

2. There are 6 scenic routes to the top of a mountain. At the top, there are 4 restaurants. How many choices are there for route and restaurant? 24

3. Dru can either go to school early for tutoring or go at the regular time. To get to school, he can take the bus, the subway, or his bicycle. Before he starts class, he gets either hot chocolate or orange juice. How many choices does he have for his morning routine? 12

Cooperative Learning

4. Explain to a partner how to find the choices in number **2** in **Practice.** Multiply the number of scenic routes by the number of restaurants: 6 × 4 = 24.

5. Write a problem that has choices for different things. Ask a friend to count the total number of choices. Check the work. Answers will vary.

More practice is provided in Exercises 86 and 87 of the Workbook.

15·2 ▶ Permutations

Getting Started
Relate permutations to choosing club officers. Suppose Jim, Sue, and Al run for President, Secretary, or Treasurer. Once a student is chosen at random to be President, he or she cannot be Secretary or Treasurer. This leaves only 2 choices for Secretary. Once a person is chosen for Secretary, only one is left to be Treasurer.

You can arrange a group of objects in different ways. These are called **permutations.**

ABC   BAC   CAB   ACB   BCA   CBA

You can also count the number of arrangements using multiplication. There are 3 letters and 3 choices for the first position. For each position, there is one less letter to choose from than for the last position.

1st position		2nd position		3rd position	
3 letters		2 letters left		1 letter left	
3	×	2	×	1	= 6

There are 6 ways to arrange the letters A, B, and C.

▶ **EXAMPLE 1**

How many different ways can 5 students stand in line?

There are 5 positions.	1st	2nd	3rd	4th	5th
Count the number of choices for each position.	5	4	3	2	1

Multiply. $5 \times 4 \times 3 \times 2 \times 1 = 120$

There are 120 ways 5 students can stand in line.

▶ **EXAMPLE 2**

There are 15 students in a class. How many ways can you pick a president, vice president, and secretary?

There are 3 positions.	P	VP	S
Count the number of choices.	15	14	13

Multiply. $15 \times 14 \times 13 = 2{,}730$

There are 2,730 ways to elect the 3 officers.

▶ **EXAMPLE 3**

There are 10 runners in a race. How many ways can the runners finish first, second, and third?

There are 3 positions.	1st	2nd	3rd
Count the number of choices.	10	9	8

Multiply. $10 \times 9 \times 8 = 720$

There are 720 ways for 10 runners to finish first, second, and third.

Try These

Find each number of permutations.

1. How many ways can you award first place and second place in a contest with 10 entries?

There are 2 positions.	1st	2nd
Count the number of choices.	10	9
Multiply.	10 ▧ × ▧ 9

   ▧ 90
   90

   First and second place can be awarded ▧ ways.
   90

2. How many ways can you arrange the letters E, F, G, and H?

   There are ▧ 4 positions.

	E	F	G	H
Count the number of choices.	4	2		
	▧	3	▧	1

   Multiply. $4\,▧ × 3 × ▧ × 1$
   2

   ▧ 24

   E, F, G, and H can be arranged ▧ ways.
   24

Practice

Find each number of permutations.

1. How many ways can 3 people stand in a line? 6

2. How many ways can you arrange the letters M, N, O, P, Q? 120

3. There are 6 people on a committee. How many ways are there to elect a chairperson and recorder? 30

4. A competition has 5 finalists. They can win first, second, and third place. In how many ways can the finalists win? 60

Cooperative Learning

5. Explain to a partner how to find the number of permutations in number **3** in **Practice.** Possible answer: There are 6 options for the first choice. There are 5 options for the second choice. The product of 6 and 5 is 30.

6. Write a question that asks how many ways there are to arrange a group of objects. Be sure to include the number of objects and what the objects are. Ask a partner to answer the question. Answers will vary and may be very large.

More practice is provided in Exercises 86 and 87 of the Workbook.

15·3 ▸ Combinations

Here are the different ways you can choose two pieces
of fruit from an Apple, Orange, Banana, and Plum:

A and O	O and A	B and A	P and A
A and B	O and B	B and O	P and O
A and P	O and P	B and P	P and B

In a **combination**, the order does not matter. There are
6 combinations of 2 pieces of fruit chosen from 4
different fruits. You can also use a formula to find the
number of combinations.

Number of combinations of 2 objects from 4:

$$\frac{\text{number of arrangements of 2 objects from 4}}{\text{number of arrangements of 2 objects}}$$

Number of fruit combinations $= \dfrac{4 \cdot 3}{2 \cdot 1} = \dfrac{\overset{2}{\cancel{4}} \cdot 3}{\cancel{2} \cdot 1} = \dfrac{6}{1} = 6$

▸ **EXAMPLE 1**

How many ways are there to choose 3 different pizza
toppings if there are 12 to choose from?

Find the number of arrangements $12 \cdot 11 \cdot 10$
of 3 objects chosen from 12.

Find the number of arrangements $3 \cdot 2 \cdot 1$
of 3 objects.

Divide. $\dfrac{12 \cdot 11 \cdot 10}{3 \cdot 2 \cdot 1} = 220$

There are 220 combinations of 3 pizza toppings.

▸ **EXAMPLE 2**

How many ways can a teacher choose 5 volunteers
from a class of 12?

Find the number of arrangements $12 \cdot 11 \cdot 10 \cdot 9 \cdot 8$
of 5 objects chosen from 12.

Find the number of arrangements $5 \cdot 4 \cdot 3 \cdot 2 \cdot 1$
of 5 objects.

Divide. $\dfrac{12 \cdot 11 \cdot 10 \cdot 9 \cdot 8}{5 \cdot 4 \cdot 3 \cdot 2 \cdot 1} = 792$

The teacher can choose 5 helpers in 792 different ways.

Try These

Find each number of combinations.

1. How many ways can you choose 3 photos from 6?

Find the number of arrangements of 3 photos chosen from 6. $6 \times 5 \times 4$

Find the number of arrangements of 3 photos. $\blacksquare \times \blacksquare \times \blacksquare$ (over $3\ 2\ 1$)

Divide. $\dfrac{\overset{6}{\blacksquare} \times \overset{5}{\blacksquare} \times \overset{4}{\blacksquare}}{3\blacksquare \times 2\blacksquare \times \blacksquare 1} = \blacksquare$ 20

You can choose 3 photos $\blacksquare$ 20 different ways.

2. How many ways can you choose 2 ice cream flavors from 7?

Find the number of arrangements of 2 flavors chosen from 7. $\underset{7\quad 6}{\blacksquare \times \blacksquare}$

Find the number of arrangements of 2 flavors. 2×1

Divide. $\dfrac{\overset{7}{\blacksquare} \times \overset{6}{\blacksquare}}{2\blacksquare \times \blacksquare 1} = \blacksquare$ 21   (21)

There are $\blacksquare$ different ways to choose 2 flavors.

Practice

Find each number of combinations.

1. How many ways can you choose 3 flowers from an arrangement of 5?   10

2. How many ways can a student choose 2 exam questions from a group of 8?   28

3. How many ways can you choose 3 CDs from a collection of 10?   120

4. How many ways can 8 friends choose 3 to ride in a cab?   56

5. How many ways can you chose 1 sandwich from 6?   6

Cooperative Learning

6. Explain to a partner how to find the number of combinations in number **2** in **Practice.** Possible answer: Find the number of arrangements of 2 questions chosen from 8: 8×7. Find the number of arrangements of 2 questions: 2×1. Divide: $\dfrac{8 \times 7}{2 \times 1} = 28$.

7. Write a problem that you can solve using combinations. Be sure to include the number of objects in the group and the number you want to choose. Ask a partner to solve the problem. Check the work. Answers will vary.

More practice is provided in Exercises 86, 88, and 89 of the Workbook.

Getting Started
Discuss the
meaning of
probable as *likely
to be,* such as the
probable chance of rain.

15·4 ▶ Probability

When you toss a coin, two things can happen. It can land on heads. Or, it can land on tails. The coin has an equally likely chance of landing on heads or tails. So, the coin lands **at random**. The results—heads or tails—are called the **outcomes** of a coin toss.

▶ **EXAMPLE 1**

How many possible outcomes are there for the spinner?

List the possible outcomes. R, R, Y, 1, 2, 3

Count the outcomes. 6

There are 6 possible outcomes for the spinner.

An outcome or a group of outcomes is called an **event**. **Probability** is the chance that an event will happen. When you find the probability that a coin lands on heads, heads is the event.

You can find the probability by finding a ratio.

Math Fact
A ratio is a comparison of two numbers.

Probability of an event = $\dfrac{\text{number of outcomes in the event}}{\text{total number of outcomes}}$

There is a short way to show probability. *P*(event) means the probability of an event. In the coin toss, *P*(heads) means the probability that the coin lands on heads. So, $P(\text{heads}) = \frac{1}{2}$.

A probability of 1 means the event will always happen. A probability of 0 means the event is impossible.

▶ **EXAMPLE 2**

A cube is numbered 0–5. What is the chance that the cube lands on a number less than 6?

List and count the possible outcomes. $0, 1, 2, 3, 4, 5 \rightarrow 6$

Count the numbers less than 6. $0, 1, 2, 3, 4, 5 \rightarrow 6$

Write the probability ratio. Then simplify. $\frac{6}{6} = 1$

The probability that the cube lands on a number less than 6 is 1.

Try This

A number cube is marked with the
numbers 1–6. Find each probability.

P(a number less than 5)

List and count the possible outcomes.   1, 2, 3, 4, 5, 6 → 6

Count the numbers less than 5.   1, 2, 3, 4 → ■ 4

Write the probability ratio. $\dfrac{4■}{6■} = \dfrac{2}{3}$

P(a number less than 5) $= ■\dfrac{2}{3}$

Practice

A spinner is divided into 5 equal regions, numbered
1 through 5. An arrow is spun and lands on one of
the regions. Find each probability.

1. $P(3)$ $\dfrac{1}{5}$

2. P(odd number) $\dfrac{3}{5}$

3. P(a number greater than 2) $\dfrac{3}{5}$

A marble is drawn at random from a jar that contains
5 marbles. There are 2 white and 3 green marbles.
Find each probability.

4. P(green) $\dfrac{3}{5}$ **5.** P(white) $\dfrac{2}{5}$ **6.** P(yellow) $\dfrac{0}{5} = 0$

Cooperative Learning

7. Explain to a partner how to find the probability in number **2**
in **Practice.** Possible answer: Your event can occur 3 ways. There are 5 possible outcomes.
Write as a fraction: $\dfrac{3}{5}$.

8. Write a list of 6 numbers. Ask a partner to find the probability
that a number picked is divisible by 5. Answers will be a fraction between 0 and 1
and have a denominator of 6.

Getting Started
Review notation.
Point out that
P(letter) stands for
the probability of drawing a
letter from the jar.

15·5 ▶ Complementary Events

5 outcomes: A, B, C, 1, 2
3 letters: A, B, C
2 numbers: 1, 2

Look at the jar to find the probabilities.

$P(\text{letter}) = \frac{3}{5}$ There are 3 letters.

$P(\textit{not} \text{ a letter}) = \frac{2}{5}$ There are 2 that are *not* letters.

Add the probabilities. $\frac{3}{5} + \frac{2}{5} = \frac{5}{5} = 1$

When you add the probability that an event happens and the probability that the event does *not* happen, the sum is always 1. These are called **complementary events.**

$$P(\text{event}) + P(\textit{not} \text{ the event}) = 1$$

To find the probability an event does *not* happen, you can subtract from 1.

$$P(\textit{not} \text{ the event}) = 1 - P(\text{event})$$

▶ **EXAMPLE 1**

Find the probability the spinner does *not* land on 8.

Find $P(8)$. $\frac{1}{8}$

Write the formula. $P(\textit{not } 8) = 1 - P(8)$

Substitute $\frac{1}{8}$ for $P(8)$. $P(\textit{not } 8) = 1 - \frac{1}{8}$

$$P(\textit{not } 8) = \frac{8}{8} - \frac{1}{8}$$

$$P(\textit{not } 8) = \frac{7}{8}$$

The probability the spinner does *not* land on 8 is $\frac{7}{8}$.

▶ **EXAMPLE 2**

The probability that it will rain this weekend is $\frac{3}{4}$. What is the probability that it will not rain?

Find $P(\text{rain})$. $\frac{3}{4}$

Write the formula. $P(\textit{not} \text{ rain}) = 1 - P(\text{rain})$

Substitute $\frac{3}{4}$ for $P(\text{rain})$. $P(\textit{not} \text{ rain}) = 1 - \frac{3}{4}$

$$P(\textit{not} \text{ rain}) = \frac{4}{4} - \frac{3}{4}$$

$$P(\textit{not} \text{ rain}) = \frac{1}{4}$$

The probability that it will *not* rain is $\frac{1}{4}$.

Find each probability.

1. The probability that Leslie makes a free throw is $\frac{4}{5}$. What is the probability that she misses a free throw?

   Find *P*(makes free throw).

   Write the formula. $P(\text{miss}) = 1 - \blacksquare$

   $\frac{4}{5}$ Substitute $\blacksquare$ for *P*(makes free throw).

   $P(\text{miss}) = \frac{\blacksquare 5}{\blacksquare 5} - \frac{4}{5}$

   $P(\text{makes free throw})$

   Simplify. $P(\text{miss}) = \frac{\blacksquare 1}{\blacksquare 5}$

   $P(\text{miss}) = \blacksquare \frac{1}{5}$

2. The probability that Lily guesses wrong on a multiple choice question is $\frac{2}{3}$. Find the probability that she guesses correctly.

   Find *P*(wrong).

   $\frac{2}{3} \blacksquare$ *P*(correct)

   Write the formula. $\blacksquare = 1 - P(\text{wrong})$

   Substitute $\blacksquare$ for *P*(wrong). $\blacksquare = 1 - \frac{\blacksquare 2}{\blacksquare 3}$

   $\frac{2}{3}$ *P*(correct)

   Simplify. $\frac{2}{3}$ *P*(correct) $\blacksquare = \frac{\blacksquare 1}{\blacksquare 3}$

   $P(\text{correct}) = \blacksquare \frac{1}{3}$

Practice

Pick a letter at random from the word PROBABILITY. Find each probability.

1. *P*(*not* a B) $\frac{9}{11}$

2. *P*(*not* a vowel) $\frac{7}{11}$

3. *P*(*not* a Q) $\frac{11}{11} = 1$

Find each probability.

4. The probability that Jasmine gets a hit at bat is $\frac{2}{5}$. What is the probability that she does not get a hit? $\frac{3}{5}$

5. A jar contains 3 blue and 2 orange marbles. Pick a marble at random. What is the probability that you do not pick a blue marble? $\frac{2}{5}$

6. The probability that Liberty wins is $\frac{9}{10}$. What is the probability that the team loses? $\frac{1}{10}$

Cooperative Learning

7. Possible answer: Write the formula $P(\text{no hit}) = 1 - P(\text{hit})$; $P(\text{no hit}) = 1 - \frac{2}{5}$; $P(\text{no hit}) = \frac{5}{5} - \frac{2}{5} = \frac{3}{5}$.

7. Explain to a partner how to find the probability in number **4** in **Practice**. See above.

8. Describe an event and include its probability. Ask a partner to find the probability that the event does *not* happen. Answers will be between 0 and 1.

More practice is provided in Exercises 86 and 90 of the Workbook.

Have one group of students
ask for a probability, such as
P(even), and another group
find the probability. $(\frac{1}{2})$

15·6 ▶ Independent Events

You know how to find the probability of tossing a coin and having it land heads up. If you toss the coin again, the result of the first toss does not affect this toss. The two coin tosses are **independent events**.

A **compound event** is two or more events. To find the probability of a compound event, find the probability of each event and multiply.

$$\begin{array}{ccc} \text{Probability of} & \times & \text{Probability of} & = & \text{Probability of} \\ \text{First Event} & & \text{Second Event} & & \text{Compound Event} \end{array}$$

▶ **EXAMPLE 1**

Lana flips a coin twice. What is the probability it will land heads then tails?

Find P(heads).　　　　　　　　$\frac{1}{2}$

Find P(tails).　　　　　　　　$\frac{1}{2}$

Multiply P(heads) and P(tails).　$\frac{1}{2} \times \frac{1}{2} = \frac{1}{4}$

The probability of tossing heads then tails is $\frac{1}{4}$.

A compound event can have more than two events.

▶ **EXAMPLE 2**

Spin the spinner, pick a letter from the cards, and then spin the spinner again. Find the probability that the spinner lands on an even number, you pick the letter G, and the spinner lands on 5.

Find P(even).　　　　　　　　$\frac{3}{8}$

Find P(G).　　　　　　　　　$\frac{3}{6}$

Find P(5).　　　　　　　　　$\frac{1}{8}$

Multiply P(even), P(G), and P(tails).　$\frac{3}{8} \times \frac{3}{6} \times \frac{1}{8} = \frac{9}{384}$

Simplify.　　　　　　　　　$\frac{9}{384} = \frac{3}{128}$

The probability of getting an even number, a G and then a 5 is $\frac{3}{128}$.

Try These

Use the jar and the spinner to find each probability.

1. picking a green marble from the jar and spinning a 5

   Find P(green marble). $\frac{3}{\blacksquare 5}$

   Find P(5). $\frac{1}{\blacksquare 6}$ $\frac{1}{6}$

   Multiply. $\frac{3}{5}\blacksquare \times \blacksquare = \blacksquare \frac{3}{30}$

   The probabilty of picking a green marble and then spinning 5 is $\blacksquare$. $\frac{1}{10}$

2. picking a white marble and spinning an odd number

   Find P(white marble). $\frac{2}{\blacksquare 5}$

   Find P(odd). $\frac{3}{\blacksquare 6}$ $\frac{3}{6}$

   Multiply. $\frac{2}{5}\blacksquare \times \blacksquare = \blacksquare \frac{6}{30}$

   The probability of getting a white marble and then an odd number is $\blacksquare$. $\frac{1}{5}$

Practice

Use the jar, the spinner, the cards, and the coin above to find each probability.

1. You pick a white marble from the jar and an F from the cards. $\frac{1}{15}$
2. You spin an even number and the coin lands on heads. $\frac{1}{4}$
3. Pick a green marble from the jar and pick an R from the cards. $\frac{1}{10}$
4. You pick a vowel from the cards, a green marble from the jar, and spin 7. 0

Cooperative Learning

5. Explain to a partner how to find the probability in 2 in **Practice**. Multiply P(even number) and P(heads).

6. Write a problem with two independent events. Ask a partner to find the probability of the compound event. Answers should be the product of the two probabilities.

More practice is provided in Exercises 86 and 90 of the Workbook.

15·7 Dependent Events

Sometimes an event can affect a second event. These are called **dependent events.**

A jar contains 3 grey marbles and 2 green marbles. Find the probability that you pick a grey marble, keep it, and then pick another grey marble. To do this, find each probability separately. Then, multiply. Find the probability that you pick a grey the first time. There are 3 greys out of 5 marbles. So, $P(\text{grey}) = \frac{3}{5}$.

When you pick the second marble, one grey marble is gone. There are only 2 grey marbles left and 4 left in all. So, $P(\text{another grey})$ is $\frac{2}{4}$ or $\frac{1}{2}$.

The probability of picking a grey and then another grey:

$$\frac{3}{5} \times \frac{2}{4} = \frac{6}{20} = \frac{3}{10}$$

▶ **EXAMPLE 1**

April has a bag of marbles. There are 3 blue and 4 yellow. She picks one, and then picks another. What is the probability that she picks a blue and then a yellow?

Math Fact
After the first pick, 1 blue is gone. So, there are only 6 marbles left.

Find the probability of picking a blue. $\quad \frac{3}{7}$

Find the probability of then picking a yellow. $\quad \frac{4}{6}$

Multiply. Then simplify. $\quad \frac{3}{7} \times \frac{4}{6} = \frac{12}{42} = \frac{2}{7}$

The probability is $\frac{2}{7}$ that she picks a blue and then a yellow.

▶ **EXAMPLE 2**

Find the probability that you pick an A, keep it, and then pick a vowel from the word ALPHABET.

Math Fact
After you pick an A, there are only 7 letters left. Two letters are vowels.

Find the probability of picking an A. $\quad \frac{2}{8}$

Find the probability of picking a vowel. $\quad \frac{2}{7}$

Multiply. Then simplify. $\quad \frac{2}{8} \times \frac{2}{7} = \frac{4}{56} = \frac{1}{14}$

The probability of picking an A and then a vowel is $\frac{1}{14}$.

Try These

A bag contains 5 red marbles and 1 green marble. Without looking, you pick a marble, keep it, and then pick another.

1. Find the probability that both marbles are red.

Find the probability that the first is red. ■ $\frac{5}{6}$

Find how many are left. 4 ■ red, 5 total

Find the probability that the second is red. ■ $\frac{4}{5}$

Multiply. $\frac{5}{6}$ ■ × ■ $\frac{4}{5}$ = ■ $\frac{20}{30}$ = ■ $\frac{2}{3}$

The probability of red, red is ■. $\frac{2}{3}$

2. Find the probability that both marbles are green.

Find the probability that the first is green. ■ $\frac{1}{6}$

Find how many are left. ■ 0 green, ■ 5 total

Find the probability that the second is green. ■ $\frac{0}{5}$

Multiply. $\frac{1}{6}$ ■ × ■ $\frac{0}{5}$ = ■0

The probability of green, green is ■. 0

Practice

A bag contains 2 green marbles and 3 yellow marbles. You pick a marble, keep it, and then pick another.

1. Find the probability that both marbles are green. $\frac{1}{10}$

2. Find the probability that both marbles are yellow. $\frac{3}{10}$

3. Find the probability that the first marble is green and the second is yellow. $\frac{3}{10}$

4. Find the probability that the first marble is yellow and the second is green. $\frac{3}{10}$

5. Possible answer: Divide the number of green marbles by the total number of marbles: $\frac{2}{5}$. Divide the number of yellow marbles by the total number of marbles after one green marble has been removed: $\frac{3}{4}$. Multiply the fractions: $\frac{2}{5} \cdot \frac{3}{4} = \frac{6}{20}$.

Cooperative Learning

5. Explain to a partner how to find the probability in number **3** in **Practice**. See above.

6. Listen while a partner explains how to find the probability in number **4** in **Practice**. Possible answer: Divide the number of yellow marbles by the total number of marbles: $\frac{3}{5}$. Divide the number of green marbles by the total number of marbles after one yellow marble has been removed: $\frac{2}{4}$. Multiply.

Getting Started
Review the
distinction
between a
permutation, where order
matters, and a combination,
where order does not matter.

15·8 Calculator: Permutations and Combinations

Use a calculator to find these permutations and combinations.

EXAMPLE 1

How many ways can you award first, second, and third place from 20 entries?

There are 3 places.   1st   2nd   3rd

Multiply the number of choices for each.   20 • 19 • 18

Use your calculator to simplify.   Display

Enter 20 by pressing: | 2 | 0 | 20

Multiply by 19 by pressing: | × | 1 | 9 | 380

Multiply by 18 by pressing: | × | 1 | 8 | = | 6840

First, second, and third places can be awarded 6,840 ways.

EXAMPLE 2

How many ways can you choose 4 gifts from 18 shops?

Find the number of arrangements of   18 • 17 • 16 • 15
4 gifts chosen from 18.

Find the number of arrangements of   4 • 3 • 2 • 1
4 gifts.

Divide. $\dfrac{18 \cdot 17 \cdot 16 \cdot 15}{4 \cdot 3 \cdot 2 \cdot 1}$

Use your calculator to simplify.   Display

Enter 18 by pressing: | 1 | 8 | 18

Multiply by 17 by pressing: | × | 1 | 7 | 306

Multiply by 16 by pressing: | × | 1 | 6 | 4896

Multiply by 15 by pressing: | × | 1 | 5 | = | 73440

Math Fact
Multiplying by 1 does not
change a number.

Multiply 4 • 3 • 2 • 1
by pressing: | 4 | × | 3 | × | 2 | = | 24

Divide 73,440 by 24
by pressing: | 7 | 3 | 4 | 4 | 0 | 73440

                                | ÷ | 2 | 4 | = | 3060

You can choose 4 gifts 3,060 ways.

Practice

Find each number of permutations or combinations.

1. How many ways can 9 students stand in a line? 362,880

2. How many ways can 20 runners finish first and second? 380

3. How many ways can 22 entries win first, second, third, and fourth place? 175,560

4. How many ways can a teacher pick 3 volunteers from a class of 20? 1,140

5. How many ways can you choose 4 photos from 25? 12,650

6. How many ways can you pick 2 flavors of ice cream from 22? 231

On-the-Job Math

WEATHER FORECASTING

What do you think "20% chance of rain" means? It does not really mean there are 20 chances out of 100 for rain today. Probability and predicting are only part of weather forecasting. It is really much more complicated.

Meteorologists are people who study and predict weather. They use computers to predict rainfall. They also input data such as temperature, wind speed, and humidity. The computer gives a forecast. It tells where and when it might rain. It also shows how much it might rain.

So what does "20% chance of rain" mean? It means that there is a 20% chance it *might* rain in your area. This is a low chance for rain. What if it said "80% chance of rain"? This is a much higher chance. Now you know how to tell when to bring an umbrella.

15·9 Problem Solving: Another Kind of Probability

You have already found the probability of an event by counting the number of possible outcomes. You found this probability based on what could happen. You can also find probability based on what has already happened. This is called **empirical probability.**

You can find this new kind of probability in almost the same way. Probabilities of this kind are usually given as a percent.

▶ **EXAMPLE**

A factory made CD cases. In 50 cases, 3 were defective. Find the probability that a case is defective.

READ **What do you need to find out?**
You need to find the probability that a case is defective.

PLAN **What do you need to do?**
You need to divide the number of defective cases by the total number of cases.

DO **Follow the plan.**

Find the number of defective cases. $\quad 3$

Find the total number of cases. $\quad 50$

Find P(defective). $\quad \dfrac{\text{number of defective cases}}{\text{total number of cases}} = \dfrac{3}{50}$

Write the fraction as a percent. $\quad \dfrac{3}{50} = .06 = 6\%$

Math Fact
To change a fraction to a percent, divide the numerator by the denominator.

$50\overline{)3} = .06$

CHECK **Does your answer make sense?**
The number 3 is much smaller than the number 50, so the percent of defective cases should be small. ✓

The probability a case is defective is 6%.

Try These

1. Maria scored on 5 of her last 8 free throws. Find the probability that she will make a free throw.

   Find the number of free throws she made.   ■ 5

   Find the total number of free throws.   8

   Find P(makes free throw). $\dfrac{\text{number of free throws made}}{\text{total number of free throws}} = \dfrac{■\ 5}{■\ 8}$

   Write the fraction as a percent. $\dfrac{5\ ■}{8\ ■} = ■ = 62.5\%$
   0.625

   The probability Maria will make a free throw is ■. 62.5%

2. A telephone survey asked 50 people what they had for breakfast. 15 people said they had cereal. Find the probability a person had cereal for breakfast.

   Find the number of people who had cereal.   ■ 15

   Find the total number of people asked.   ■ 50

   Find P(cereal). $\dfrac{\text{number of people who had cereal}}{\text{total number of people asked}} = \dfrac{■\ 15}{■\ 50}$

   Write the fraction as a percent. $\dfrac{15\ ■}{50\ ■} = ■ = ■\%$
   $0.3\quad 30$

   The probability a person had cereal is ■.
   30%

Practice

1. A reporter asks 25 people if they read the newspaper. 23 people answer "yes." What is the probability a person reads the paper? 92%

2. A small light bulb factory made 1,200 cases of light bulbs. 24 cases had a defective light bulb. Find the probability that a case contains a defective light bulb. 2%

   3. Possible answer: Divide the number of people asked by the number of people who read the paper. ($\frac{23}{25}$); rewrite the decimal as a percent. $\frac{23}{25} = .92 = 92\%$.

Cooperative Learning

3. Explain to a partner how to find the probability in number **1** in **Practice**. See above.

4. Write a probability question that can be answered using what has already happened. Have a partner answer the question. Answers will vary.

More practice is provided in Exercise 92 of the Workbook.

Getting Started
Discuss what
information is
used to make a
prediction. Ask for examples
in sports and the news, such
as batting averages and
voting results.

15·10 ▷ Application: Predicting Outcomes

You can use probability to predict outcomes. When you know the probability of an event, you can find how many times it may happen in the future by multiplying.

▶ **EXAMPLE 1**

The probability that a tulip bulb will open is 80%. How many bulbs would you expect to open out of 200 bulbs?

Find 80% of 200.

Write the percent as a decimal.　　.8

Multiply.　　$.8 \cdot 200 = 160$

You would expect 160 bulbs to open.

▶ **EXAMPLE 2**

Mo plays baseball. He gets a hit 34% of the time he is at bat. How many hits would you expect in 450 times at bat?

Find 34% of 450.

Write the percent as a decimal.　　.34

Multiply.　　$.34 \cdot 450 = 153$

You would expect Mo to get a hit 153 times in 450 times at bat.

The number you find is only a guess. The answer will not always be a whole number.

▶ **EXAMPLE 3**

The probability of a defective CD case is 3%. How many defective cases would you expect in a group of 50 cases?

Find 3% of 50.

Write the percent as a decimal.　　.03

Multiply.　　$.03 \cdot 50 = 1.5$

You would expect 1.5 defective CD cases in 50.

Try These

1. 10% of popcorn kernels do not pop. Out of 450 kernels, how many would you expect to not pop?

   Find 10% of 450.

   Write the percent as a decimal.   ■ .1

   Multiply.   .1 ■ • 450 = ■ 45

   You would expect ■ kernels not to pop.
   45

2. John plays soccer. He makes 40% of his goal shots. If he takes 6 shots, how many goals does he expect to make?

   Find 40% of ■. 6

   Write the percent as a decimal.   ■ .4

.4	6	2.4
■ •	■ =	■

   Multiply.

   He expects to make ■ goals.
   2.4

Practice

1. 40% of the people in a survey exercise at least once a week. How many people in 30 do you expect exercise at least once a week? 12 people

2. In the winter, it snows on 25% of the days. On how many days would you expect it to snow in 40 days?   10 days

3. In a spark plug factory, 2% of the spark plugs are defective. How many defective spark plugs would you expect to find if you tested 500? 10 defective spark plugs

4. Chris plays tennis. She only misses her serve 8% of the time. In 30 serves, how many does she expect to miss? 2.4 missed serves

5. Dawn dives for oysters. She finds a pearl in 5% of her oysters. How many pearls should she expect if she finds 20 oysters? 1 pearl

Cooperative Learning

6. Explain to a partner how to find the number of snowy days in 2 in **Practice**. Possible answer: Find 25% of 40. Write 25% as a decimal. (.25) Multiply .25 and 40.

7. Make up a percentage for how many days a week you exercise. Ask a partner to find how many times you expect to exercise in 100 days. Check the work. Answers will vary.

Summary

You can find the total number of choices by multiplying the number of each different choice.
You need to multiply to find permutations and combinations.
To find the probability of an event, divide the number of ways the event can occur by the total number of possible outcomes.
A probability of 0 means the event will never happen. A probability of 1 means it will always happen.
The probability of a complementary event is the probability of the event subtracted from 1.
When finding the probability of a compound event, first find the probability of each event. Then, multiply the probabilities.
You can find empirical probability based on what has happened.
Use probability to tell how many times you expect an event to happen.

More vocabulary review is provided in Exercise 141 of the Classroom Resource Binder.

permutations
combination
outcomes
event
probability
complementary events
independent events
dependent events

Vocabulary Review

Complete the sentences with the words from the box.

1. Different ways of arranging a group of objects in order are ____. permutations

2. Opposite events are called ____. complementary events

3. A ____ tells you how likely something is to happen. probabili

4. A ____ is a group of objects in which the order they are chosen does not matter. combination

5. If the outcome of one event affects the outcome of a second event, the two events are ____. dependent events

6. If the outcome of one event does not affect the outcome of a second event, the two events are ____. independent ever

7. An ____ is an outcome or a group of outcomes. event

8. Results of an activity, experiment, or game are called ____. outcomes

Chapter Quiz   **More assessment** is provided in the Classroom Resource Binder.

Find the total number of choices.

1. Karl has 4 pairs of pants and 7 shirts. How many choices does he have for 1 pair of pants and 1 shirt? 28

Find each number of permutations.

2. How many ways can 4 people stand in a line? 24

3. Eight runners compete for first and second prizes in a race. How many ways can the runners win prizes? 56

Find each number of combinations.

4. How many ways can you choose 2 pizza toppings from 10? 45

5. How many ways can a teacher choose 3 volunteers from 12 students? 220

A number cube is marked with numbers 1 through 6. Find each probability for one roll.

6. $P(2)$ $\frac{1}{6}$

7. $P(\text{odd})$ $\frac{3}{6}$ or $\frac{1}{2}$

8. $P(6)$ $\frac{1}{6}$

9. $P(\text{not }6)$ $\frac{5}{6}$

10. $P(\text{not odd})$ $\frac{3}{6}$ or $\frac{1}{2}$

11. $P(\text{not }7)$ 1

Find each probability.

12. Pick a letter at random from the word MATH and then from the word ALGEBRA. What is the probability you pick an A and then another A? $\frac{2}{28}$ or $\frac{1}{14}$

13. A bag has 4 blue marbles and 3 white marbles. You pick one at random, keep it, and then pick another. What is the probability you pick a blue and then a white marble? $\frac{12}{42}$ or $\frac{2}{7}$

14. A newspaper samples 400 residents and finds 300 like the new park. What is the probability a person will like the new park? 75%

Find the expected outcome.

15. During August, it rains on 70% of the days. How many days would you expect it to rain in 10 days? 7 days

Additional Practice for this chapter is provided on p. 427 of this text.

Unit 5 Review

1. What is the missing length of the triangle? A

   A. $s = \sqrt{51}$ m
   B. $s = \sqrt{3}$ m
   C. $s = \sqrt{17}$ m
   D. $s = 3$ m

2. Find the distance between the points $(-2, -1)$ and $(2, 4)$. B
   A. $d = 8$
   B. $d = \sqrt{41}$
   C. $d = 4\sqrt{2}$
   D. $d = 9$

3. At Maple School, 2 out of 5 students have a brother or sister in high school. There are 350 students at Maple School. How many students at Maple School have a brother or sister in high school? A
   A. 140 students
   B. 250 students
   C. 240 students
   D. not given

4. The formula $y = \frac{120}{x}$ shows the time it takes to travel 120 miles. x represents the rate (mph) and y represents the time in hours. If you travel 40 mph, how long will the trip take? D
   A. 4 hours
   B. 8 hours
   C. 2 hours
   D. 3 hours

5. In Denver, Colorado, the sun shines 80% of the days. How many sunny days can you expect in 365 days? C
   A. 300 days
   B. 296 days
   C. 292 days
   D. 320 days

6. A survey shows that 90 of the 120 households in a neighborhood have more than two children. What is the probability that a household has more than two children? B
   A. 90%
   B. 75%
   C. 60%
   D. 25%

Critical Thinking

A bag contains 3 green marbles and 4 blue marbles. You pick one at random and keep it. You then pick another. What is the probability that you pick two green marbles? $\frac{6}{42}$ or $\frac{1}{7}$

CHALLENGE Suppose 2 yellow marbles are added to the bag. You pick a marble at random and keep it. You pick another and again keep it. What is the probability that you pick two yellow marbles? $\frac{2}{72}$ or $\frac{1}{36}$

Critical Thinking See the Classroom Resource Binder for a scoring rubric to assess this Critical Thinking Question.

Student Handbook
Table of Contents

ADDITIONAL PRACTICE
Chapter 1: Numbers for Algebra

Graph on a number line.

1. 4

$$-2\ -1\ \ 0\ \ 1\ \ 2\ \ 3\ \ 4\ \ 5$$

2. ⁻6

$$-8\ -7\ -6\ -5\ -4\ -3\ -2$$

3. 0

$$-3\ -2\ -1\ \ 0\ \ 1\ \ 2\ \ 3$$

Compare. Use > or <.

4. ⁻9 and ⁻3 <

5. 1 and ⁻6 >

6. 0 and 4 <

Find the absolute value of each integer.

7. $|8|$ 8

8. $|{}^-13|$ 13

9. $|{}^+20|$ 20

Find the opposite of each integer.

10. 14 −14

11. ⁻4 4

12. ⁺9 ⁻9

Simplify.

13. ⁻5 + 8 3

14. 7 − 9 ⁻2

15. ⁻5 + 10 5

16. ⁻3 − 10 ⁻13

17. (⁻3)(⁻7) 21

18. (6)(⁻2) ⁻12

19. ⁻20 ÷ ⁻4 5

20. ⁻15 ÷ 5 ⁻3

21. (⁻5)² 25

Guess, test, and revise to solve the problem.

22. A restaurant manager ordered twice as many paper napkins as cloth napkins. He ordered 210 napkins in all. How many of each did he order?
140 paper; 70 cloth

Use the graph of Alex's savings to answer the question.

23. In which month did Alex have the most money in savings? August

24. How much were Alex's savings in July? $100

Six Months of Savings

ADDITIONAL PRACTICE
Chapter 2: Tools for Algebra

Simplify.

1. $17 - 16 \div 4$ 13

2. $3 \cdot (12 - 4) \div 4$ 6

3. $10 - 2(5 + 2)$ −4

4. $6 + 3 \cdot 12$ 42

5. $6 + 2 \cdot 5 - 6$ 10

6. $-16 + 3 \cdot 0 \div 42$ −16

Evaluate each variable expression.

7. $2a - 6$ when a is 1 −4

8. $t \div 12$ when t is 36 3

9. $7(c - 4)$ when c is 4 0

10. $-5b$ when b is −6 30

**Tell whether the expressions form an equation.
Write *yes* or *no*.**

11. -12 and $2x$ when x is −6 yes

12. 6×6 and $4(16 - 6)$ no

Name the property shown.

13. $32 + 0 = 32$
Identity Property of Addition

14. $12 \cdot 1 = 12$
Identity Property of Multiplication

15. $(x \cdot 5) \cdot 7 = x \cdot (5 \cdot 7)$
Associative Property of Multiplication

16. $10 + y = y + 10$
Commutative Property of Addition

Simplify each expression.

17. $5x + 3x$ 8x

18. $2ab + 3ab - 7ab$ −2ab

19. $16(1 - a)$ 16 − 16a

20. $12x - 4y + 3x$ 15x − 4y

21. $6c + 4 - 3 + c$ 7c + 1

22. $3 + 7a - 6 + 6a$ 13a − 3

23. $3(x + 4)$ 3x + 12

24. $10(n - 3)$ 10n − 30

25. $-(a + 7)$ −a − 7

26. $-(5 - x)$ −5 + x

27. $15x + 5(x - 4)$ 20x − 20

28. $5 - (x + 8)$ −3 − x

Write a variable equation for the sentence.

29. Jaime's age is 4 more years than Megan's. $j = m + 4$

**Use the formula $P = 2l + 2w$ to find the perimeter of
each rectangle.**

30. $l = 3$ cm and $w = 7$ cm 20 cm

31. $l = 30$ ft and $w = 3$ ft 66 ft

ADDITIONAL PRACTICE
Chapter 3: Solving Equations

Tell whether the number is the solution of the equation.
Write *yes* or *no*.

1. $5; 6x + 20 = 50$ yes

2. $-3; 16 = 3y + 6$ no

3. $0; 4 = 12 - 8a$ no

4. $2; 3w - 7 = -1$ yes

Solve. Then, check the solution.

5. $k + 3 = 17$ 14

6. $-2 = 6 + d$ −8

7. $8 = b - 1$ 9

8. $w - 15 = 5$ 20

9. $\frac{x}{4} = -3$ −12

10. $10 = \frac{p}{2}$ 20

11. $8n = 24$ 3

12. $-28 = 4s$ −7

13. $2 = 3a - 7$ 3

14. $1 + \frac{y}{5} = 1$ 0

15. $12 = -2(q + 5)$ −11

16. $6(t - 1) = 18$ 4

17. $-c + 8 = 3c$ 2

18. $7x = 4 + 3x$ 1

19. $-(n + 4) = 12$ −16

20. $12a = -4a - 16$ −1

Find the number.

21. What is 45% of 80? 36

22. 5% of 20 is what number? 1

Find the discount or the sale price.

23. A $20 book is on sale for 15% off. Find the sale price. $17.00

24. Find the discount on a $10 t-shirt. It is 20% off. $2.00

ADDITIONAL PRACTICE
Chapter 4: Introducing Functions

Use graph paper. Draw coordinate axes. Graph and
label each point.   See Additional Answers p. 480.

1. A at $(-3, 4)$

2. B at $(4, 0)$

3. C at $(6, -2)$

4. Write the ordered pairs. Graph.

Time (s)	Height (m)
1	3
2	7
3	12

See Additional Answers p. 480.

5. Copy and complete the table.

x	12 − 2x	y
−1	12 − 2(− 1)	? 14
0	?	? 12 − 2(0), 12
1	?	? 12 − 2(1), 10
2	?	? 12 − 2(2), 8

Tell whether each group of ordered pairs is a function.
Write *yes* or *no*.

6. $(-1, 3)$, $(0, 3)$, $(1, 3)$, $(2, 7)$ yes

7. $(-1, 0)$, $(0, 0)$, $(0, 6)$, $(2, 9)$ no

8.   yes

9.   no

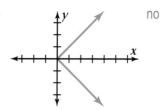

Find the value of each function.

10. $f(4)$ when $f(x) = 8 + x$ $f(4) = 12$

11. $f(-2)$ when $f(x) = 3x + 12$ $f(-2) = 6$

Use table or $d = 55t + 20$.

12. What is the distance when
the time is 3 hours? 185

Time	Distance
1 hour	75 miles
2 hours	130 miles
3 hours	185 miles

Use the bar graph.

13. In which year were there the
fewest employees? 2001

ADDITIONAL PRACTICE
Chapter 5: Linear Equations and Functions

Tell whether each ordered pair is a solution of the equation. Write *yes* or *no*.

1. $(1, 16)$; $y = 11 + 3x$
no

2. $(5, -19)$; $y = 1 - 4x$
yes

3. $(14, -5)$; $y = 2 - \dfrac{x}{2}$
yes

Make a table of values for each equation. Then, graph the equation.   **4.–6.** See Additional Answers p. 480.

4. $y = 2x + 10$

5. $y = 9 - x$

6. $y = 1 + \dfrac{x}{-2}$

Find the slope of each line that contains the points.

7. $(12, 4)$ and $(11, 1)$
3

8. $(5, 9)$ and $(6, 9)$
0

9. $(1, 5)$ and $(1, 15)$
no slope

Tell whether the lines containing each pair of points are *parallel* or *perpendicular*.

10. $(4, 13)$ $(-4, 0)$ and $(16, 0)$ $(3, 8)$
perpendicular

11. $(-4, 8)$ $(2, -10)$ and $(6, 2)$ $(4, 8)$
parallel

Find the *x*-intercept and *y*-intercept of each line.

12. $y = 8x - 24$
x-intercept: 3; y-intercept: -24

13. $y = x - 14$
x-intercept: 14; y-intercept: -14

14. $y = -9x + 18$
x-intercept: 2; y-intercept: 18

Graph each line.   **15.–16.** See Additional Answers p. 480.

15. *y*-intercept: -5; slope: 4

16. $(3, 3)$; slope: $\dfrac{1}{4}$

17. Write the equation $6x + y = 12$ in slope-intercept form. $y = -6x + 12$

Find the slope to solve the problem.

18. At 6:00 A.M. Shane passes the 4 mile mark. At 7:00 A.M. he passes the 11 mile mark. If Shane continues at the same rate, where will he be at 9:00 A.M.? 25 mile mark

The price of renting a video varies directly with the number of days. It costs $6.00 to rent a video for 2 days.

19. Find *k* in the equation for the price of renting a video. Use $P = kd$. 3

ADDITIONAL PRACTICE
Chapter 6: Writing Linear Equations

Write the equation of the line described.

1. with slope $= -1$ and y-intercept $= -3$ $y = -x - 3$

2. through $(-5, 4)$ and with slope $= 0$ $y = 4$

3. through $(1, 9)$ and with slope $= 4$
   $y = 4x + 5$

4. through $(2, 3)$ and $(4, 1)$
   $y = -x + 5$

5. with y-intercept $= 6$ and parallel to $y = x - 2$
   $y = x + 6$

6. through $(1, 3)$ and perpendicular to $y = \frac{-1}{2}x - 1$
   $y = 2x + 1$

Write the equation of each line.

7.

$y = 2x - 4$

8.

$y = -2x + 2$

9.
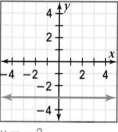
$y = -3$

Find the pattern. Then, write the equation.

10.

Pints	Gallons
2	16
3	24
4	32

Multiply pints by 8 to find gallons. $8p = g$.

11.

x	y
2	4
3	5
4	6

Add 2 to x to find y. $x + 2 = y$

Use the formula $l = \frac{2}{25}g + 75$ to answer the question. Use l for length and g for mass.

12. What is the length in millimeters of a spring when the mass is 500 grams? $l = 115$ mm

ADDITIONAL PRACTICE
Chapter 7: Inequalities

Solve each inequality. Then, graph on a number line.

1. $m < 1$

2. $x \le 2$

3. $c > -8$

4. $d - 1 < -6$

5. $y + 5 \ge 5$

6. $\dfrac{m}{-2} > -3$

7. $4a < 16$

8. $-4y - 8 > 12$

9. $\dfrac{n}{-5} - 1 \ge 0$

1.–9. See Additional Answers p. 480.

Write *yes* or *no*. Tell whether each point is a solution of $y > -2x + 2$.

10. $(-3, 4)$ no

11. $(2, 1)$ yes

12. $(1, 0)$ no

Graph the solution of each inequality on a coordinate plane. **13.–18.** See Additional Answers p. 481.

13. $y \ge -3x - 3$

14. $y < \dfrac{3}{4}x - 1$

15. $y > 2x - 2$

16. $y \le x + 4$

17. $y < \dfrac{1}{2}x + 1$

18. $y > x$

Write and solve the inequality.

19. Marcus is selling some of his old books to a used bookstore. How many $2 books does he need to sell to make at least $30.00? $2b \ge 30$; $b \ge 15$; Marcus needs to sell at least 15 books.

Solve by looking at the graph.

20. Rachel has $20.00 to spend on dried fruit. Apricots are $5.00 per pound, and raisins are $2.00 per pound. The ordered pair (apricots, raisins) tells how many pounds of each. The inequality gives the ordered pairs that have a total less than or equal to $20.00. Can Rachel buy 3 pounds of apricots and 3 pounds of raisins? No; (3, 3) is not in the shaded region.

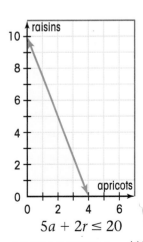

$5a + 2r \le 20$

Tell whether the ordered pair is a solution of the system. Write *yes* or *no*.

1. $(4, 4)$; $x + y = 8$
$2x + y = 1$
no

2. $(-1, 5)$; $y > x + 4$
$y < 4x + 8$
no

3. $(-1, -4)$; $y > -5$
$y \leq x + 2$
yes

Graph each system to find its solution. **4.–7.** See Additional Answers p. 481.

4. $y = x + 4$
$y = 2x + 6$

5. $y = 6$
$y = 2x - 6$

6. $y \leq x + 1$
$y \leq x - 7$

7. $y \geq x + 2$
$y \leq 2x + 6$

Use substitution to find the solution of each system.

8. $y = x + 8$
$y = 5x$
$(2, 10)$

9. $y = x$
$y = -4x + 10$
$(2, 2)$

10. $y = x + 5$
$y = -x - 5$
$(-5, 0)$

Find the solution of each system with addition, subtraction, or multiplication.

11. $x + y = 9$
$x - y = 5$ $(7, 2)$

12. $-x + y = -5$
$x + y = -9$ $(-2, -7)$

13. $x + 3y = -6$
$x - 3y = 12$ $(3, -3)$

14. $2x - 3y = -7$
$x + 4y = 2$ $(-2, 1)$

15. $5x - y = 4$
$3x - 2y = -6$ $(2, 6)$

16. $2x + 3y = -8$
$6x + 2y = 4$ $(2, -4)$

17. Mr. Jones went to a bank to change a $100 bill. He received 6 bills total. All of the bills were $10 bills or $20 bills. How many did he receive of each?
He received 4 $20 bills and 2 $10 bills.

The deli owner makes a profit of $2.00 on each pound of beef and $1.00 on each pound of pork. She orders at least 10 pounds total. She needs at most 7 pounds of beef and at most 6 pounds of pork. The graph shows these inequalities: $b \leq 7$, $p \leq 6$, and $b + p \geq 10$.

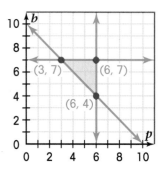

18. Find the maximum profit the deli can make. Use the graph of the inequalities and the equation Profit = $2b + 1p$. 6 pounds of pork and 7 pounds of beef yields the maximum profit. $19

ADDITIONAL PRACTICE
Chapter 9: More About Data and Data Analysis

Find the mean, median, and mode.

1. 9, 6, 8, 8, 3, 5, 6, 9, 9
mean, 7; median, 8; mode, 9

2. 80, 77, 75, 80, 91, 80, 52, 83, 75
mean, 77; median, 80; mode, 80

Find the minimum, maximum, and range.

3. 10, 15, 9, 7, 11, 9, 2
min., 2; max., 15; range, 13

4. 15, 20, 22, 10, 22, 10, 22, 12, 20
min., 10; max., 22; range, 12

5. Make a frequency table for the set of data of class grades: A, B, B, C, F, C, A, C, B, B, A, B, A, F, B, A, B. See Additional Answers p. 481.

6. How many grades are above a C? 12 grades

Make a stem-and-leaf plot for each set of data. 7.–8. See Additional Answers p. 481.

7. 40, 45, 49, 54, 54, 64, 65, 66

8. 80, 77, 75, 80, 91, 70, 62, 84, 75

Tell whether the correlation is positive or negative.

9.

positive

10.

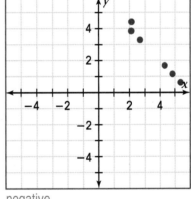

negative

Find the mean, median, and mode of each set of data. Then, tell which best describes the data.

11. 2, 3, 3, 5, 42
11; 3; 3; median and mode

12. 58, 2, 62, 90, 78, 2, 114
58; 62; 2; mean and median

Find the quartiles in each set of data.

13. 11, 13, 15, 17, 19, 21, 23
13; 17; 21

14. 48, 55, 35, 36, 29, 49, 25
29; 36; 49

ADDITIONAL PRACTICE
Chapter 10: Exponents and Functions

Use exponents to rewrite each power.

1. $xxxx$ x^4

2. $abbb$ ab^3

3. $2mmnnn$ $2m^2n^3$

Find the value of each power.

4. $(-2)^3$ -8

5. w^3 when w is 4 64

6. w^2 when w is 10 100

Multiply. Write using positive exponents.

7. $5x^2 \bullet 3x^3$ $15x^5$

8. $b^4c^3 \bullet b^4c^3$ b^8c^6

9. $(a^7)^2$ a^{14}

10. $4x^0 \bullet 2x^8$ $8x^8$

11. $x^{-1}y \bullet x^6y^{-2}$ $\dfrac{x^5}{y}$

12. $(a^0)^5$ 1

Divide. Write using positive exponents.

13. $\dfrac{b^{10}}{b^5}$ b^5

14. $\dfrac{x^8y}{x^2}$ x^6y

15. $\dfrac{8c^{12}d^2}{4cd}$ $2c^{11}d$

16. $\dfrac{b^{14}}{b^{14}}$ 1

17. $\dfrac{3c^{-2}}{3c^2}$ $\dfrac{1}{c^4}$

18. $\dfrac{y^{-7}z^4}{y^3z}$ $\dfrac{z^3}{y^{10}}$

Find each number named in scientific notation.

19. 5×10^3 $5,000$

20. 1.1×10^4 $11,000$

21. 3.6×10^{-5} $.000036$

22. 9.4×10^6 $9,400,000$

23. 9×10^{-2} $.09$

24. 4.09×10^5 $409,000$

25. Find five ordered pairs for the function $y = 3 \bullet 2^x$. Make a table. Graph the function on a coordinate plane. See Additional Answers p. 482.

26. Use a tree diagram to find how many different choices of shirt and shorts you can wear if you have three shirts (white, yellow, and red) and two pairs of shorts (green and blue). See Additional Answers p. 482.

27. Find the total after 3 years. Use the formula $T = 200(1.1)^x$. $266.20

ADDITIONAL PRACTICE
Chapter 11: Quadratic Functions and Equations

1. Find a, b, and c for $y = x^2 + 4x + 12$ 1, 4, 12

Make a table of values for each function. Then, graph.
Use $x = 2, 1, 0, -1, -2, -3$. 3.–5. See Additional Answers p. 482.

2. $y = x^2$ **3.** $y = x^2 + x$ **4.** $y = x^2 + 5$

Tell whether the graph opens upward or downward.
Tell whether it has a minimum or a maximum.

5. $y = 3x^2$
upward; minimum

6. $y = -7x^2 + 3$
downward; maximum

7. $y = 6x^2$
upward; minimum

Find the zeros of each quadratic function from its graph.

8. $y = \dfrac{x^2}{2} + 3$ no zeros

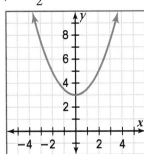

9. $y = -x^2 + 2x + 3$ 3 and −1

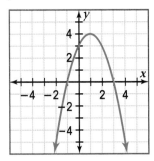

Find the value.

10. square roots of 49
7 and −7

11. $\sqrt{64}$ 8

12. $-\sqrt{25}$ −5

Solve each equation.

13. $x^2 = 36$
6 and −6

14. $x^2 + 10 = 59$
7 and −7

15. $0 = x^2 - 11x + 30$
5 and 6

16. The area of a rectangle is 400 square feet. The length is 4 times the width. Find the length and width.
The length is 40 feet and the width is 10 feet.

Solve using the vertical motion formula:
$h = -16t^2 + vt + s$.

17. A book falls off a building 500 feet high. At what time is the book 356 feet above the ground? 3 seconds

ADDITIONAL PRACTICE
Chapter 12: Polynomials and Factoring

Name the type of polynomial.

1. $2xy + 8$
binomial

2. $x^2 - x - y^2$
trinomial

3. $-4y$
monomial

Combine each pair of polynomials.

4. Add $y^2 + 5y - 8$ and $3y^2 + 2y + 6$.
$4y^2 + 7y - 2$

5. Subtract $x^2 - 3$ from $-2x^2 + 4x + 4$.
$-3x^2 + 4x + 7$

Multiply.

6. $3(x^2 + 5x + 6)$
$3x^2 + 15x + 18$

7. $-2a(a - 4)$
$-2a^2 + 8a$

8. $2b(b^2 - 3b - 10)$
$2b^3 - 6b^2 - 20b$

9. $(x + 5)(x + 6)$
$x^2 + 11x + 30$

10. $(a - 1)(a - 9)$
$a^2 - 10a + 9$

11. $(y - 2)(y + 10)$
$y^2 + 8y - 20$

Tell whether the first expression is a factor of the second expression. Write *yes* or *no*.

12. Is $3y$ a factor of $15y^2$? yes

13. Is $2x^2$ a factor of $6xy^2$? no

Factor by finding the greatest common factor.

14. $a^2 + 6a$
$a(a + 6)$

15. $3n^3 + 12n$
$3n(n^2 + 4)$

16. $12x^2 + 6y$
$6(2x^2 + y)$

Factor as the product of two binomials.

17. $y^2 - 11y + 30$
$(y - 5)(y - 6)$

18. $x^2 + 10x - 11$
$(x - 1)(x + 11)$

19. $y^2 - y - 30$
$(y + 5)(y - 6)$

20. $x^2 + 14x + 13$
$(x + 1)(x + 13)$

21. $x^2 - 81$
$(x + 9)(x - 9)$

22. $y^2 + 16y + 64$
$(y + 8)(y + 8)$

Solve each equation. Use factoring or the quadratic formula.

23. $x(2x + 8)=0$
$x = 0$ or -4

24. $(y - 5)(y - 8) = 0$
$y = 5$ or 8

25. $x^2 + 4x + 3 = 0$
$x = -1$ or -3

26. $x^2 - 4 = 0$
$x = 2$ or -2

27. $x^2 - 4x = 0$
$x = 0$ or 4

28. $x^2 + 20x + 75$
$x = -15$ or -5

29. Use the formula $d = \frac{s^2 - 3s}{2}$ to find the number of diagonals in a polygon with 5 sides. 5 diagonals

ADDITIONAL PRACTICE
Chapter 13: Radicals and Geometry

Between what two whole numbers is each radical.

1. $\sqrt{24}$ 4 and 5

2. $\sqrt{40}$ 6 and 7

3. $\sqrt{7}$ 2 and 3

Simplify.

4. $\sqrt{18}$ $3\sqrt{2}$

5. $\sqrt{24}$ $2\sqrt{6}$

6. $9\sqrt{3} + 2\sqrt{6} - 7\sqrt{3}$ $2\sqrt{3} + 2\sqrt{6}$

7. $3\sqrt{5} - 12\sqrt{5}$ $-9\sqrt{5}$

8. $5\sqrt{2} + \sqrt{8}$ $7\sqrt{2}$

9. $4 \cdot 5\sqrt{6}$ $20\sqrt{6}$

10. $7\sqrt{3} \cdot 2\sqrt{10}$ $14\sqrt{30}$

11. $\frac{9\sqrt{12}}{6}$ $3\sqrt{3}$

12. $\frac{15\sqrt{8}}{3\sqrt{2}}$ 10

Solve.

13. $8\sqrt{m} - 5 = 32$
$m = 21$

14. $\sqrt{3y} + 2 = 8$
$y = 12$

15. $\sqrt{10p - 1} = 7$
$p = 5$

Find the length of each missing side.

16.

17.

18.

$d = 10$ m
$e = 10\sqrt{2}$ m

19.

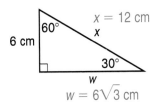
$x = 12$ cm
$w = 6\sqrt{3}$ cm

20.

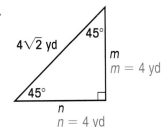
$m = 4$ yd
$n = 4$ yd

21.

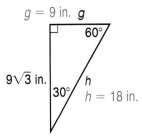
$g = 9$ in.
$h = 18$ in.

22. Tell whether a triangle with sides 18 m, 24 m, and 30 m is a right triangle. yes

23. Graph the points $(4, -3)$ and $(-2, 5)$. Then find the distance between the two points. 10 units

ADDITIONAL PRACTICE
Chapter 14: Rational Expressions and Equations

Evaluate each expression.

1. $\frac{a^2 - 7}{a + 6}$ when a is 4 $\frac{9}{10}$

2. $\frac{a^2 - 1}{a + 1}$ when a is -5 -6

Find the values that make the
rational expression undefined.

3. $\frac{2y + 5}{y(y - 7)}$
0 or 7

4. $\frac{b - 2}{(b - 8)(b + 9)}$
8 or -9

Simplify each rational expression.

5. $\frac{(x - 5)(x + 3)}{2x(x - 5)}$ $\frac{x + 3}{2x}$

6. $\frac{8x(x - 9)}{(x - 9)(x + 9)}$ $\frac{8x}{x + 9}$

Find the least common multiple for each pair
of expressions.

7. $4y$ and $y + 7$
$4y(y + 7)$

8. $16a$ and $8a^2$
$16a^2$

9. $x + 9$ and $x - 9$
$(x + 9)(x - 9)$

Add, subtract, multiply, or divide.

10. $\frac{3}{4} + \frac{2}{5}$ $\frac{23}{20}$

11. $\frac{4}{y} - \frac{3}{2y^2}$ $\frac{8y - 3}{2y^2}$

12. $\frac{2y}{8} + \frac{4}{y}$ $\frac{2y^2 + 32}{8y}$

13. $\frac{x}{9} - \frac{5}{3x}$ $\frac{x^2 - 15}{9x}$

14. $\frac{3a}{4b} \cdot \frac{12b^2}{9a^2}$ $\frac{b}{a}$

15. $\frac{t^2}{16} \div \frac{t}{4}$ $\frac{t}{4}$

16. $\frac{4x - 16}{3x} \div \frac{2x - 8}{5x^2}$ $\frac{10x}{3}$

17. $\frac{x^2 + 2x - 63}{2x} \cdot \frac{3x^2}{x^2 - 81}$ $\frac{3x(x - 7)}{2(x - 9)}$

Solve.

18. $\frac{5}{x} + \frac{3}{x} = \frac{4}{2}$ $x = 4$

19. $\frac{1}{2} - \frac{3}{6n} = \frac{3}{n}$ $n = 7$

20. $\frac{4}{12} - \frac{5}{3a} = 2$ $a = -1$

21. $\frac{3}{n + 3} = \frac{6}{n}$ $n = -6$

22. $\frac{a^2}{12} = \frac{a}{2}$ $a = 0$ or 6

23. $\frac{4}{8} = \frac{y - 1}{y + 3}$ $y = 5$

Use a proportion to solve the problem.

24. At Park High School, 2 out of 3 seniors will go to the
prom. If 30 students go to the prom, how many
seniors are there?   45 seniors

Use $y = \frac{100}{x}$ to solve the problem. x represents the rate (mph),
and y represents time (hours) it takes to complete the trip.

25. How many hours will the trip take if you travel 50 mph?   2 hours

Find the total number of choices.

1. An architect offers 5 door styles and 8 door knob styles. How many ways can you choose 1 door and 1 door knob? 40

Find each number of permutations.

2. How many ways can you arrange the letters MATH? 24

Find each number of combinations.

3. How many ways can you choose 3 days from 7 days? 35

A jar contains 1 yellow marble, 4 blue marbles, and 3 white marbles. Pick one at random. Find each probability.

4. P(blue) $\frac{4}{8}$ or $\frac{1}{2}$ 5. P(red) 0   6. P(not white) $\frac{5}{8}$

Pick a letter at random from the word GEOMETRY. Find each probability.

7. P(E) $\frac{2}{8}$ or $\frac{1}{4}$ 8. P(vowel) $\frac{3}{8}$ 9. P(not a vowel) $\frac{5}{8}$

Find each probability.

10. Flip a coin 3 times. Find the probability that it lands heads, tails, heads. $\frac{1}{8}$

11. A bag contains 4 red and 2 green marbles. You pick one, keep it, and then pick another. What is the probability that you pick two green marbles? $\frac{2}{30}$ or $\frac{1}{15}$

12. In an order of 500 lightbulbs, 3 are defective. What is the probability that a lightbulb is defective? .6%

Find the expected outcome.

13. Eighty percent of adults read the newspaper each day. In a group of 200 adults, how many would you expect to read the newspaper? 160 adults

Formulas from Algebra

The Coordinate Axes

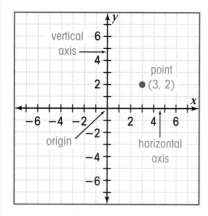

Ordered Pair (x, y)
Origin $(0, 0)$

$$\text{Slope} = \frac{\text{rise}}{\text{run}}$$

Slope-intercept Form of an Equation

$y = mx + b$
m is the slope, b is the y-intercept.

Direct Variation

$y = kx$, k is a positive number.

Inverse Variation

$y = \dfrac{k}{x}$, k is a positive number.

Quadratic Formula

$x = \dfrac{-b \pm \sqrt{b^2 - 4ac}}{2a}$ gives the values of x when $y = 0$ in the equation $y = ax^2 + bx + c$.

Probability

$$P\,(\text{event}) = \frac{\text{number of ways an event can happen}}{\text{total number of outcomes}}$$

Formulas from Geometry

▶ Perimeter and Area

Perimeter

Rectangle
$P = 2l + 2w$

Square
$P = 4s$

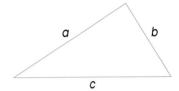

Triangle
$P = a + b + c$

Area

Rectangle
$A = lw$

Square
$A = s^2$

Volume

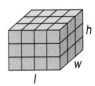

Box
$V = lwh$

▶Right Triangles

Right Triangle

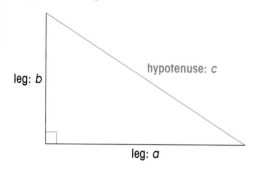

leg: b

hypotenuse: c

leg: a

Pythagorean Theorem

$$a^2 + b^2 = c^2$$

Special Right Triangles

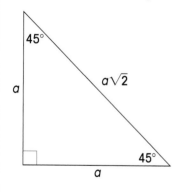

45°

$a\sqrt{2}$

a

45°

a

a

leg = leg
hypotenuse = leg • $\sqrt{2}$

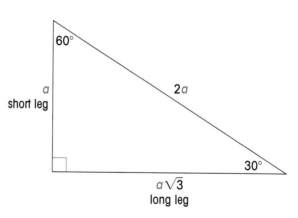

60°

a
short leg

$2a$

30°

$a\sqrt{3}$
long leg

long leg = short leg • $\sqrt{3}$
hypotenuse = 2 • short leg

Table of Squares 1–50

Number	Square
1	1
2	4
3	9
4	16
5	25
6	36
7	49
8	64
9	81
10	100
11	121
12	144
13	169
14	196
15	225
16	256
17	289
18	324
19	361
20	400
21	441
22	484
23	529
24	576
25	625

Number	Square
26	676
27	729
28	784
29	841
30	900
31	961
32	1,024
33	1,089
34	1,156
35	1,225
36	1,296
37	1,369
38	1,444
39	1,521
40	1,600
41	1,681
42	1,764
43	1,849
44	1,936
45	2,025
46	2,116
47	2,209
48	2,304
49	2,401
50	2,500

Table of Squares 51–100

Number	Square		Number	Square
51	2,601		76	5,776
52	2,704		77	5,929
53	2,809		78	6,084
54	2,916		79	6,241
55	3,025		80	6,400
56	3,136		81	6,561
57	3,249		82	6,724
58	3,364		83	6,889
59	3,481		84	7,056
60	3,600		85	7,225
61	3,721		86	7,396
62	3,844		87	7,569
63	3,969		88	7,744
64	4,096		89	7,921
65	4,225		90	8,100
66	4,356		91	8,281
67	4,489		92	8,464
68	4,624		93	8,649
69	4,761		94	8,836
70	4,900		95	9,025
71	5,041		96	9,216
72	5,184		97	9,409
73	5,329		98	9,604
74	5,476		99	9,801
75	5,625		100	10,000

Table of Square Roots 1–50

Number	Square Root		Number	Square Root
1	1.000		26	5.099
2	1.414		27	5.196
3	1.732		28	5.292
4	2.000		29	5.385
5	2.236		30	5.477
6	2.449		31	5.568
7	2.646		32	5.657
8	2.828		33	5.745
9	3.000		34	5.831
10	3.162		35	5.916
11	3.317		36	6.000
12	3.464		37	6.083
13	3.606		38	6.164
14	3.742		39	6.245
15	3.873		40	6.325
16	4.000		41	6.403
17	4.123		42	6.481
18	4.243		43	6.557
19	4.359		44	6.633
20	4.472		45	6.708
21	4.583		46	6.782
22	4.690		47	6.856
23	4.796		48	6.928
24	4.899		49	7.000
25	5.000		50	7.071

Table of Squares Roots 51–100

Number	Square Root
51	7.141
52	7.211
53	7.280
54	7.348
55	7.416
56	7.483
57	7.550
58	7.616
59	7.681
60	7.746
61	7.810
62	7.874
63	7.937
64	8.000
65	8.062
66	8.124
67	8.185
68	8.246
69	8.307
70	8.367
71	8.426
72	8.485
73	8.544
74	8.602
75	8.660

Number	Square Root
76	8.718
77	8.775
78	8.832
79	8.888
80	8.944
81	9.000
82	9.055
83	9.110
84	9.165
85	9.220
86	9.274
87	9.327
88	9.381
89	9.434
90	9.487
91	9.539
92	9.592
93	9.644
94	9.695
95	9.747
96	9.798
97	9.849
98	9.899
99	9.950
100	10.000

Glossary

absolute value   the distance between 0 and an integer on the number line

Addition Property of Opposites   the sum of a number and its opposite is 0

Associative Property   more than two numbers can be added or multiplied in groups of two. The way the numbers are grouped does not matter

at random   each outcome is equally likely to happen

bar graph   a way of showing information by using bars

base   a factor; in 3^2, 3 is the base used as a factor 2 times

binomial   a polynomial with two terms

broken–line graph   a graph made up of different pieces of straight lines

check   substitute the solution for the variable

coefficient   a number that multiplies a variable

combination   a group of objects in which order does not matter; in counting combinations, ABC is the same as CAB

Commutative Property   the order of two numbers does not matter when you add or multiply

complementary events   events that are opposites; if winning is the event, then losing is the complementary event

compound event   two or more events

compound interest   interest earned on your previous interest

constants   numbers, or quantities, that do not change

coordinate axes   two perpendicular number lines

coordinate plane   a plane with coordinate axes drawn on it

cross products   the products of numbers or expressions diagonally across from each other in a proportion

data   information gathered from surveys or experiments

degree 2   describes an equation whose largest exponent is 2

dependent events   events for which the outcome of one affects the outcome of the other

direct variation $y = kx$; k is a positive number; as one variable increases, the other increases

discount   the amount or percent a price is reduced

Distance Formula   a way to find the distance between two points using the Pythagorean Theorem

Distributive Property   to multiply a sum or difference by a number, multiply each number of the sum or difference

eliminating a variable   removing one variable in a system of equations

empirical probability probability based on what has already happened

equation a statement that two expressions are equal

equivalent having the same value

equivalent equations variable equations with the same solutions

evaluate find the value of an expression

event an outcome or group of outcomes that you are looking for

exponent tells how many times the base is used as a factor

exponential functions functions of the form $y = a \cdot b^x$, where b is a positive number not equal to 1

expression a number, or a group of numbers written with operation signs

factor to write an expression as the product of its factors

factors numbers multiplied to give a product; the product divided by the factor gives a 0 remainder

frequency table a table that shows counts of items in different groups

function a group of ordered pairs where no two ordered pairs have the same first number

function notation a way to write an equation to show it is a function

graph of a solution points on the number line that show the solution

graph of an ordered pair a dot that shows the location of an ordered pair

greatest common factor (GCF) the largest common factor of two or more terms

horizontal lines lines with slope = 0

hypotenuse the side across from the right angle of a right triangle

Identity Property adding 0, or multiplying by 1, does not change a number

independent events events whose outcomes do not affect each other

inequality greater than, greater than or equal to, less than, less than or equal to

$\geq$ the symbol for "is greater than or equal to" also means "at least" or "no less than"

$\leq$ the symbol for "is less than or equal to" also means "at most" or "no greater than"

integers numbers in the set ... ‾3, ‾2, ‾1, 0, 1, 2, 3, ...

inverse operations operations that "undo" each other; addition and subtraction are inverse operations, and multiplication and division are inverse operations

inverse variation a rational equation in the form $y = \dfrac{k}{x}$ where k is a positive constant

irrational number numbers with decimals that do not end and do not repeat

least common denominator (LCD) the smallest common denominator

least common multiple (LCM) the smallest common multiple of two or more numbers that is not 0

like terms numbers or terms that have the same variable with the same exponent

linear equation an equation whose graph is a straight line

maximum the largest number in a group of numbers

mean sum of the data divided by the number of data; also called average

median the middle number in a group of numbers when the numbers are in order from smallest to largest

minimum the smallest number in a group of numbers

mode the number that appears most often in a group of numbers

monomial an expression with one term; a number, a variable, or the product of a number and a variable

negative correlation the data in one set increase while the data in the second set decrease

negative numbers the numbers to the left of zero on the number line

opposites numbers with the same absolute value on opposite sides of zero on the number line; -3 and 3 are opposites

ordered pairs two numbers in a special order; ordered pairs give the locations of points

origin the point where the coordinate axes cross each other

outcomes the results of an activity, experiment, or game

parallel lines lines that have the same slope

permutations ways of putting a group of objects in order; there are six permutations for three letters: $ABC, ACB, BAC, BCA, CAB, CBA$

perpendicular lines two lines with slopes that are negative reciprocals

polynomial a term or the sum or difference of terms

positive correlation the data in two sets increase together

positive numbers the numbers to the right of zero on the number line

power the result of multiplying when factors are the same

probability the chance of something happening

properties of equality adding, subtracting, multiplying, or dividing both sides of an equation by the same number gives an equivalent equation

proportion a statement that two ratios are equal

Pythagorean Theorem a formula for finding the length of a side of a right triangle when you know the lengths of the other sides; $a^2 + b^2 = c^2$

Pythagorean triple three positive whole numbers that satisfy the Pythagorean Theorem; the numbers can be the measures of the sides of a right triangle

quadratic equation   an equation with one variable that has degree 2

quadratic formula   formula to find the solutions of a quadratic equation in the form $ax^2 + bx + c = 0$

quadratic function   an equation in the form $y = ax^2 + bx + c$

quartiles   numbers that divide a set of data into four parts

radical   square root written as a number under a radical sign

radical equation   an equation that has a variable under a radical sign

range   the difference between the largest and smallest number in a group of numbers

rational equation   an equation that contains rational expressions

rational expression   the quotient of two variable expressions; can be written as a fraction

rational number   a number that can be written as a fraction

revise   change; to change a guess when you have more information

right triangle   a triangle with one right angle and two acute angles

rise   the change between two points on a line in an up-and-down direction

run   the change between two points on a line in a left-to-right direction

sale price   the regular price minus the discount

scatter plot   graph that shows two sets of related data as ordered pairs

scientific notation   a number written as the product of two factors; the first factor is a decimal and the second factor is a power of ten

simplify   carry out the operations; find the value

slope   the steepness of a straight line

slope-intercept form $y = mx + b$; m is the slope and b is the y-intercept

solution   a value of the variable that makes the equation true

solve   find the solution of an equation

square   raise a number to the second power

square root   a number that when multiplied by itself gives the original number; the square root of 16 is 4; in symbols, $\sqrt{16} = 4$

standard form $Ax + By = C$

statistics   the study of collecting and organizing data

stem-and-leaf plot   tool that uses place value to arrange and display data

substitute   replace a variable with a number

system of linear equations   two or more linear equations with the same variables

system of linear inequalities   two or more linear inequalities with the same variables

terms   parts of an expression separated by a + or − sign

tree diagram   a way of showing choices so you can count them

30°–60°–90° triangle   a right triangle whose acute angles measure 30° and 60°

45°–45°–90° triangle   a right triangle whose acute angles both measure 45°

trinomial   a polynomial with three terms

undefined   when a rational expression has zero as the denominator; has no value

variable   a letter that represents a number

variable equation   an equation containing a variable

vertical line test   a test you use on a graph to tell if the graph is a function

vertical lines   lines with no slope

x-intercept   the x-value of the ordered pair at the point where a line crosses the x-axis

y-intercept   the y-value of the ordered pair at the point where a line crosses the y-axis

Zero Product Property   if the product of two numbers is 0, then one of the numbers must be 0

Zero Property of Multiplication   the product of any number and 0 is 0

zeros   the values of x where a function crosses the x-axis

Selected Answers

UNIT ONE

Chapter 1 *Numbers for Algebra*

Lesson 1.1 (Page 5)

Try These
1. left **2.** right **3.** left; less; <
4. right; greater; >

Practice
1.

3.

```
  +--+--+--+--+--+--+-->
 −10−9−8−7−6−5−4
```

5.

```
  +--+--+--+--+--+--+-->
 −1  0  1  2  3  4  5
```

7.

```
  +--+--+--+--+--+--+-->
 −7−6−5−4−3−2−1
```

9. > **11.** < **13.** > **15.** <

Lesson 1.2 (Page 7)

Try These
1. 8; 8 **2.** 12; 12 **3.** negative; positive; 15
4. positive; negative; ⁻20

Practice
1. 2 **3.** 3 **5.** 5 **7.** 1 **9.** 8 **11.** 9 **13.** 5
15. ⁻7 **17.** 22 **19.** 0

Lesson 1.3 (Page 9)

Try These
1. absolute values; 5; 5; subtract; 0; 0; 0
2. absolute values; 3; 4; subtract; 1; 4; 1

Practice
1. 3 **3.** ⁻9 **5.** ⁻6 **7.** ⁻6 **9.** 6 **11.** ⁻9
13. ⁻7 **15.** 6

Lesson 1.4 (Page 11)

Try These
1. ⁻4; Add; +; 5; ⁻5; ⁻5 **2.** +3; ⁻3; +3;
subtract; −; 4; absolute; ⁻4

Practice
1. 2 **3.** ⁻1 **5.** 13 **7.** 6 **9.** ⁻2 **11.** 9
13. ⁻23 **15.** 50

Lesson 1.5 (Page 13)

Try These
1. 21; positive; 21; 21
2. absolute values; 32; positive integer;
negative; ⁻32; ⁻32
3. absolute values; 6; 30; positive integer;
positive; ⁻30; ⁻30
4. absolute values; 3; 0; zero; 0; 0

Practice
1. 15 **3.** 7 **5.** 18 **7.** ⁻45 **9.** 6 **11.** 18
13. ⁻28 **15.** 200

Lesson 1.6 (Page 15)

Try These
1. 9; 3; positive; 3; 3 **2.** 0; 0; 0
3. absolute values; 24; 6; 4; positive; ⁻4; ⁻4
4. absolute values; 30; 5; 6; negative; ⁻6; ⁻6

Practice
1. 5 **3.** ⁻1 **5.** 0 **7.** 4 **9.** 2 **11.** ⁻3
13. undefined **15.** ⁻6

Lesson 1.7 (Page 17)

Try These
1. addition; +; ⁻4; 6; 6 **2.** ⁻15; ⁻26; ⁻20; ⁻20
3. ⁻15; ⁻20; ⁻20 **4.** ⁻8; ⁻20; ⁻20; ⁻6; ⁻6

Practice
1. 15 **3.** 12 **5.** ⁻2 **7.** ⁻32 **9.** ⁻9 **11.** 0
13. 6 **15.** ⁻6 **17.** ⁻12

Lesson 1.8 (Page 19)

Try These
1. 3; ⁻5; ⁻5; ⁻125; ⁻125 **2.** 3; 3; 3; 3; 3; 81;
81

Practice
1. 36 **3.** 8 **5.** ⁻169 **7.** ⁻27,000 **9.** 6,561
11. 16 **13.** ⁻27 **15.** ⁻64 **17.** 64 **19.** 1

Lesson 1.9 (Page 21)

Practice
1. ⁻284 **2.** 45 **3.** ⁻24 **4.** ⁻82 **5.** 26
6. 1,653 **7.** ⁻1,633 **8.** ⁻19

Lesson 1.10 (Page 23)

Try These
1. $29; $28; $28; $28; $14; $28
2. 6; 6; 8; 8; 8; 4

Practice
1. $35.00 in July, $105.00 in August
3. 110 adult tickets, 130 student tickets

Lesson 1.11 (Page 25)

Try These

1. March; ⁻8; March; 8
2. 6; ⁻8; 6; ⁻8; 14

Practice

1. December   **3.** 7°

Chapter 2 *Tools for Algebra*

Lesson 2.1 (Page 31)

Try These

1. Multiply; 12; 12; 8; 20; 20
2. power; 9; −1; −1

Practice

1. 7   **3.** 31   **5.** −1   **7.** 11   **9.** −3   **11.** −5
13. 31   **15.** 11   **17.** 5   **19.** 25   **21.** 0

Lesson 2.2 (Page 33)

Try These

1. subtraction; 4; 2; 18; 18
2. addition; power; 8; 8; 8; 0; 0

Practice

1. 16   **3.** 20   **5.** 20   **7.** 2   **9.** −3   **11.** 2
13. 6   **15.** 10   **17.** 7   **19.** 7   **21.** 8

Lesson 2.3 (Page 35)

Try These

1. •; •; •   **2.** •; •; ÷; •; ÷; +

Practice

1. •   **3.** •, −   **5.** •, +   **7.** •, •   **9.** •, ÷
11. +, •   **13.** •, ÷   **15.** •, •, +, •

Lesson 2.4 (Page 37)

Try These

1. 4; y^3; −x **2.** multiply; 5; −10; 3
3. like   **4.** unlike

Practice

1. 3n, 4p, 2   **3.** 7a^3b^2c **5.** 1, −7   **7.** −2, 3
9. 1, 2, 1   **11.** like

Lesson 2.5 (Page 39)

Try These

1. like terms; 6x **2.** like terms; −5y; −2y
3. 6a; 14   **4.** like terms; 2c^2

Practice

1. 10x^3 **3.** −11b **5.** 3a **7.** 3r + 3s
9. −4x + 2y^2 **11.** −4a + 3b **13.** 4t + 10
15. 3x − 3x^2

Lesson 2.6 (Page 41)

Try These

1. −2; − 3; −3   **2.** x; y; 2; −4; 4; 4; 16; 16

Practice

1. 8   **3.** −9   **5.** −12   **7.** −96   **9.** 9

Lesson 2.7 (Page 43)

Try These

1. 10; 10; 5; 5; true
2. x; 5; 5; 15; 20; 19; 20; ≠

Practice

1. yes   **3.** yes   **5.** yes   **7.** no   **9.** no
11. no   **13.** yes

Lesson 2.8 (Page 45)

Try These

1. 0; Identity Property of Addition
2. Associative Property of Addition; 5; 5

Practice

1. Commutative Property of Addition
3. Addition Property of Opposites
5. Identity Property of Addition
7. Commutative; 3d
9. Addition of opposites; 6m
11. Commutative; x **13.** Commutative; 3

Lesson 2.9 (Page 47)

Try These

1. 1; Identity Property of Multiplication
2. 0; Zero Property of Multiplication
3. Associative Property of Multiplication; 5
4. Commutative Property of Multiplication; b

Practice

1. Commutative Property of Multiplication
3. Associative Property of Multiplication
5. Identity Property of Multiplication
7. commutative; ⁻8d **9.** associative; h
11. identity; 1

Lesson 2.10 (Page 49)

Try These

1. 2; 2; 2; 2; 2; 2; 2; 2r − 2
2. 4; 4; 4; 4; 4; 4a + 4c

Practice

1. 14 − 7y **3.** −24 + 2k **5.** −15 + 5x
7. 4a − 28   **9.** −18 + 6d **11.** 6 − 4n
13. 2x + 2k **15.** 10w + 20

Lesson 2.11 (Page 51)

Try These

1. Distributive Property; 4; 4; 12; 7; 4x − 7
2. n; 5; 11; 5m + 11n

Practice

1. 2a + 2   **3.** −r − 2   **5.** 6y − 58   **7.** 7b − 4

9. $4t + 6$ **11.** $11p$ **13.** $3m$ **15.** $3x - 8$
17. $-3p + 8$ **19.** $5 - m$ **21.** $5y - 2x$

Lesson 2.12 (Page 53)
Practice
1. 214 **3.** 7.7 **5.** 31 **7.** 6.75

Lesson 2.13 (Page 55)
Try These
1. •; • **2.** +; +; +; +
Practice
1. $A = lw$ **3.** $t = y - 5$

Lesson 2.14 (Page 57)
Try These
1. perimeter; 23; 17; 34; 74; 74 ft
2. area; 14; 336; 336 yd^2
Practice
1. 47 m **3.** 72 in.^{2} **5.** 16 yd^2 **7.** 12 cm^3

Chapter 3 *Solving Equations*

Lesson 3.1 (Page 63)
Try These
1. 8; -3; is not **2.** n; 5; 10; 6; is
Practice
1. yes **3.** yes **5.** yes **7.** yes **9.** yes
11. no **13.** no **15.** yes **17.** yes
19. no **21.** no

Lesson 3.2 (Page 65)
Try These
1. -5; -5; -10; -4 **2.** -4; -4; -12; 14; 14
Practice
1. $7 = 7$; $10 - 7 = 3$ **3.** $-5 = -5$;
$7 = 12 + (-5)$ **5.** $6 = 6$; $(2)(6) = 12$
7. $10 = 10$; $(-2)(10) - 3 = -23$;
9. $0 = 0$; $8 + 6(0) = 8$
11. $-2 = -2$; $-3(-2) + 1 = 7$

Lesson 3.3 (Page 67)
Try These
1. subtracted; subtract; $-$; $-$
2. multiplied; multiply; 3; 3
Practice
1. 5 **3.** • **5.** -3 **7.** 4 **9.** 2

Lesson 3.4 (Page 69)
Try These
1. Subtract; $-$ **2.** Multiply; •

Practice
1. $-$ **3.** $\div$ **5.** $-$ **7.** $\div$ **9.** $-$ **11.** $+$

Lesson 3.5 (Page 71)
Try These
1. 8; 8; 8; -11; -11; -11; -11; -11; -3; -3
2. 6; 6; 6; 18; 0; 18; 18; 18; 18; 24; 24
Practice
1. 6 **3.** 12 **5.** 3 **7.** -15 **9.** -8 **11.** -4
13. -21 **15.** -5

Lesson 3.6 (Page 73)
Try These
1. 5; 5; 5; 0; -10; -10; -10; -10; -15
2. 4; 4; 4; 10; 0; 10; 10; 10; 6
Practice
1. 30 **3.** 27 **5.** 20 **7.** -11 **9.** -6
11. -6 **13.** 12 **15.** -20 **17.** -16

Lesson 3.7 (Page 75)
Try These
1. -5; -5; -5; 35; 35; 35; -7
2. -4; -4; -4; 24; 24; 24; -6
Practice
1. 24 **3.** 18 **5.** -28 **7.** -20 **9.** -24
11. -50 **13.** 72 **15.** 15 **17.** 100

Lesson 3.8 (Page 77)
Try These
1. 30; 30; 30; -30 **2.** 8; 0; 0; 0; 0
Practice
1. 7 **3.** 8 **5.** -6 **7.** -5 **9.** -24 **11.** -5
13. 10 **15.** -1 **17.** -8

Lesson 3.9 (Page 79)
Try These
1. 8; 8; 8; 20; 5; 5; 5; 4; 4; 4; 20; 12
2. subtract; 6; 6; 8; multiply; -2; -2; -16;
 -16; 8; 14
Practice
1. 2 **3.** 7 **5.** -28 **7.** -2 **9.** 25 **11.** -16

Lesson 3.10 (Page 81)
Try These
1. s; 20; subtract; 20; 20; 20; -10; -5; -5; -5;
 2; 2; 2; -2; 10
2. Distributive Property; n; 4; $4n$; 12; 12; 12; 4;
 4; 4; 4; 1; 1; 1 -2; -8
Practice
1. 3 **3.** -9 **5.** 13 **7.** -8 **9.** 11

Lesson 3.11 (Page 83)

Try These
1. $6t$; $6t$; $6t$; $7t$; 14; 14; 14; $7t$; 7; 7; 7; -2; -2
2. $12k$; $12k$; $12k$; terms; $8k$; 24; 24; 24; -24; 8; 8; 8; -3; -3

Practice
1. 3 3. 6 5. 7 7. -4 9. -3 11. 2

Lesson 3.12 (Page 85)

Practice
1. yes 2. yes 3. yes 4. no 5. yes 6. no

Lesson 3.13 (Page 87)

Try These
1. w; 44; 44 2. n; 6; 6

Practice
1. $n = .55 \cdot 80$; 44 3. $.25 \cdot 100 = n$; 25
5. $.05 \cdot 160 = n$; 8

Lesson 3.14 (Page 89)

Try These
1. .25; 6; $6.00
2. regular price; 24; 18; $18.00

Practice
1. $1.50 3. $36.00 5. $24.00

UNIT TWO

Chapter 4 *Introducing Functions*

Lesson 4.1 (Page 97)

Try These
1. 5 2. 2 3. left; 2 4. 3

Practice
1. right 1 unit, up 3 units
3. up 2 units from the origin
5. left 4 units from the origin
7. left 2 units, down 5 units
9. left 5 units, down 4 units

Lesson 4.2 (Page 99)

Try These
1. 2; up 2. left; 3

Practice
1.–15.

Lesson 4.3 (Page 101)

Try These
1. 2, -2, (3, -6), 2; -2; (3, -6) 2. feet; 2; -2; (3, -6)

Practice
1. (1, -5), (2, 0), (3, 5);

Lesson 4.4 (Page 103)

Try These
1. 0; 0; 3; 3; 1; 6; (1, 6); 0; 3; (1, 6)
2. $2x + 4$; 2; 0; 0; 1; 1; 6; 2; 0; (1, 6)

Practice
1. Possible answers: (-1, -4), (0, 1), (1, 6)
3. Possible answers: (-1, -2), (0, 0), (1, 2)
5. -4; $2(0 - 1)$, -2; $2(1 - 1)$, 0; $2(2 - 1)$, 2; (-1, -4), (0, -2), (1, 0), (2, 2)

Lesson 4.5 (Page 105)

Try These
1. 3; only one; is 2. crosses; is not

Practice
1. no 3. yes 5. no

Lesson 4.6 (Page 107)

Try These
1. $f(x)$ 2. $f(x)$; $6(x + x^2)$ 3. -2; 2; 5; 5
4. 0; 0; 0; 4; 20; 20

Practice
1. $f(x) = 4 + x$ 3. $f(x) = 3(x - 5)$

5. $f(0) = -9$ **7.** $f(8) = 24$ **9.** $f(-3) = -1$

Lesson 4.7 (Page 109)

Practice

1. 19; 0.5(4) + 18, 20; 0.5(6) + 18, 21;
0.5(8) + 18, 22

2. 80; 10(4 + 6), 100; 10(6 + 6), 120;
10(8 + 6), 140

Lesson 4.8 (Page 111)

Try These

1. equation; 100; 1,200; 1,204; $1,204
2. table; $28

Practice

1. table; $16 **3.** equation; $64
5. The cost increases.

Lesson 4.9 (Page 113)

Try These

1. 5; 5 **2.** 6; 4; 6; 2

Practice

1. 3 students **3.** 3 more students

Chapter 5 *Linear Equations and Functions*

Lesson 5.1 (Page 119)

Try These

1. 0; 2; 2; 0; 2; 0; 2; 1; is not
2. −3; 13; 13; −3; 13; 12; 13; 13; is

Practice

1. yes **3.** yes **5.** yes **7.** no **9.** no
11. yes **13.** no **15.** yes

Lesson 5.2 (Page 121)

Try These

1. 4; 3; 2; 4; 3; 2; 4; 3; 2
2. 1; 0; −1; 1; 0; −1; 1; 0; −1

Practice

1.

3.

5.

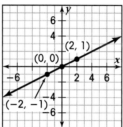

Lesson 5.3 (Page 123)

Try These

1. y; −3; 8; x; 3; −5; 8; −5; $-\dfrac{8}{5}$

2. y; 2; −6; x; 3; −3; −6; −3; 2; 2

Practice

1. $\dfrac{3}{2}$ **3.** $\dfrac{5}{-3}$ **5.** $\dfrac{-5}{9}$ **7.** $\dfrac{8}{5}$

9. $\dfrac{1}{2}$ **11.** 0 **13.** 1

Lesson 5.4 (Page 125)

Try These

1. 8; 0; −1; 9; −10; 0; −10; 0; 0
2. vertical; vertical; no; no

Practice

1. 0 **3.** 0 **5.** no slope **7.** no slope **9.** 0

Lesson 5.5 (Page 127)

Try These

1. −2; 4; −1; 4; $\dfrac{6}{5}$; 3; −3; 6; −1; $\dfrac{6}{7}$; $\dfrac{6}{5}$; $\dfrac{6}{7}$;
are not

2. −2; 7; −1; 2; 3; 5; 4; −1; −4; $\dfrac{1}{3}$; 3; $\dfrac{1}{3}$;
are not

Practice

1. yes **3.** yes **5.** yes

Lesson 5.6 (Page 129)

Try These

1. 0; 0; 3; −3; 3; −1; −1 **2.** 0; 0; 0; 3; 3

Practice

1. x-intercept: −1; y-intercept: 1
3. x-intercept: 2; y-intercept: −2
5. x-intercept: −2; y-intercept: 10
7. x-intercept: 6; y-intercept: −3
9. x-intercept: 0; y-intercept: 0
11. x-intercept: −3; y-intercept: 9

Lesson 5.7 (Page 131)

Try These

1. 0; −2; 2; 1; 1; 0; 1; 0
2. 1; 1; 4; 3; 4; −3; 4; −3

Practice

1.

3.

5.

7.

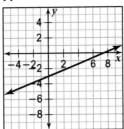

Lesson 5.8 (Page 133)

Try These

1. 1; 5 **2.** $\frac{3}{2}$; −1; $\frac{3}{2}$; −1 **3.** 0; 4; 0; 4; 0
4. −1; 3; −1; 3

Practice

1. slope: $\frac{1}{2}$; y-intercept: 3

3. slope: $-\frac{2}{3}$; y-intercept: 6

5. slope: $\frac{3}{4}$; y-intercept: 0

7. slope: −2; y-intercept: −4

9. slope: $\frac{1}{3}$; y-intercept: 1

11. slope: 3; y-intercept: 6

Lesson 5.9 (Page 135)

Try These

1. $3x$; $3x$; $3x$; −4; $\frac{3}{4}x$

2. $4x$; $4x$; $4x$; −1; −1; −1; −1; −4; $4x$; $4x$; 4

Practice

1. $y = -3x + 1$ **3.** $y = -5x + 10$
5. $y = -6x + 6$ **7.** $y = -3x + 10$
9. $y = \dfrac{-2x}{3}$ **11.** $y = -2x + 3$

Lesson 5.10 (Page 137)

Practice

1. −13 **2.** 6 **3.** 7 **4.** 14 **5.** 24 **6.** −5
7. 1.8 **8.** 10 **9.** 32

Lesson 5.11 (Page 139)

Try These

1. 24; 5; 1; 8; 8 **2.** 1; 6; 6; 6

Practice

1. Gracie will earn $40.
3. The bus could travel 300 miles.

Lesson 5.12 (Page 141)

Try These
1. 9; 3; 3   **2.** 3; n; 15; 45; $45.00

Practice
1. 2   **3.** 8

Chapter 6 *Writing Linear Equations*

Lesson 6.1 (Page 147)

Try These
1. $\frac{1}{2}$; 1; $\frac{1}{2}$; 1; $\frac{1}{2}$; 1   **2.** 3; 0; 3; 0; 3   **3.** 1; 3; m; b; 1; 3; 1; 3; 3

Practice
1. $y = -4x - 3$
3. $y = -x + 2$; Possible check: Use (1, 1); $1 = -1 + 2$.

Lesson 6.2 (Page 149)

Try These
1. $\frac{1}{2}$; $\frac{1}{2}$; 2; $\frac{1}{2}$; 3; 2; $\frac{1}{2}$; 2; 2; $y = \frac{1}{2}x + 2$
2. -3; -3; 2; -3; 0; 6; -3; 6; 6; $y = -3x + 6$

Practice
1. $y = -2x + 3$ **3.** $y = \frac{3}{2}x + 1$
5. $y = \frac{1}{4}x + 2$ **7.** $y = x$

Lesson 6.3 (Page 151)

Try These
1. 3; 3; 3; 5; 5; -1; -1; 1; -4; -1; -4; -4; $y = 3x - 1$
2. $-\frac{1}{2}$; $-\frac{1}{2}$; $-\frac{1}{2}$; 4; 4; 4; $-\frac{1}{2}$; 4; 3; 2; 3; $y = -\frac{1}{2}x + 4$

Practice
1. $y = -\frac{1}{2}x + 5$ **3.** $y = -x + 10$
5. $y = 6$ **7.** $y = \frac{1}{2}x$ **9.** $y = x$

Lesson 6.4 (Page 153)

Try These
1. -1; -1; -1; -1 **2.** 5; 5; 5; 5

Practice
1. $x = 2$ **3.** $y = 2$

Lesson 6.5 (Page 155)

Try These
1. -4; $\frac{1}{4}$; $\frac{1}{4}$; 1; 4; 0; $\frac{1}{4}x$
2. -2; -2; -5; 5; $-2x - 5$

Practice
1. $y = 4x + 1$ **3.** $y = -\frac{1}{2}x - 3$
5. $y = \frac{1}{2}x - 6$

Lesson 6.6 (Page 157)

Practice
1. true   **3.** false   **5.** false

Lesson 6.7 (Page 159)

Try These
1. 50; 40; 5; 5; divide by 5; ÷
2. 1; 29; 30; 30; 87; multiply by 30; 30

Practice
1. $y = x - 3$ **3.** $m = j + 6$

Lesson 6.8 (Page 161)

Try These
1. 75; $\frac{2}{25}$; 75; $\frac{2}{25}$; 75; $\frac{2}{25}$; 75   **2.** 100; 83; 83

Practice
1. 485 cc   **3.** 700 cc

UNIT 3

Chapter 7 *Inequalities*

Lesson 7.1 (Page 169)

Try These
1. solid; right   **2.** open; left   **3.** open; right
4. solid; left

Practice
1.

3.

5.

7.

9.

$$-7\,-6\,-5\,-4\,-3\,-2\,-1\quad 0$$

11.

$$-13\quad -11\quad -9\quad -7$$

13.

$$-9\,-8\,-7\,-6\,-5\,-4\,-3\,-2$$

15.

$$-12\quad -10\quad -8\quad -6$$

Lesson 7.2 (Page 171)

Try These

1. 4; 4; 1   **2.** 4; 4; 4; 1

Practice

1. $y > 2$;

$$0\ \ 1\ \ 2\ \ 3\ \ 4\ \ 5\ \ 6\ \ 7$$

3. $b < 7$;

$$2\ \ 3\ \ 4\ \ 5\ \ 6\ \ 7\ \ 8\ \ 9$$

5. $s > -2$;

$$-4\,-3\,-2\,-1\ \ 0\ \ 1\ \ 2\ \ 3$$

7. $x < 1$;

$$-4\,-3\,-2\,-1\ \ 0\ \ 1\ \ 2\ \ 3$$

9. $w < -9$;

$$-13\quad -11\quad -9\quad -7$$

Lesson 7.3 (Page 173)

Try These

1. -3; -3; $\geq$; -3; change; $\geq$ **2.** -6; -6; $<$; -6; change; $<$

Practice

1. $x > 8$;

$$6\ \ 7\ \ 8\ \ 9\ \ 10\ 11\ 12\ 13$$

3. $f < 36$;

$$31\ 32\ 33\ 34\ 35\ 36\ 37\ 38$$

5. $m \geq -30$;

$$-32\quad -30\quad -28\quad -26$$

7. $x \leq -20$;

$$-24\quad -22\quad -20\quad -18$$

9. $x < -20$ **11.** $f < 0$
13. $m \leq 35$ **15.** $x \leq -30$

Lesson 7.4 (Page 175)

Try These

1. 6; 6; 6; 6; 3; 18
2. 4; 4; 4; -18; -6; $<$; -18; $<$

Practice

1. $x > 12$;

$$10\ 11\ 12\ 13\ 14\ 15\ 16\ 17$$

3. $x \leq -2$;

$$-7\,-6\,-5\,-4\,-3\,-2\,-1\ \ 0$$

5. $m \geq 6$;

$$4\ \ 5\ \ 6\ \ 7\ \ 8\ \ 9\ \ 10\ 11$$

7. $x > 5$ **9.** $m \geq -21$ **11.** $a < 3$

Lesson 7.5 (Page 177)

Try These

1. -1; 0; 0; -1; 0; -2; 0; 0; is not
2. 2; 3; 3; 2; 3; 2; is not

Practice

1. yes   **3.** no   **5.** no   **7.** yes

Lesson 7.6 (Page 179)

Try These

1. $(0, -2)$; $\dfrac{2}{5}$; solid   **2.** $(0, 0)$; 1; dotted

Practice

1.

3.

5.

Lesson 7.7 (Page 181)
Practice
1. yes   **3.** yes   **5.** no   **7.** no

Lesson 7.8 (Page 183)
Try These
1. $>;>;>;$ 500; 500   **2.** $\geq; \geq; \geq;$ 40; 40

Practice
1. $12t < 48; t < 4$ tickets
3. $7 + p \geq 15; p \geq 8$ pages

Lesson 7.9 (Page 185)
Try These
1. (6, 6); is not; will not   **2.** (8, 4); will

Practice
1. Yes; (10, 20) is in the shaded region.
3. No; (10, 25) is on the dotted line and not in the shaded region.

Chapter 8 *Systems of Equations and Inequalities*

Lesson 8.1 (Page 191)
Try These
1. $-2; 0; -2; -2; 0; 2;$ is
2. $6; 1; 6; 1; 4; 6; 1; -11;$ is not

Practice
1. yes   **3.** no   **5.** yes   **7.** yes

Lesson 8.2 (Page 193)
Try These
1. $-1; -2; -2; -2; -1$ **2.** 4; 2; 2; 4; 2; 4

Practice
1. (−1, 0);

3. (1, −1);

5. no solution;

7. (−6, −1);

9. $(-1, 1)$;

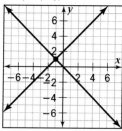

Lesson 8.3 (Page 195)

Try These

1. -2; -2; -1; -2; -2; -1; -2; -1; -2; -1; -1; -2; -1

2. $4x$; $4x$; 3; 3; 3; 12; 3; 12; 3; 12; 3; 12; 12; 12; 3; 12; 12; 3; 12

Practice

1. $(2, 4)$ **3.** $(-3, -2)$ **5.** $(-3, -1)$

Lesson 8.4 (Page 197)

Try These

1. Add; 0; 2; y; -2; -6; 3; 3; 3; x; -12; -6; -6; 3; -6; 3; -6; 3

2. Subtract: -2; x; -2; -2; y; -2; -4; -5; -2; -5; -2; -5; -2; -5

Practice

1. $(5, 1)$ **3.** $(-2, -1)$ **5.** $(4, 11)$

Lesson 8.5 (Page 199)

Try These

1. 3; 6; 0; x; 1; 1; y; 1; -1; 1; -1

2. opposites; -2; -2; Add; 1; 0; y; 0; 0; x; 0; 0

Practice

1. $(0, 2)$ **3.** $(-3, -1)$ **5.** $(-2, -4)$

Lesson 8.6 (Page 201)

Try These

1. 9; -20; -22; x; 2; 2; y; -12; 3; 2; 3

2. 15; 4; y; 1; 1; x; -4; -2; -2; 1

Practice

1. $(6, -4)$ **3.** $(-5, 9)$ **5.** $(-2, 1)$

Lesson 8.7 (Page 203)

Try These

1. 3; 4; 4; 4; 3; 4; 4; is

2. 3; -1; -1; 3; -1; 10; -1; 3; -1; 3; is not

Practice

1. yes   **3.** yes   **5.** no

Lesson 8.8 (Page 205)

Try These

1. dark shaded; 2; 2; 2; 4

2. dark shaded; 2; 1; 2; 2; 2; 0; 2; 1; 2; -2; 2; -1

Practice

1.

3.

5.

7.

9.

Lesson 8.9 (Page 207)
Practice
1. yes **3.** no **5.** yes

Lesson 8.10 (Page 209)
Try These
1. $+; =; +; =$ **2.** $-10; 4; -6; 10; 10.00$
Practice
1. $x + y = 4, x - y = 2; (3, 1)$
3. $3x + 2y = 9, x + 2y = 7;$ Tomatoes cost $1.00 a pound; Broccoli costs $3.00 a pound.

Lesson 8.11 (Page 211)
Try These
1. $\geq; \geq; \leq$
2. 4; 12; 6; 4; 12; 6; 13; 16; 15; 12; 4
Practice
1. $b \leq 7; p \leq 6; b + p \geq 10$

Chapter 9 *More About Data and Data Analysis*

Lesson 9.1 (Page 217)
Try These
1. $4; -5$ **2.** 2; 4; 4; 2; 3; 15; 15; 3; 3
Practice
1. 30 **3.** 451 **5.** -10 **7.** -5 **9.** 30 boxes

Lesson 9.2 (Page 219)
Try These
1. 1; 1
2. 1; 1; 4; 4; 8; 8; 10; 12; 8; 8; 12; 6; 6
Practice
1. -3 **3.** 16 **5.** -1 and 0
7. 4 **9.** 22 **11.** 3

Lesson 9.3 (Page 221)
Try These
1. minimum; 1; maximum; 9; 1; 9
2. $-5; -2; 3; 9; 12;$ minimum; $-5;$ maximum; 12; minimum; maximum; 12; $-5;$ 17; 17
Practice
1. 0; 12; 12 **3.** $-9; -2; 7$ **5.** $-6; 3; 9$
7. 59; 752; 693

Lesson 9.4 (Page 223)
Try These
1. |||, 3; ||||, 5; ||, 2; 10 **2.** 2; 6–8 h
3. 5; 3; 8; 8
Practice
1. |||| |, 6; |||, 3; |||, 3; 12. **3.** 1–10 years

Lesson 9.5 (Page 225)
Try These
1. 235; 236; 238; 241; 247; 248; 254; 5; 6; 8; 1; 7; 8; 25; 4
2. 560 to 569; 550 to 559; 550 to 559; 560 to 569
Practice
1.

Stem	Leaves
1	4 5
2	1 1 3 8
3	1 3 5 6
4	2 8

3.

Stem	Leaves
72	0 4
73	5
74	8 8 8 9
75	8
76	14

Lesson 9.6 (Page 227)
Try These
1. pair; scatter plot
2. increase; positive

Practice

1. negative correlation

Lesson 9.7 (Page 229)

Practice

1. 714.25   **3.** 930.5   **5.** 674.8   **7.** 102.2

Lesson 9.8 (Page 231)

Try These

1. 3; 4; mean; median; mode   **2.** 315; 315; 12; 46; mode; mean; median

Practice

1. mean 34, median 32, modes 3 and 60; mean, median

3. mean 50, median 48, mode 15; mean, median

Lesson 9.9 (Page 233)

Try These

1. 4; 3; 7; 3; 4; 7   **2.** 33; 27; 44; $27; $33; $44

Practice

1. 84, 88, 94   **3.** 3, 5, 8

UNIT FOUR

Chapter 10 *Exponents and Functions*

Lesson 10.1 (Page 241)

Try These

1. n; n; n; 3; 3   **2.** y; y; 1; 2; 2   **3.** 2; -2; 4
4. 4; 3; 3; 3; 3; 81

Practice

1. g^3 **3.** a^2b^4 **5.** r^2 **7.** y^5 **9.** 64
11. -32 **13.** 1

Lesson 10.2 (Page 243)

Try These

1. bb; 6; $3b^6$
2. -10; -10; Rearrange; -10; -10; 3; 2; $-10c^3d^2$

Practice

1. c^4 **3.** x^6 **5.** x^2y **7.** $6ab$ **9.** $2x^2$
11. $-3a^4d^3$ **13.** $12ab^6$ **15.** $8h^5g^6$
17. $-3y^3$

Lesson 10.3 (Page 245)

Try These

1. 10; 3; 1; 2; 3; 2   **2.** 3; 4; 4; 4; 12

Practice

1. x^{10} **3.** w^5x^6 **5.** b^8c^{12} **7.** $3a^4$ **9.** $30c^6q^4$
11. a^9 **13.** d^{10} **15.** y^{20} **17.** $-32n^7p$

Lesson 10.4 (Page 247)

Try These

1. 2; 2; $2w$; $2w$ **2.** abb; 2; ab^2

Practice

1. b **3.** $5cd$ **5.** st^5 **7.** $6n$ **9.** $9x^2$ **11.** q^2
13. r **15.** ab **17.** $6x^4y^2$

Lesson 10.5 (Page 249)

Try These

1. 6; 3; 3; $4x^3$ **2.** 2; 4; 5; 3; 2; 4; 2; g^4h^2

Practice

1. b^2 **3.** $3r^4$ **5.** c^4d^2 **7.** $5m^3n^3$ **9.** x^5y^3
11. $6x^2y^2$

Lesson 10.6 (Page 251)

Try These

1. 0; 2; 0; 2; 2; 2; 2   **2.** 0; 1; 0; x; 1; x; x

Practice

1. b^6 **3.** c^3d^6 **5.** t^4 **7.** y^4 **9.** xz^6 **11.** 1

Lesson 10.7 (Page 253)

Try These

1. -4; 3; -4; 3; $\dfrac{1}{x^4}$; y^3; 3; 4; 3; 4

2. 2; -3; 2; -3; $\dfrac{1}{b^3}$; $\dfrac{a^2}{b^3}$; $\dfrac{a^2}{b^3}$

Practice

1. b^2 **3.** $\dfrac{d^3}{c}$ **5.** $\dfrac{r^6}{q^3}$ **7.** $\dfrac{1}{m^5}$ **9.** $b^{10}c^4$
11. $\dfrac{j^5}{k^2}$

Lesson 10.8 (Page 255)

Try These

1. .00001; 5; left; .0000908   **2.** 1,000; 1,000; 3; 1,300

Practice

1. 161   **3.** 924,000   **5.** 274,200   **7.** .026
9. .000041   **11.** .0000047   **13.** 93,000,000

Lesson 10.9 (Page 257)

Try These

1. 0; 1; 1; 5; 2; 25; 3; 125; 4; 4; 625; 1; 5; 25; 125; 4; 625

2. 4; 1; 8; 2; 16; 3; 32; 4; 4; 64; 4; 8; 16; 32; 4; 64

Practice

1.

x	4^x	y
0	4^0	1
1	4^1	4
2	4^2	16
3	4^3	64
4	4^4	256

(0, 1) (1, 4) (2, 16) (3, 64) (4, 256)

3.

x	$-2 \cdot 5^x$	y
0	$-2 \cdot 5^0$	-2
1	$-2 \cdot 5^1$	-10
2	$-2 \cdot 5^2$	-50
3	$-2 \cdot 5^3$	-250
4	$-2 \cdot 5^4$	$-1,250$

(0, ⁻2) (1, ⁻10) (2, ⁻50) (3, ⁻250) (4, ⁻1,250)

5.

x	8^x	y
0	8^0	1
1	8^1	8
2	8^2	64
3	8^3	512

(0, 1) (1, 8) (2, 64) (3, 512)

Lesson 10.10 (Page 259)

Try These

1. 4; 16; 64; 256   **2.** 1; 2; 3; 4

Practice

1.

3.

Lesson 10.11 (Page 261)

Practice

1. 2,401   **3.** 225   **5.** 6,561   **7.** 3.24

9. 792.35   **11.** 24.39

Lesson 10.12 (Page 263)

Try These

1. Black; Black; Brown; Red

2. Blue; Blue; Blue; Tan; Black; Tan; Brown; Tan; Red; 6

Practice

1. 6 choices;

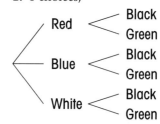

Lesson 10.13 (Page 265)

Try These
1. 2; 1.1664; 1166.4; $1166.40
2. 2; 1.3225; 661.25; $661.25

Practice
1. $a = \$1,000; r = 5\%$ **3.** $a = \$150; r = 8\%$
5. $a = \$10; r = 5\%$ **7.** $385.00
9. $50,000.00   **11.** $605.00

Chapter 11 *Quadratic Functions and Equations*

Lesson 11.1 (Page 271)

Try These
1. 5; 0; 8; 5; 0; 8
2. $6x^2$; x; 3; 6; -1; 3; 6; -1; 3

Practice
1. 2; 3; 5   **3.** 1; 1; 1   **5.** 7; 1; 6   **7.** 3; 7; 8
9. 5; 0; -4 **11.** 2, 8, -1 **13.** -3; 0; 4
15. 1; -6; -4

Lesson 11.2 (Page 273)

Try These
1. 8; 1; 1; 0; -1; -1; -2; -2; 0; 3; 8   **2.** 8; -1

Practice
1.

x	y
2	16
1	4
0	0
-1	4
-2	16

3.

x	y
2	8
1	5
0	4
-1	5
-2	8

5.

x	y
2	16
1	6
0	0
-1	-2
-2	0
-3	6
-4	16

Lesson 11.3 (Page 275)

Try These
1. 4; upward; minimum
2. a; a; -2; downward; maximum

Practice
1. downward; maximum
3. downward; maximum
5. downward; maximum
7. upward; minimum
9. upward; minimum
11. upward, minimum

Lesson 11.4 (Page 277)

Try These
1. -2; 0; 2; 0; -2; 2   **2.** no

Practice
1. -1 **3.** 3

Lesson 11.5 (Page 279)

Try These
1. 3; -3; -3; 3; -3 **2.** 6; -6; -6; 6; -6
3. -7; -7; -7 **4.** 0; 0; 0

Practice
1. 8 and -8 **3.** 10 and -10 **5.** 1 and -1
7. 11   **9.** -3 **11.** ± 9 **13.** -13 **15.** ± 15
17. 25

Lesson 11.6 (Page 281)

Try These
1. 20; 20; 20; 64; -8; 8; -8; 64; -8; 64
2. 3; 3; 3; 16; 16; 4; -4; 4; -4; 4; 16; -4; 16

Practice
1. 10 and -10 **3.** 11 and -11
5. 8 and -8 **7.** 2 and -2 **9.** 1 and -1

Lesson 11.7 (Page 283)

Try These

1. x; b; b; a; c; a
2. 1; 4; 4; 4; 4; 1; 4; 16; 0; -2; -2

Practice

1. 1 **3.** 2 and 3 **5.** -1 **7.** -2 and -4
9. no zeros **11.** -3 and -4

Lesson 11.8 (Page 285)

Practice

1. .03 and $-.03$ **3.** 8.49 and -8.49
5. .063 and $-.063$ **7.** 60 and -60
9. 99 and -99 **11.** 1.1 and -1.1

Lesson 11.9 (Page 287)

Try These

1. $2w$; 800; 800; w; 2; 800; 400; positive; 20; 20; 40; 20; 40
2. 121; positive; 11; 11

Practice

1. 12 yards

Lesson 11.10 (Page 289)

Try These

1. h; 5,000; 11,400; $-6,400$; -16; 400; 20; 20
2. s; 0; 400; 400; 400; -400; -16; 25; 5; 5

Practice

1. 10 seconds

Chapter 12 *Polynomials and Factoring*

Lesson 12.1 (Page 295)

Try These

1. 3; -3; trinomial; -3 **2.** 2; 0; binomial; 0

Practice

1. binomial, 0 **3.** binomial, 6
5. trinomial, -2 **7.** trinomial, -5
9. monomial, 0 **11.** binomial, 0
13. binomial, 0 **15.** trinomial, 24
17. binomial, -4

Lesson 12.2 (Page 297)

Try These

1. coefficients; -3; 5; -10; $-3a^2 + 5a - 10$
2. coefficients; -1; 3; 3; $-x + 3y + 3$

Practice

1. $4x^2 + 4x + 6$ **3.** $6s + 2t$
5. $-2c^2 + 6c - 5$ **7.** $x^2 + 7x - 3$
9. $2n^3 - 2n^2 - 3n - 5$ **11.** $-r^3 + 9r$

Lesson 12.3 (Page 299)

Try These

1. opposite; -4; -1; -2; $-4x^2 - x - 2$
2. $+$; $-$; like; 6; 7; $6p + 7q - 3$

Practice

1. $-3k^2 - k + 3$ **3.** $-2m + 7n$
5. $-3w^2 + 2w - 2$ **7.** $-z^3 + 5z^2 - 4z + 4$
9. $-4h + 1$ **11.** $-y - 2$ **13.** $-x + 2$

Lesson 12.4 (Page 301)

Try These

1. $-2a^2$; $6a$; $-2a^2 + 6a$
2. Distributive; $3x$; $3x$; $3x$; $3x^3$; $6x^2$; $3x$; $3x^3 - 6x^2 + 3x$

Practice

1. $6b^2 + 12b$ **3.** $3y^3 + y^2$ **5.** $-2s^2 + 6s$
7. $-4x^3 + 20x^2$ **9.** $p^3 - 4p^2 + p$

Lesson 12.5 (Page 303)

Try These

1. 2; 5; 10; 3; 10; $x^2 - 3x - 10$
2. a; a; 3; $3a$; 0; $a^2 - 9$

Practice

1. $x^2 + 3x + 2$ **3.** $y^2 + 6y + 8$
5. $a^2 + 2a - 8$ **7.** $x^2 - 25$ **9.** $y^2 - 1$
11. $a^2 - 4a + 4$ **13.** $x^2 + 7x + 10$
15. $y^2 + 6y + 9$

Lesson 12.6 (Page 305)

Try These

1. 2; 5; 5; All; is
2. 2; 3; x; 2; 3; y; is not; is not

Practice

1. yes **3.** no **5.** yes **7.** no
9. yes **11.** no

Lesson 12.7 (Page 307)

Try These

1. 2; 2; 2; 4; 4; 4; x; 4; $4(x + 2y)$
2. 3; $2ab$; $2ab$; $2ab$; 1; $3a$; 1; $2ab(3a - 1)$

Practice

1. $3(x + 3y)$ **3.** $k(3k + 8)$
5. $a(a^2 + a - 1)$ **7.** $4x^2(2 - y)$
9. $5n(4m^2 - 1)$

Lesson 12.8 (Page 309)

Try These

1. 6; 4; 7; 4; 3; 4; $(y + 3)(y + 4)$
2. a; a; 8; 4; 4; -10; -2; -8; 2; 8; $(a - 2)(a - 8)$

Practice
1. $(x + 1)(x + 4)$ **3.** $(c + 2)(c + 2)$
5. $(a - 1)(a - 3)$ **7.** $(x - 3)(x - 4)$
9. $(x + 6)(x + 5)$

Lesson 12.9 (Page 311)
Try These
1. 9; 6; 3; 3; 3; 6; 3; $(x + 6)(x - 3)$
2. a; a; 10; 5; 8; 10; 8; -8; -8; 10; 2;
   $(a - 10)(a + 2)$

Practice
1. $(x - 1)(x + 5)$ **3.** $(y + 1)(y - 6)$
5. $(a - 2)(a + 4)$ **7.** $(x + 2)(x - 8)$
9. $(k + 6)(k - 2)$

Lesson 12.10 (Page 313)
Try These
1. 6; 6; 6; $(x + 6)(x - 6)$
2. y; 10; 10; $(10 + y)(10 - y)$

Practice
1. $(x + 8)(x - 8)$ **3.** $(7 + c)(7 - c)$
5. $(a + 9)(a - 9)$ **7.** $(x + 20)(x - 20)$
9. $(b + 13)(b - 13)$ **11.** $(25 - x)(25 + 1x)$

Lesson 12.11 (Page 315)
Try These
0; $x + 2$; -2; $3x + 9$; -3; -2; -3; -2; -2; 0;
-6; -3; -3; -1; -9

Practice
1. $x = 0$ and $x = -3$ **3.** $y = 0$ and $y = 7$
5. $y = -2$ and $y = 2$ **7.** $z = -4$ and $z = -2$
9. $x = 4$ and $x = 5$

Lesson 12.12 (Page 317)
Try These
1. 4; 4; 0; 4; -4; 0; -4 **2.** 5; 5; 5; 5; 5

Practice
1. $y = -1$ **3.** $y = 4$ **5.** $a = 7$ and $a = -7$
7. $y = 3$ and $y = -5$ **9.** $a = 9$ and $a = -4$
11. $n = -7$ and $n = 4$

Lesson 12.13 (Page 319)
Practice
1. yes   **3.** yes   **5.** yes

Lesson 12.14 (Page 321)
Try These
1. 3; 3; 5; 3; 0; 3; -3; -3 **2.** 120; 19; 24; -5

Practice
1. $x = -18$ or 3; factoring
3. $x = 16$ or 3; factoring
5. $x = 0$ or 15; quadratic formula

Lesson 12.15 (Page 323)
Try These
1. 2; -4; 38; 19; 53; 53
2. 5; 5; -25; 95; 19; 89; 89

Practice
1. 60 meters   **3.** 37°F   **5.** 27 diagonals

UNIT FIVE
Chapter 13 *Radicals and Geometry*
Lesson 13.1 (Page 331)
Try These
1. 2; 9; greater; 9; 3; 2; 3
2. 9; less; 9; 3; 4; 3; 4

Practice
1. 2 and 3   **3.** 4 and 5   **5.** 2 and 3
7. 3 and 4

Lesson 13.2 (Page 333)
Try These
1. 5; 2; 5; 2; 5; 2; 5   **2.** 9; 9; 2; 3; 2; 3; 2; 3; 2

Practice
1. $2\sqrt{6}$ **3.** $2\sqrt{7}$ **5.** $2\sqrt{15}$ **7.** $2\sqrt{11}$
9. $2\sqrt{13}$ **11.** $4\sqrt{5}$ **13.** $3\sqrt{10}$ **15.** $4\sqrt{6}$

Lesson 13.3 (Page 335)
Try These
1. $2\sqrt{6}$; $\sqrt{7}$; $3\sqrt{6}$; $3\sqrt{6} + 4\sqrt{7}$
2. $2\sqrt{3}$; $2\sqrt{3}$; $6\sqrt{3}$; $\sqrt{2}$; $6\sqrt{3} - \sqrt{2}$

Practice
1. $10\sqrt{2}$ **3.** $6\sqrt{5} + 8\sqrt{6}$ **5.** $3\sqrt{2} + 3\sqrt{6}$
7. $\sqrt{2}$ **9.** $6\sqrt{5}$ **11.** $\sqrt{7} + \sqrt{6}$

Lesson 13.4 (Page 337)
Try These
1. $\sqrt{15}$; $\sqrt{3}$; 45; 5; 3; 5; 24; 5; $24\sqrt{5}$
2. $\sqrt{16}$; 4; $\frac{1}{4}$

Practice
1. $9\sqrt{10}$ **3.** 5   **5.** $6\sqrt{6}$ **7.** $9\sqrt{7}$
9. $12\sqrt{5}$ **11.** 2

Lesson 13.5 (Page 339)
Try These
1. $\sqrt{2n}$; $2n$; 2; 2; 8; 8   **2.** $5t + 1$; 1; 1; 5; 5; 3; 3

Practice
1. $x = 4$ **3.** $x = 3$ **5.** $n = 2$ **7.** $p = 11$
9. $k = 2$ **11.** $x = 4$ **13.** $w = 7$ **15.** $t = 12$

Lesson 13.6 (Page 341)

Try These

1. $t; r; s$ **2.** $x; y$

Practice

1. legs: a, b; hypotenuse: c
3. legs: s, t; hypotenuse: r
5. legs: d, e; hypotenuse: f

Lesson 13.7 (Page 343)

Try These

1. $3; 3; 9; c; \sqrt{13}$
2. $a^2 + b^2 = c^2$; 9; 15; 15; 81; 81; 81; 81; 81; square root; b; 12; 12

Practice

1. 5 m **3.** 5 m

Lesson 13.8 (Page 345)

Try These

1. $2\sqrt{2}$; leg; $2\sqrt{2} \cdot \sqrt{2}$; $2\sqrt{2}$; 4
2. hypotenuse; 12; 12; $\sqrt{2}$; 12; $\sqrt{2}$; $\sqrt{2}$; $6\sqrt{2}$; $6\sqrt{2}$; $6\sqrt{2}$; $6\sqrt{2}$

Practice

1. $b = 3$ cm; $c = 3\sqrt{2}$ cm
3. $a = 5\sqrt{2}$ in.; $b = 5\sqrt{2}$ in.

Lesson 13.9 (Page 347)

Try These

1. $10; 2; 5; 5$ **2.** short leg; $5; 5; 5\sqrt{3}$

Practice

1. long leg = $4\sqrt{3}$ in.; hypotenuse = 8 in.
3. short leg = 7 m; long leg = $7\sqrt{3}$ m
5. long leg = 12 yd; hypotenuse = $8\sqrt{3}$ yd

Lesson 13.10 (Page 349)

Practice

1. yes **3.** yes **5.** yes

Lesson 13.11 (Page 351)

Try These

1. $5; 5; 12; 12; 25; 144; 169; 169; 169$; are
2. Pythagorean Theorem; $50; 50; 120; 130$; $120; 130; 14{,}400; 16{,}900; 16{,}900; 16{,}900$; are

Practice

1. yes **3.** no **5.** no **7.** yes **9.** no

Lesson 13.12 (Page 353)

Try These

1. $-4; 3; 4; 4; 4; 2; 20; 2\sqrt{5}; 2\sqrt{5}$
2. $-3; 3; 5; 5; 5; 4; 41; \sqrt{41}; \sqrt{41}$

Practice

1. $\sqrt{53}$ units **3.** $4\sqrt{5}$ units

Chapter 14 *Rational Expressions and Equations*

Lesson 14.1 (Page 359)

Try These

1. $4; 4; 4; 7; 14; \dfrac{1}{2}; \dfrac{1}{2}$

2. $4; -4; 4; 4; -4; 8; 4; 2; 2$

Practice

1. $\dfrac{1}{2}$ **3.** $\dfrac{4}{11}$ **5.** $\dfrac{10}{19}$ **7.** -1 **9.** 12

Lesson 14.2 (Page 361)

Try These

1. denominator; $2a - 6$; a 6; 3; 3
2. denominator; $3y$; $y - 4$; y; 0; 4; $0, 4$

Practice

1. -6 **3.** 0 **5.** 0 or -5 **7.** 0 or -5

Lesson 14.3 (Page 363)

Try These

1. $3; 5$; the common factors; $3; 2; 3; \dfrac{2}{3}$

2. $2a; 2a; a - 2; \dfrac{1}{a - 2}$

Practice

1. $\dfrac{1}{4}$ **3.** $\dfrac{7}{10}$ **5.** $\dfrac{1}{4y}$ **7.** $\dfrac{a - 1}{a}$
9. $\dfrac{p + 5}{p - 5}$ **11.** $\dfrac{2}{5x}$ **13.** $\dfrac{1}{a + 2}$ **15.** $\dfrac{x - 3}{2}$

Lesson 14.4 (Page 365)

Try These

1. $20; x^2; y; 20x^2y$ **2.** $a(a + 1)$

Practice

1. 12 **3.** x^2 **5.** $2x^2y$ **7.** $x(x + 6)$
9. $18x^2$ **11.** $(x - 1)(x + 1)$

Lesson 14.5 (Page 367)

Try These

1. $5; \dfrac{5}{3x}$

2. $y^2; y^2; y; y; 4x; y^2; 3xy; y^2; 4x; 3xy; y^2;$ $\dfrac{4x - 3xy}{y^2}$

Practice

1. $\dfrac{9}{10}$ **3.** $\dfrac{17}{24}$ **5.** $\dfrac{5a}{14}$ **7.** $\dfrac{13b}{30}$ **9.** $\dfrac{4y - 6x}{xy}$

11. $\dfrac{2p + 7m}{mp}$ **13.** $\dfrac{2x + 8y}{x^2y^2}$ **15.** $\dfrac{5a - 6ab}{b^2}$

Lesson 14.6 (Page 369)
Try These

1. $4x$; $4x$; x; x; 4; 4; 16; 16; $\dfrac{x^2 - 16}{4x}$

2. $4x$; 12; $6x$; 18; $4x$; $6x$; 6; $\dfrac{10x + 6}{(x + 3)(x - 3)}$

Practice

1. $\dfrac{8y + 18}{y(y + 3)}$ **3.** $\dfrac{7y + 15}{(y + 1)(y + 3)}$

5. $\dfrac{2a^2 + a + 10}{(a + 2)(a - 2)}$ **7.** $\dfrac{-x + 18}{x(x - 3)}$

Lesson 14.7 (Page 371)
Try These

1. $\dfrac{4}{5a}$; $\dfrac{4}{5a}$

2. reciprocal; 4; $3x^2$; x; 4; y; $3x^2$; 4; $3xy$; $\dfrac{4}{3xy}$

Practice

1. $\dfrac{1}{4}$ **3.** $\dfrac{4}{5}$ **5.** $\dfrac{5}{6}$ **7.** $\dfrac{3y^2}{20}$ **9.** $\dfrac{2m^2}{3}$

11. $\dfrac{4}{9a}$ **13.** $\dfrac{a}{8}$ **15.** $\dfrac{7}{4y}$

Lesson 14.8 (Page 373)
Try These

1. a; a; 2; $9a$; $\dfrac{2}{9a}$

2. reciprocal; 5; $x^2 + 5x + 6$; 2; 2; 2; 2; 25;

$x(x + 3)$; $\dfrac{25}{x(x + 3)}$

Practice

1. $\dfrac{12y}{5}$ **3.** $\dfrac{6}{35x}$ **5.** 6 **7.** $\dfrac{1}{15}$ **9.** $\dfrac{3}{5(x + 1)}$

Lesson 14.9 (Page 375)
Try These

1. $3a$; $3a$; $3a$; $3a$; $3a$; a; 3; 5; 5

2. 10; 10; 10; 10; 10; 6; 7; -15; -15

Practice

1. $y = 2$ **3.** $m = 36$ **5.** $n = 4$ **7.** $n = 7$

9. $b = 5$ **11.** $v = 2$ **13.** $n = 4$ **15.** $z = 2$

Lesson 14.10 (Page 377)
Try These

1. 8; 3; 16; 9; 25; 5; 5

2. cross product; 2; 4; 14; 20; 2; $2y$; -3; -3

Practice

1. $x = 12$ **3.** $n = -2$ **5.** $y = 15$ **7.** $x = 2$

9. $n = 6$ or $n = -1$

Lesson 14.11 (Page 379)
Practice

1. yes **3.** yes **5.** yes **7.** no

Lesson 14.12 (Page 381)
Try These

1. 1; 20; 1; 20; 4; 20; 4; 5; 5

2. a proportion; 12 feet; 36 feet; 8 seconds; x seconds; 12; 36; 8; 12; 288; 24; 24 s

Practice

1. 7 miles **3.** 24 days of band

Lesson 14.13 (Page 383)
Try These

1. 8; 8; 3; 3 cm **2.** 12; 12; 2; 2 cm

Practice

1. $9\ h$ **3.** 8 cm

Chapter 15 *Topics From Probability*

Lesson 15.1 (Page 389)
Try These

1. 5; 5; 6; 30; 30 **2.** 4; 3; 4; 3; 12; 12

Practice

1. 16 **3.** 12

Lesson 15.2 (Page 391)
Try These

1. 10; 9; 90; 90 **2.** 4; 4; 2; 4; 2; 24; 24

Practice

1. 6 **3.** 30

Lesson 15.3 (Page 393)
Try These

1. 3; 2; 1; 6; 5; 4; 3; 2; 1; 20; 20

2. 7; 6; 7; 6; 2; 1; 21; 21

Practice

1. 10 **3.** 120 **5.** 6

Lesson 15.4 (Page 395)
Try This

4; 6; $\dfrac{2}{3}$

Practice

1. $\dfrac{1}{5}$ **3.** $\dfrac{3}{5}$ **5.** $\dfrac{2}{5}$

Lesson 15.5 (Page 397)
Try These

1. P(makes free throw); $\dfrac{4}{5}$; 5; 5; 1; 5; $\dfrac{1}{5}$

2. 2; 3; P(correct); $\frac{2}{3}$; P(correct); 2; 3; P(correct);

1; 3; $\frac{1}{3}$

Practice

1. $\frac{9}{11}$ **3.** $\frac{11}{11} = 1$ **5.** $\frac{2}{5}$

Lesson 15.6 (Page 399)

Try These

1. 5; 6; $\frac{3}{5}$; $\frac{1}{6}$; $\frac{3}{30}$; $\frac{1}{10}$ **2.** 5; 6; $\frac{2}{5}$; $\frac{3}{6}$; $\frac{6}{3}$; $\frac{1}{5}$

Practice

1. $\frac{1}{15}$ **3.** $\frac{1}{10}$

Lesson 15.7 (Page 401)

Try These

1. $\frac{5}{6}$; 4; $\frac{4}{5}$; $\frac{5}{6}$; $\frac{4}{5}$; $\frac{20}{30}$; $\frac{2}{3}$; $\frac{2}{3}$

2. $\frac{1}{6}$; 0; 5; $\frac{0}{5}$; $\frac{1}{6}$; $\frac{0}{5}$; 0; 0

Practice

1. $\frac{1}{10}$ **3.** $\frac{3}{10}$

Lesson 15.8 (Page 403)

Practice

1. 362,880 **3.** 175,560 **5.** 12,650

Lesson 15.9 (Page 405)

Try These

1. 5; 5; 8; 5; 8; 0.625; 62.5%

2. 15; 50; 15; 50; 15; 50; 0.3; 30; 30%

Practice

1. 92%

Lesson 15.10 (Page 407)

Try These

1. .1; .1; 45; 45 **2.** 6; .4; .4; 6; 2.4; 2.4

Practice

1. 12 people **3.** 10 defective spark plugs

5. 1 pearl

ADDITIONAL PRACTICE

Chapter 1 *Numbers for Algebra*

(Page 413)

1.

2.

3.

4. < **5.** > **6.** < **7.** 8 **8.** 13 **9.** 20

10. -14 **11.** 4 **12.** -9 **13.** 3 **14.** -2

15. 5 **16.** -13 **17.** 21 **18.** -12 **19.** 5

20. -3 **21.** 25 **22.** 140 paper; 70 cloth

23. August **24.** $100

Chapter 2 *Tools for Algebra*

(Page 414)

1. 13 **2.** 6 **3.** -4 **4.** 42 **5.** 10 **6.** -16

7. -4 **8.** 3 **9.** 0 **10.** 30 **11.** yes

12. no **13.** Identity Property of Addition

14. Identity Property of Multiplication

15. Associative Property of Multiplication

16. Commutative Property of Addition

17. $8x$ **18.** $-2ab$ **19.** $16 - 16a$

20. $15x - 4y$ **21.** $7c + 1$ **22.** $13a - 3$

23. $3x + 12$ **24.** $10n - 30$ **25.** $-a - 7$

26. $-5 + x$ **27.** $20x - 20$ **28.** $-3 - x$

29. $j = m + 4$ **30.** 20 cm **31.** 66 ft

Chapter 3 *Solving Equations*

(Page 415)

1. yes **2.** no **3.** no **4.** yes **5.** 14 **6.** -8

7. 9 **8.** 20 **9.** -12 **10.** 20 **11.** 3

12. -7 **13.** 3 **14.** 0 **15.** -11 **16.** 4

17. 2 **18.** 1 **19.** -16 **20.** -1 **21.** 36

22. 1 **23.** $17.00 **24.** $2.00

Chapter 4 *Introducing Functions*

(Page 416)

1.–3.

4. (1, 3), (2, 7), (3, 12);

5. 14; 12 − 2(0), 12; 12 − 2(1), 10; 12 − 2(2), 8
6. yes **7.** no **8.** yes **9.** no **10.** $f(4) = 12$
11. $f(-2) = 6$ **12.** 185 **13.** 2001

Chapter 5 *Linear Equations and Functions* (Page 417)

1. no **2.** yes **3.** yes
4.

5.

6.

7. 3 **8.** 0 **9.** no slope
10. perpendicular **11.** parallel
12. x-intercept: 3; y-intercept: −24
13. x-intercept: 14; y-intercept: −14
14. x-intercept: 2; y-intercept: 18
15.

16.

17. $y = -6x + 12$ **18.** 25 mile mark **19.** 3

Chapter 6 *Writing Linear Equations* (Page 418)

1. $y = -x - 3$ **2.** $y = 4$ **3.** $y = 4x + 5$
4. $y = -x + 5$ **5.** $y = x + 6$ **6.** $y = 2x + 1$
7. $y = 2x - 4$ **8.** $y = -2x + 2$ **9.** $y = -3$
10. Multiply pints by 8 to find gallons. $8p = g$
11. Add 2 to x to find y. $x + 2 = y$
12. $l = 115$ mm

Chapter 7 *Inequalities* (Page 419)

1. $m < 1$

```
  +--+--+--+--+--+--+--⊕--+--+-->
 −4 −3 −2 −1  0  1  2  3
```

2. $x \le 2$

```
  +--+--+--+--+--+--+--●--+--+-->
 −3 −2 −1  0  1  2  3  4
```

3. $c > -8$

```
  +--+--⊕--+--+--+--+--+--+-->
 −10 −9 −8 −7 −6 −5 −4 −3
```

4. $d < -5$

```
  +--+--+--+--+--⊕--+--+--+-->
 −10 −9 −8 −7 −6 −5 −4 −3
```

5. $y \geq 0$

(number line: $-2\ -1\ 0\ 1\ 2\ 3\ 4\ 5$)

6. $m < 6$

(number line: $1\ 2\ 3\ 4\ 5\ 6\ 7\ 8$)

7. $a < 4$

(number line: $-1\ 0\ 1\ 2\ 3\ 4\ 5\ 6$)

8. $y < -5$

(number line: $-10\ -9\ -8\ -7\ -6\ -5\ -4\ -3$)

9. $n \leq -5$

(number line: $-10\ -9\ -8\ -7\ -6\ -5\ -4\ -3$)

10. no **11.** yes **12.** no

13.

14.

15.

16.

17.

18.

19. $2b \geq 30$; $b \geq 15$; Marcus needs to sell at least 15 books.

20. No; (3, 3) is not in the shaded region.

Chapter 8 *Systems of Equations and Inequalities* (Page 420)

1. no **2.** no **3.** yes

4. $(-2, 2)$;

(graph showing two lines intersecting at (−2, 2))

5. $(6, 6)$;

6.

7.

8. $(2, 10)$ **9.** $(2, 2)$ **10.** $(-5, 0)$ **11.** $(7, 2)$
12. $(-2, -7)$ **13.** $(3, -3)$ **14.** $(-2, 1)$
15. $(2, 6)$ **16.** $(2, -4)$
17. He received 4 $20 bills and 2 $10 bills.
18. 6 pounds of pork and 7 pounds of beef yields the maximum profit. $19.

Chapter 9 *More About Data and Data Analysis* (Page 421)

1. mean, 7; median, 8; mode, 9
2. mean, 77; median, 80; mode, 80
3. min., 2; max., 15; range, 13
4. min., 10; max., 22; range, 12

5.

Grade	Tally	Frequency
A	ⅢⅠ	5
B	ⅢⅠ II	7
C	III	3
F	II	2
		Total 17

6. 12 grades

7.

Stem	Leaves
4	0 5 9
5	4 4
6	4 5 6

8.

Stem	Leaves
6	2
7	0 5 5 7
8	0 0 4
9	1

9. positive **10.** negative
11. 11; 3; 3; median and mode
12. 58; 62; 2; mean and median
13. 13; 17; 21 **14.** 29; 36; 49

Chapter 10 *Exponents and Functions* (Page 422)

1. x^4 **2.** ab^3 **3.** $2m^2n^3$ **4.** -8 **5.** 64

6. 100 **7.** $15x^5$ **8.** b^8c^6 **9.** a^{14} **10.** $8x^8$

11. $\dfrac{x^5}{y}$ **12.** 1 **13.** b^5 **14.** x^6y **15.** $2c^{11}d$

16. 1 **17.** $\dfrac{1}{c^4}$ **18.** $\dfrac{z^3}{y^{10}}$ **19.** 5,000

20. 11,000 **21.** .000036
22. 9,400,000 **23.** .09 **24.** 409,000
25. $(0, 3), (1, 6), (2, 12), (3, 24), (4, 48)$

26. 6 choices;

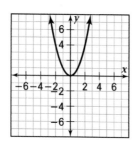

White	Green — White shirt and green shorts
	Blue — White shirt and blue shorts
Yellow	Green — Yellow shirt and green shorts
	Blue — Yellow shirt and blue shorts
Red	Green — Red shirt and green shorts
	Blue — Red shirt and blue shorts

27. $266.20

Chapter 11 *Quadratic Functions and Equations* (Page 423)

1. 1, 4, 12

2.

x	y
2	4
1	1
0	0
−1	1
−2	4
−3	9

3.

x	y
2	6
1	2
0	0
−1	0
−2	2
−3	6

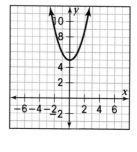

4.

x	y
2	9
1	6
0	5
−1	6
−2	9
−3	14

5. upward; minimum
6. downward; maximum
7. upward; minimum   **8.** no zeros
9. 3 and −1   **10.** 7 and −7   **11.** 8   **12.** −5
13. 6 and −6   **14.** 7 and −7   **15.** 5 and 6
16. The length is 40 feet and the width is 10 feet.   **17.** 3 seconds

Chapter 12 *Polynomials and Factoring* (Page 424)

1. binomial   **2.** trinomial   **3.** monomial
4. $4y^2 + 7y - 2$ **5.** $-3x^2 + 4x + 7$
6. $3x^2 + 15x + 18$ **7.** $-2a^2 + 8a$
8. $2b^3 - 6b^2 - 20b$ **9.** $x^2 + 11x + 30$
10. $a^2 - 10a + 9$ **11.** $y^2 + 8y - 20$ **12.** yes
13. no   **14.** $a(a + 6)$ **15.** $3n(n^2 + 4)$
16. $6(2x^2 + y)$ **17.** $(y - 5)(y - 6)$
18. $(x - 1)(x + 11)$ **19.** $(y + 5)(y - 6)$
20. $(x + 1)(x + 13)$ **21.** $(x + 9)(x - 9)$
22. $(y + 8)(y + 8)$ **23.** $x = 0$ or -4
24. $y = 5$ or 8 **25.** $x = -1$ or -3
26. $x = 2$ or -2 **27.** $x = 0$ or 4

28. $x = -15$ or -5 **29.** 5 diagonals

Chapter 13 *Radicals and Geometry*

(Page 425)

1. 4 and 5   **2.** 6 and 7   **3.** 2 and 3   **4.** $3\sqrt{2}$
5. $2\sqrt{6}$ **6.** $2\sqrt{3} + 2\sqrt{6}$ **7.** $-9\sqrt{5}$ **8.** $7\sqrt{2}$
9. $20\sqrt{6}$ **10.** $14\sqrt{30}$ **11.** $3\sqrt{3}$ **12.** 10
13. $m = 21$ **14.** $y = 12$ **15.** $p = 5$ **16.** 6 in.
17. $\sqrt{34}$ cm   **18.** $d = 10$ m; $e = 10\sqrt{2}$ m
19. $w = 6\sqrt{3}$ cm; $x = 12$ cm   **20.** $m = 4$ yd;
$n = 4$ yd   **21.** $g = 9$ in.; $h = 18$ in.   **22.** yes
23. 10 units.

Chapter 14 *Rational Expressions and Equations* (Page 426)

1. $\dfrac{9}{10}$ **2.** -6 **3.** 0 or 7   **4.** 8 or -9

5. $\dfrac{x + 3}{2x}$ **6.** $\dfrac{8x}{x + 9}$ **7.** $4y(y + 7)$ **8.** $16a^2$

9. $(x + 9)(x - 9)$

10. $\dfrac{23}{20}$ **11.** $\dfrac{8y - 3}{2y^2}$ **12.** $\dfrac{2y^2 + 32}{8y}$

13. $\dfrac{x^2 - 15}{9x}$ **14.** $\dfrac{b}{a}$ **15.** $\dfrac{t}{4}$ **16.** $\dfrac{10x}{3}$

17. $\dfrac{3x(x - 7)}{2(x - 9)}$ **18.** $x = 4$ **19.** $n = 7$
20. $a = -1$ **21.** $n = -6$ **22.** $a = 0$ or 6
23. $y = 5$ **24.** 45 seniors   **25.** 2 hours

Chapter 15 *Topics from Probability*

(Page 427)

1. 40   **2.** 24   **3.** 35   **4.** $\dfrac{4}{8}$ or $\dfrac{1}{2}$

5. 0   **6.** $\dfrac{5}{8}$ **7.** $\dfrac{2}{8}$ or $\dfrac{1}{4}$ **8.** $\dfrac{3}{8}$ **9.** $\dfrac{5}{8}$ **10.** $\dfrac{1}{8}$

11. $\dfrac{2}{30}$ or $\dfrac{1}{15}$ **12.** .6%   **13.** 160 adults

Index

Photo Credits

p. 2: Andrea Booher, Stone
p. 21: Chris Noble, Stone
p. 28: Rob Crandall, The Image Works
p. 53: Chad Ehlers, Stone
p. 60: Duomo, Corbis
p. 85: David Young-Wolff, PhotoEdit
p. 94: NASA, Science Source, Photo Researchers Inc.
p. 116: Kevin R. Morris, Corbis
p. 137: Courtesy of Evelyn Granville
p. 144: Davis Barber, PhotoEdit
p. 157: Bettmann, Corbis
p. 166: Mitch Kezar, Stone
p. 181: Courtesy of IBM
p. 188: M. Granitsas, The Image Works
p. 207: Matthew Borkoski, Stock Bostonp. 214: Bob Daemmrich, The Image Works
p. 229: David Grossman, Photo Researchers Inc.
p. 238: Visuals Unlimited

p. 261: Bettmann, Corbis
p. 268: Gary S. Settles, Photo Researchers Inc.
p. 285: Ronald Royer, Science Photo Library, Photo Researchers Inc.
p. 292: Richard Hamilton Smith, Corbis
p. 319: The Granger Collection
p. 328: Lowell Georgia, Corbis
p. 349: Steven Peters, Stone
p. 356: Paul A. Souders, Corbis
p. 379: Carol & Mike Werner, Stock Boston
p. 386: George Lepp, Corbis
p. 403: Bob Daemmrich, Stock Boston

Cover:
Nautilus Shell: PhotoDisc, Inc.
Cheetah: Tom Brakefield, Corbis
Coins: PhotoDisc, Inc.
Ruler: Corbis

Additional Answers

Unit Two
Chapter 4 Introducing Functions
Lesson 4·3, page 101

Practice 1.–2.

1.

2.

Chapter Quiz, page 115, 1.–4.

1.–3.

4.

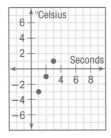

Chapter 5 Linear Equations and Functions
Lesson 5·2, page 121

Practice 1.–6.

1.

2.

3.

4.

5.

6.

Lesson 5·7, page 131

Practice 1.–8.

1.

2.

3.

4.

5.

6.

7.

8.

Chapter Quiz, page 143, **4.–6., 18.–21.**

4.

5.

6.

18.

19.

20.

21.

22.

Unit Three
Chapter 6 Writing Linear Equations
Lesson 6·1, page 147

Cooperative Learning 6.

6.

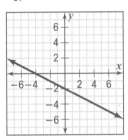

Lesson 6·3, page 149

Cooperative Learning 10.

10.

Lesson 6·3, page 151

Cooperative Learning 11.

11.

Lesson 6·5, page 155

Cooperative Learning 7.

7.

Unit Three
Chapter 7 Inequalities
Lesson 7·2, page 171

Practice 1.–10.

1.

2.

3.

4.

5.

6.

7. $\leftarrow$|—|—|—|—|—|—|○—|—|—|$\rightarrow$
$-4\,-3\,-2\,-1\ \ 0\ \ 1\ \ 2\ \ 3$

8. $\leftarrow$|—|—●—|—|—|—|—|$\rightarrow$
$\ \ 8\ \ 9\ 10\ 11\ 12\ 13\ 14\ 15$

9. $\leftarrow$|—|—|—|—○—|—|—|$\rightarrow$
$-13\ \ -11\ \ \ -9\ \ \ \ -7$

10. $\leftarrow$|—○—|—|—|—|—|$\rightarrow$
$-11\ \ -9\ \ \ -7\ \ \ -5$

Lesson 7·3, page 173

Practice 1.–8.

1. $\leftarrow$|—|—○—|—|—|—|—|$\rightarrow$
$\ \ 6\ \ 7\ \ 8\ \ 9\ 10\ 11\ 12\ 13$

2. $\leftarrow$|—|—●—|—|—|—|—|$\rightarrow$
$\ \ 0\ \ 1\ \ 2\ \ 3\ \ 4\ \ 5\ \ 6\ \ 7$

3. $\leftarrow$|—|—|—|—|—○—|—|$\rightarrow$
$31\ 32\ 33\ 34\ 35\ 36\ 37\ 38$

4. $\leftarrow$|—|—○—|—|—|—|—|$\rightarrow$
$\ \ 1\ \ 2\ \ 3\ \ 4\ \ 5\ \ 6\ \ 7\ \ 8$

5. $\leftarrow$|—|—●—|—|—|—|$\rightarrow$
$-32\ \ \ -30\ \ \ -28\ \ \ -26$

6. $\leftarrow$|—|—○—|—|—|—|—|$\rightarrow$
$-2\,-1\ \ 0\ \ 1\ \ 2\ \ 3\ \ 4\ \ 5$

7. $\leftarrow$|—|—|—|—●—|—|$\rightarrow$
$-24\ \ \ -22\ \ \ -20\ \ \ -18$

8. $\leftarrow$|—●—|—|—|—|—|—|$\rightarrow$
$-8\,-6\,-4\,-2\ \ 0\ \ 2\ \ 4\ \ 6$

Lesson 7·4, page 175

Practice 1.–6.

1. $\leftarrow$|—|—○—|—|—|—|—|$\rightarrow$
$10\ 11\ 12\ 13\ 14\ 15\ 16\ 17$

2. $\leftarrow$|—|—|—|—|—○—|—|$\rightarrow$
$\ \ 1\ \ 2\ \ 3\ \ 4\ \ 5\ \ 6\ \ 7\ \ 8$

3. $\leftarrow$|—|—|—|—|—●—|—|$\rightarrow$
$-7\,-6\,-5\,-4\,-3\,-2\,-1\ \ 0$

4. $\leftarrow$|—|—○—|—|—|—|—|$\rightarrow$
$\ \ 1\ \ 2\ \ 3\ \ 4\ \ 5\ \ 6\ \ 7\ \ 8$

5. $\leftarrow$|—|—●—|—|—|—|—|$\rightarrow$
$\ \ 4\ \ 5\ \ 6\ \ 7\ \ 8\ \ 9\ 10\ 11$

6. $\leftarrow$|—|—|—|—|—●—|—|$\rightarrow$
$10\ 11\ 12\ 13\ 14\ 15\ 16\ 17$

Lesson 7·7, page 179

Practice 1.–6.

1.

2.

3.

4.

5.

6.
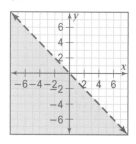

Chapter Quiz, page 187, *1.–9., 13.–18.*

1. $\leftarrow$|—○—|—|—|—|—|$\rightarrow$
$\ \ 2\ \ 3\ \ 4\ \ 5\ \ 6\ \ 7\ \ 8\ \ 9$

2. $\leftarrow$|—|—|—|—●—|—|$\rightarrow$
$-11\ \ \ -9\ \ \ -7\ \ \ -5$

3. $\leftarrow$|—|—●—|—|—|—|$\rightarrow$
$\ \ 4\ \ 5\ \ 6\ \ 7\ \ 8\ \ 9\ 10\ 11$

4. $\leftarrow$|—|—|—|—●—|—|$\rightarrow$
$-1\ \ 0\ \ 1\ \ 2\ \ 3\ \ 4\ \ 5\ \ 6$

5. $\leftarrow$|—|—○—|—|—|—|$\rightarrow$
$\ \ 4\ \ 5\ \ 6\ \ 7\ \ 8\ \ 9\ 10\ 11$

6.

7.

8.

9.

Practice 1.–9.

1.

2.

13.

14.

3.

4.

15.

16.

5.

6.

17.

18.

7.

8.

9.

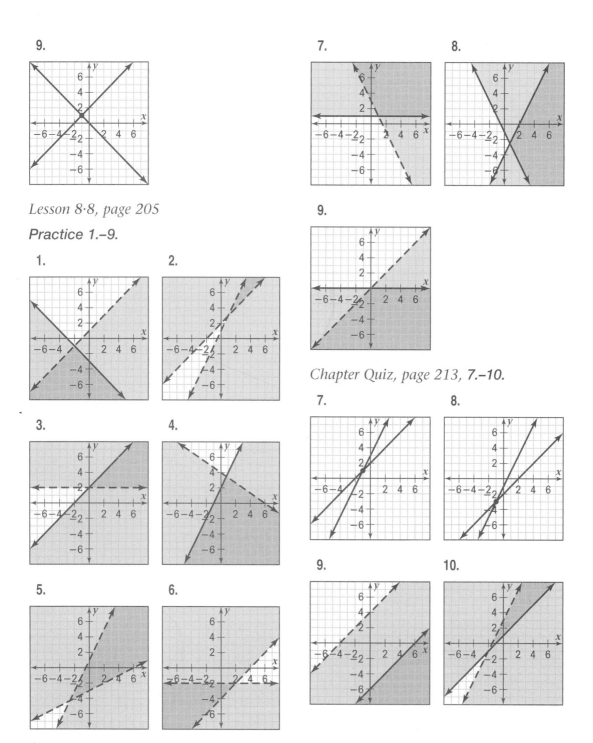

Lesson 8·8, page 205

Practice 1.–9.

1.

2.

7.

8.

9.

Chapter Quiz, page 213, 7.–10.

3.

4.

7.

8.

5.

6.

9.

10.

Chapter 9 More about Data and Data Analysis

Lesson 9·4, page 223

Practice 4.

4.

Sizes	Tally	Frequency
S	JHHT I	6
M	IIII	4
L	JHHT	5
	Total	15

Lesson 9·6, page 227

Practice 1.–2.

1.

2.

Chapter Quiz, page 235, 5.

5.

Sizes	Tally	Frequency
S	JHHT	5
M	JHHT I	6
L	IIII	4
	Total	15

Chapter 10 Exponents and Functions

Lesson 10·2, page 257

Practice 1.–6.

1.

x	4^x	y
0	4^0	1
1	4^1	4
2	4^2	16
3	4^3	64
4	4^4	256

2.

x	3^x	y
0	3^0	1
1	3^1	3
2	3^2	9
3	3^3	27
4	3^4	81

3.

x	$-2 \cdot 5^x$	y
0	$-2 \cdot 5^0$	-2
1	$-2 \cdot 5^1$	-10
2	$-2 \cdot 5^2$	-50
3	$-2 \cdot 5^3$	-250
4	$-2 \cdot 5^4$	$-1,250$

4.

x	10^x	y
0	10^0	1
1	10^1	10
2	10^2	100
3	10^3	1,000

5.

x	8^x	y
0	8^0	1
1	8^1	8
2	8^2	64
3	8^3	512

6.

x	20^x	y
0	20^0	1
1	20^1	20
2	20^2	400
3	20^3	8,000

Lesson 10·10, page 259

Practice 1.–3.

1.

2.

3.

Lesson 10·12, page 263

Practice 1.–2.

1.

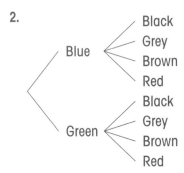

2.

Blue
- Black
- Grey
- Brown
- Red

Green
- Black
- Grey
- Brown
- Red

Chapter Quiz, page 267, **25.–26.**

25.

26.

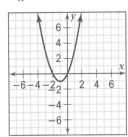

Black —
- Red
- Yellow
- Blue
- Green

Brown —
- Red
- Yellow
- Blue
- Green

Chapter 11 Quadratic Functions and Equations

Lesson 11·2, page 273

Practice 1.–6.

1.

2.

3.

4.

5.

6.

Chapter Quiz, page 291, 3.–5.

3.

4.

5.

Chapter 12 Polynomials and Factoring

Lesson 12·12, page 326

Practice 25.

25.

Poster —

Square —
- White — Black / Red
- Yellow — Black / Red
- Blue — Black / Red

Rectangle —
- White — Black / Red
- Yellow — Black / Red
- Blue — Black / Red

Additional Answers   479

Additional Practice

Chapter 4 Introducing Functions
Page 416, 1.–4.

1.–3.

4. (1, 3), (2, 7), (3, 12);

Chapter 5 Linear Equations and Functions
Page 417, 4.–6., 15.–16.

4.

5.

6.

15.

16.

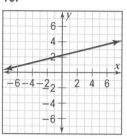

Chapter 7 Inequalities
Page 419, 1.–9., 13.–18.

1. $m < 1$

2. $x \le 2$

3. $c > -8$

4. $d < -5$

5. $y \ge 0$

6. $m < 6$

7. $a < 4$

8. $y < -5$

9. $n \le -5$

13.

14.

6.

7.

15.

16.

Chapter 9 More About Data and Data Analysis

Page 421, 5., 7.–8.

5.

Grade	Tally	Frequency
A	ЖНТ	5
B	ЖНТ II	7
C	III	3
F	II	2
	Total	17

17.

18.

7.

Stem	Leaves
4	0 5 9
5	4 4
6	4 5 6

8.

Stem	Leaves
6	2
7	0 5 5 7
8	0 0 4
9	1

Chapter 8 Systems of Equations and Inequalities

Page 420, 4.–7.

4. $(-2, 2)$

5. $(6, 6)$

Chapter 10 Exponents and Functions

Page 422, 25.–26.

25. (0, 3), (1, 6), (2, 12), (3, 24), (4, 48)

26. 6 choices;

White — Green — White shirt and green shorts
White — Blue — White shirt and blue shorts

Yellow — Green — Yellow shirt and green shorts
Yellow — Blue — Yellow shirt and blue shorts

Red — Green — Red shirt and green shorts
Red — Blue — Red shirt and blue shorts

Chapter 11 Quadratic Functions and Equations

Page 423, 2.–4.

2.

x	y
2	4
1	1
0	0
−1	1
−2	4
−3	9

3.

x	y
2	6
1	2
0	0
−1	0
−2	2
−3	6

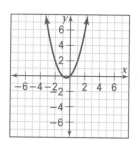

4.

x	y
2	9
1	6
0	5
−1	6
−2	9
−3	14